THE WASHERDRIER AND TUMBLEDRIER MANUAL

Graham Dixon

DIY Plumbing ☐ Maintenance ☐ Repair

First edition published 1990
Revised second edition published 1993
Reprinted 1994
Revised third edition published 1999
Reprinted 2000 (with minor amendments)
Reprinted 2001

Published by: Haynes Publishing, Sparkford, Nr
Yeovil, Somerset BA22 7JJ, England

British Library Cataloguing in Publication Data
A catalogue record for this book is available
from the British Library

ISBN 1 85960 328 9

Printed in the USA.

**While every effort is taken to ensure the
accuracy of the information given in this
book, no liability can be accepted by the
author or publishers for any loss, damage or
injury caused by errors in, or omissions from,
the information given. Because the author
and the publishers have no control over the
way the information contained within this
publication is used or put into practice, no
warranty is given or implied as to the
suitability of the advice for specific
applications. Therefore, no liability can be
accepted for any consequential loss,
damage, or injury however caused, arising
as a result of the information herein.**

Contents

Contents

Contents

Contents

Acknowledgements

The author would like to extend his thanks and gratitude to the following people and organisations for their help in the compilation of certain sections of this book.

Oracstar Ltd
Lever Bros.
Crabtree Electrical Industries Ltd.

Thanks also to Andrew Morland for much of the photographic work and Martin Coltman and Jack Whitehead for artwork. Special thanks to Keith Lavender for the loan of the machine used in the cover shot.

The author would like to point out that any references to manufacturer's names or model numbers, etc., used throughout this manual are for identification and reference purposes only. Whilst every precaution has been taken to ensure that all information is factual in every detail, the author cannot accept any liability for any errors or omissions or for any damage or injury caused by using this manual.

Introduction

Today's modern automatic washing machines/tumbledriers are the highly refined offspring of their predecessors. Many refinements have been made to aid production and to cut costs for the manufacturer, although it is fair to say that improvements to washing and spin speeds have also been incorporated. The automatic washing machine has changed little in its basic operation over the years, apart from the obvious cosmetic changes and additions of faster spin speeds and increased wash variations. Environmental concerns are now taken into consideration by most manufacturers and efforts made to make domestic appliances in general more efficient in the way they use resources such as water and detergents. In recent years the washing machine and tumbledrier have been combined in the washerdrier. These changes have not significantly increased the overall cost of automatic machines and in real terms, they are actually cheaper now than twenty five years ago. With the use of electronics to control motor speeds and the high demand for machines, mass production techniques and a competitive market have kept costs relatively low.

The main drawback has been in the cost of repairs and servicing your appliance once the guarantee has expired. Many people opted for the five year cover offered by manufacturers only to find that in some cases only the defective part is covered and not the wear and tear, and in particular, not the labour charge for fitting the replacement part.

This may result in even a small repair, e.g. replacement of a belt, costing around £60. The breakdown of which is the cost of the belt approximately £10 is waived, but the call-out and repair charge of £50 or more plus VAT is levied.

This book looks in detail at the combined automatic washerdrier and separate dry-only machines. The aim of the book is to help you to understand these machines and to show that they are not as complex as one may at first sight imagine. In fact, the majority of all repairs are within the scope of most owners. With a little thought, planning and understanding of how your machine and its components operate, you will not only be able to save money but also gain the satisfaction of completing a repair yourself, often without the delay encountered when contacting a repair company. Even if you are on a five year cover, repair it yourself when parts are less than labour charge and pass on to the manufacturer the jobs needing expensive parts. **Note:** *This action may invalidate subsequent claims in some instances.*

This book has been written for those who possess little or no practical knowledge of front loading washerdriers and tumbledriers. Seasoned DIY car mechanics will find the book useful as many of the problems found with the washing machine are similar to those on cars, e.g. worn or noisy bearings, faulty hoses, suspension, etc. The information will also be useful for those wishing to gain employment in the service industry. Those already in the service industry will find much of the information of help when they are studying for their servicing NVQ.

Approached in a logical step-by-step manner, not as a haphazard guess, most if not all faults are within the capabilities of the DIY person. The book is best read cover to cover to gain the gist of flowchart use and to familiarise yourself with procedures and the best ways to locate and rectify faults that may occur. You can then use the book as a quick reference guide before and during repairs. It is impossible to deal specifically with any particular machine as models vary considerably with each manufacturer having their own style of pumps, hoses, bearing sizes, etc., but the concept of an automatic washer, washerdrier or tumbledrier differs very little between manufacturers. This will become apparent after reading through the book.

Having read the book, you will become more aware of safety around the home due to a better understanding of electrical items and their limitations. Regular checks for faults, which can be rectified prior to failure or accident, greatly increase the safety of your appliances. You will gain more efficient use of your items through understanding their correct operation.

The machines in the photo sequences have been selected as a cross section of some of the most popular ones found in homes today. Both old and new machines are used in the sequences to highlight actual fault areas and faults to look out for. All names and model numbers are used for customer reference purposes only. At all times, before working on a machine, make sure that it is isolated from both the electrical supply, i.e. switch off socket and remove plug, and from the water supply by turning off the feed taps. This ensures your safety and that of the machine and its surroundings.

This book has been split into two separate sections: first, the combined washerdrier, both vented and condenser types (this section covers all aspects of the machine including parts of the drier) and secondly, the separate dry-only machines in detail. **Note:** *The sections on* Basics, Safety, Motors *and* Timers, *etc., are common to both versions therefore it is essential to read the whole book.*

The washerdrier

There are two main types of automatic washerdriers:

a) Vented washerdriers allow the warm moisture-laden air to escape through a vent usually positioned at the rear of the machine, easily spotted by its large diameter. This type of machine requires a hose to vent the moisture-laden air out of the room, either through an open window or through a wall vent system (explained later in the book). The machine can be used without venting but this results in moisture-laden air discharged by the machine on a drying cycle condensing on cold surfaces in the same room (i.e. windows, cupboards, walls, etc.). For the machine to be used economically, and in order to avoid problems with damp walls and cupboards, etc., it is advisable to vent the machine in some way.

b) Condenser washerdriers use the same system of rotating the wash load in a stream of warm air following the final spin but do not vent the resulting moisture-laden air out of the machine. The warm moist air is allowed to pass over an internal condenser unit within the machine. This unit is kept cool by passing a small amount of cold water through it via an extra cold water inlet valve, and when the warm air meets this cold surface the moisture is condensed from it. The resulting liquid is allowed to collect at the bottom of the outer tub ready to be discharged by the outlet pump through the drain hose of the machine. The warm air with the moisture removed is then recycled via the drier heater making this style of machine more economical than the straight vent to atmosphere machines described in a. The condenser washerdrier requires no extra fittings than is needed for a normal automatic washing machine.

Both versions have many parts in common and although the size and shape of the parts may change, depending on manufacturer, the basic principles are the same. Washerdrier machines, as the name implies, are a combination of an automatic washing machine and a tumbledrier in one machine. As with any combination, compromises have to be made in order to run smoothly and the load size and drying time will not suit every situation.

Combining the auto washer with the tumbledrier is beneficial for the manufacturer. The automatic washing machine already has a drum for the load, a means of rotating it (clockwise and anti-clockwise) and an outlet pump to discharge the water produced by the condenser machines. In simple terms, all that is needed in addition to turn it into a drier would be a fan to circulate air, a heater to warm the air, a means of ducting the air through the drum and a means of timing the length of the dry cycle. Condenser machines would require the addition of an extra cold water valve, plus a condenser unit which could be a simple trickle bar within the wash tub or externally mounted on the outer of the wash tub or inner of the cabinet of the machine.

The repair and maintenance of automatic washerdriers is similar to ordinary automatic washing machines and many parts such as valves, pumps, pressure switches, etc., may be common to other machines within the manufacturer's range of both wash only and combined washerdriers. The main differences are the addition of fan and heater to supply warm air, larger vents on outer tub, door seals with hot air intake aperture and timers with dry cycle position. Some machines will also have separate timers for the drying cycle, more of these in the *Timers (programmers)* chapter. Another difference is the restricted space within the machine in which to carry out repairs. This is due to the added bulk of the fan and heater assembly as well as the external condenser unit on condenser machines.

Faults, repair and maintenance of the machine must be considered as a whole. Many faults will interrelate between the washing sequence of the machine and the drying action, therefore a simple division between the two operations is not always possible. An understanding of all the parts is essential, their correct operation, the way in which they function, the interrelating between them, associated faults and potential areas for trouble. To this end, each item is examined individually and how it relates to other working parts is described in detail. This will help in building up an overall picture of how the machine works, the details of each section and ultimately the interaction of all components during a wash and dry cycle. Where possible, specific faults are given with help regarding checks/action to be carried out.

Dry-only machines

The tumbledrier has been with us for many years now. The basic function is to circulate warm air through the damp clothes for a given period of time selected by the user, followed with a cool tumble prior to switching off at the selected time. This is a relatively simple operation requiring a drum to hold the load, a heater to warm the air and a fan to circulate the warm air through the drum. As with the washing machine, the drum is rotated to allow the whole load to gain maximum benefit from the warm airflow. In most instances the motor that revolves the drum also drives the fan used for air circulation. Being a dedicated machine (drying only) it works much more efficiently than its combined washerdrier counterpart. There are several reasons for this. The drum capacity can be much larger as it is not necessary to have a water-tight outer tub thus allowing for a larger drum taking up nearly all the available space within the cabinet. The larger machines (those with cabinets the same size as a washing machine) can take the same size load, i.e. 5kg (11lb) wash load can be transferred directly into the 5kg load tumbledrier. The smaller models with a 2.7kg (6lb) load capacity, convenient if space is restricted, operates in exactly the same way as the larger models.

The larger drum allows for better movement of the clothing through the airflow, ensuring more even and quicker drying even though the clothing increases in bulk during the drying process. This increase in bulk/size of the load during drying is why the combined washerdrier can dry only half its wash load. A larger wattage heater can be used (if necessary) with a greater surface area for warming the air.

Again, owing to the increase in usable space, a larger fan can be used for circulating the air.

Over the years, additions to the basic principles have been made. Drum rotation on early and current basic machines is in one direction only. Nowadays, the option is to have reverse drum action similar to the wash action (clockwise and counter clockwise). This obviously requires a more complex motor, which is capable of rotation in both directions, and a more complex timer or motor reversal system. Temperature control again on early and current basic models is relatively straightforward with selections of high or low, but on the more recent and expensive machines, auto sensing is now a feature. This system senses the moisture content of the load being dried and switches off when a pre-selected degree of dryness has been reached. The advantage of auto sensing is that it switches off when dry unlike the more basic machine that carries on tumbling and heating for the set time regardless of whether the clothes are dry or not.

Further refinements and extras include computer control (electronic in place of mechanical), intermittent tumble after the drying process is complete which prevents the load compacting at the end of the cycle if left unattended for any length of time prior to removal. Condenser tumbledriers are also available. These operate in a similar manner to the combined washerdrier system by condensing the moisture rather than venting it. Some require water supply and outlet whilst others use cold air instead of water to aid condensing, with a removable container

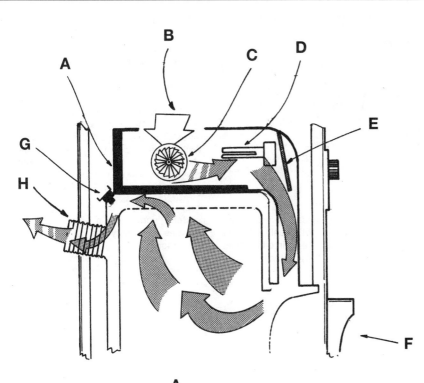

Simple vented type combined washerdrier. This cutaway drawing illustrates the basic components of a vented washerdrier and highlights how few extra parts are required over and above a wash-only machine. The fan unit, duct and heaters make up part of the top tub weight (A). Cold air is drawn in from the interior shell space of the machine (B) by fan (C). The air drawn in is blown over the heating elements (D) and in doing so, lifts flap (E). Access to the inner drum is by an extra flange/inlet to the door gasket/seal (F). The now warm air picks up moisture from the wash load on its way through the contra-rotating drum. The moisture-laden air escapes through the contra-rotating drum. Thermostat (G) monitors the air temperature within the outer tub. The moisture-laden air escapes through the vent positioned on the rear of the outer tub unit. A convoluted hose (H) guides the warm moist air to the exterior of the machine. Note: *A filter is normally situated on the outlet hose to the rear of the machine*

Shown are the basic components and operation of a typical condenser combined washerdrier

A Heater duct
B Heating element (maybe two or more)
C Circulation fan motor
D Air circulation fan
E Condenser unit externally mounted in this instance on the back of the outer tub
F Cold water inlet to spray bar or trickle plate
G Normal sump hose to pump

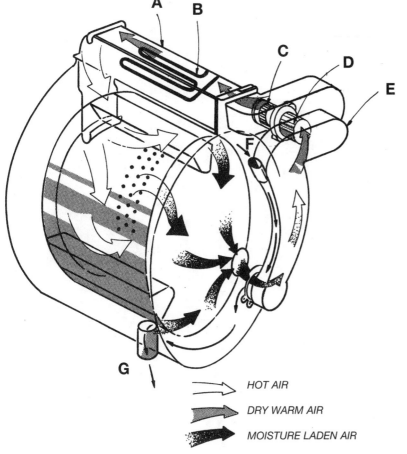

HOT AIR

DRY WARM AIR

MOISTURE LADEN AIR

WATER AND CONDENSATE

to catch the condensation. The container requires regular emptying (once every two dry cycles on average if not permanently drained in a similar way to the automatic washer, i.e. pump and outlet).

The tumbledriers covered in this book heat the air used in the drying process by electricity, but domestic tumbledriers are now available which heat by gas. Although commercial machines have had this option for several years, it is relatively new to the domestic user. Because of the stringent gas regulations and the obvious need for safety, do not attempt installation or any inspection or repair on this type of product. The installation and repair of gas machines must be done by those with the correct knowledge, equipment and gas qualifications.

The main benefits of the larger dry-only machines (same sized cabinet as the washing machine), are that they can dry a full wash load, giving the ability to be drying one load whilst another load is being washed, thus saving a lot of time. **Note:** *Do not use both machines from a single socket via an adapter. See* Basics – electrical. *The separate drier is also quicker and more efficient than combined washerdriers if used correctly.*

Drawbacks

For households with restricted space, finding room for another appliance the same size as a washing machine can be a problem. Some of the smaller machines can stand on work surfaces if necessary and some of the larger models can stack on top of a washing machine (these usually need to be of the same make and require a stacking frame for safety). Some of the smaller machines can be wall mounted by using a suitable bracket obtainable from the manufacturer. **Note:** *See also the chapter on venting.*

Chapter 1
Emergency procedures

With symptoms such as leaking, flooding, unusual noises, blowing fuses, etc., the following procedure should be carried out. It is essential that the machine is NOT allowed to continue its programme until the fault has been located and rectified.

Firstly – do not panic

A Isolate the machine from the mains supply, i.e. turn the machine off, switch off at the wall socket, and remove the plug from the socket. **B** Turn off the hot and cold taps to which the fill hoses of the machine are connected. This is done because, even with the power turned off, if a valve is at fault it could be jammed in the open position. The machine will still fill, as turning the power or the machine off will make no difference to this type of fault. **C** At this point, the power and water should be disconnected. Even now, if there is still water in the machine, it could be leaking. Any remaining water can be extracted from the machine by syphoning, which is done simply by lifting the outlet hose from its usual position and lowering it to below the level of water in the machine. This will allow water to drain (unless of course, there is a blockage in the outlet hose!) To stop the water, lift the hose above the height of the machine. Repeat this process until the machine is empty. **D** Do not open the door to remove the clothes until all the previous steps have been carried out and a few minutes have elapsed to allow the load in the machine to cool. In cases where the machine was on a very hot wash, wait about half an hour. When all of these steps have been carried out, and the clothes have been removed from the drum, it is then possible to calmly sit down and start to work out what the problem may be, and form the plan of action in a logical manner.

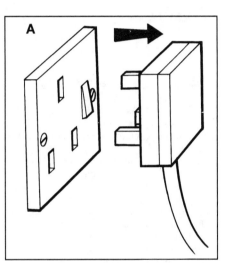
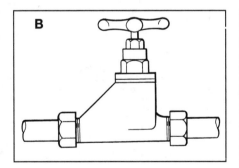

Chapter 2
Tools and equipment

Modern automatic washing machines do not require very specialised tools. Many of the routine repairs such as blocked pumps, renewal of door seals and hoses can normally be completed with a selection of the following tools: crossblade and flatblade screwdrivers, combination pliers, simple multimeter, pliers.

Most people who are DIY-orientated will own one or more of these items already. A useful addition to this selection would be a self-locking wrench, a socket and/or box spanner set, soft-face hammer and circlip pliers. These would help with the larger jobs, such as motor removal and bearing removal, etc.

Bearing removal/renewal for instance may also require specific equipment such as bearing pullers. As these can be expensive to buy, it is advisable to hire them from a tool hire specialist for the short period that you require them. Local garages may also be willing to let you hire them for a small deposit.

It will not prove difficult to build up a selection of tools capable of tackling the faults that you are likely to encounter on your machine. Most of the large DIY stores will stock the tools that you require, often at a good saving.

When buying tools check the quality. A cheap spanner or socket set is a waste of money if it bends or snaps after a short period of use. Having said that, there are many tools on the market that are of a reasonable quality and are inexpensive. Try to buy the best that your budget will allow. Remember, the tools that you buy are a long-term investment and should give years of useful service.

As with any investment, it is wise to look after it and tools should be treated in the same way. Having spent time and money on tools, they should be kept in a clean and serviceable condition. Ensure that they are clean and dry before storage.

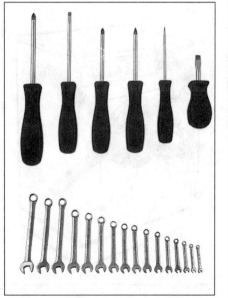

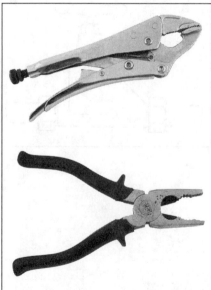

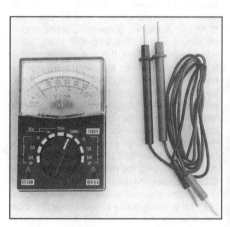

Chapter 3
A general safety guide

Electricity at all voltages is to be respected. Those who do not observe the basic rules of electricity are not only a danger to themselves but to those around them.

Electrical accidents should be regarded as avoidable. Most are due to plain carelessness and the failure to follow basic rules of electricity even when they are known by the injured party.

There are in the region of sixteen million homes in Britain supplied with electricity, each home having on average twenty five electrical appliances. With such a volume of items, it may be a surprise to find that fatalities due to electrical accidents are less than eighty per year. Although this is a small percentage figure in terms of population and only 1% of the 8000 deaths resulting from accidents in the home, it is still too high.

The most common causes of shocks or fires from electrical appliances fall into three categories;

1 Faulty wiring of the appliances. i.e. frayed or damaged flex or cables, incorrect fuse, poor socket, poor/damaged plug, incorrectly wired plug, etc.

2 Misuse of the appliance. Hairdriers and similar electrical items being used in the bathroom. This also includes the installation of washing machines, etc., incorrectly installed in bathrooms. Rules regarding electrical items in bathrooms are strict for good reason. See *Do's* and *Dont's*. Electrical power tools used outside in the rain or in wet conditions. The combination of water and electricity greatly increases the possibility of you or someone else being injured.

3 Continuing to use an electrical appliance knowing it to be unsafe, i.e. cracked casing, faulty plug, damaged cable, faulty on/off switch, etc.

By being aware of the need for safety, several of the above faults can be avoided. Others can be eliminated by regular inspection and immediate correction of faults, failure or wear. As for misuse, this may be due to a purely foolhardy approach or genuine ignorance of potential danger. This can be overcome by understanding and above all, acting upon the guidelines in this book. If at any time you feel you lack the ability to do a particular job yourself, then it is best not to try. You can still carry out the diagnosis of the problem thus ensuring that any work carried out by a repair company is correct. This alone can sometimes save a lot of time and expense.

Switch off! Always withdraw plug and disconnect from mains.

Appliances vary – make sure you have a suitable replacement part.

For screws use a screwdriver, for nuts a spanner.

Examine and clean all connections before fitting new parts.

Tighten all screws and nuts firmly (knurled nuts, use pliers).

Your safety depends on these simple rules:

Fuses: Up to 250 watts 1A; 750 watts 3A; 750 to 3000 watts 13A.

Insulation is for your protection. Don't interfere.

Renew worn or damaged appliance flex.

Secure flex clamps and all protective covers.

Test physically and electrically on completion.

Do's

● Thoroughly read all the information in this book prior to putting it into practice.
● Isolate any appliance before repair and/or inspection commences.
● Make sure that the correct rated fuse is used.
● Correctly fit the mains plug *(Basics – Electrical)*, ensuring the connections are in the correct position, tight and with the cord clamp fitted on the outer of the cable.
● Check that the socket used is in good condition and has a sound earth path. *See Basics – Electrical.*
● Take time to consider the problem at hand and allow enough time to complete the job without rushing.
● Keep a methodical approach to the stripdown of the item and make notes. This helps greatly with subsequent reassembly.
● Double check everything, ask or seek help if in doubt.
● Ensure an RCD, see *Jargon*, is in circuit when functionally testing a machine, and when using electrical equipment outdoors.

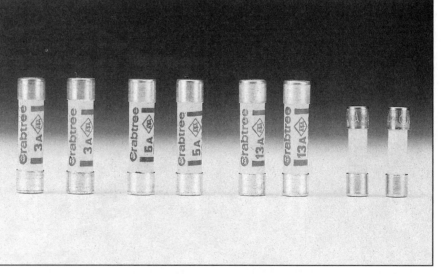

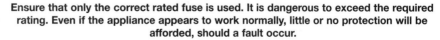
Ensure that only the correct rated fuse is used. It is dangerous to exceed the required rating. Even if the appliance appears to work normally, little or no protection will be afforded, should a fault occur.

Don'ts

● Do not work on any machine that is still plugged in/connected to the mains supply even if the socket switch is OFF. Always isolate fully.

● Do not install or allow the use of washing machines, tumbledriers or any portable mains appliance in bathrooms or shower rooms. It may seem harmless to run an extension lead from a convenient socket on the landing so that an appliance can be used in the bathroom, but it is extremely dangerous and MUST NOT be done under any circumstances.

● Do not use mains powered equipment outdoors in damp conditions or in the rain.

● Do not repair damaged wiring or cables with insulation tape under any circumstances.

● Do not sacrifice safety by effecting a temporary repair.

WARNING: *Never leave bare wires outside terminals.*

Note: *The wires in a mains lead are coloured in accordance with the following code: Green and Yellow – Earth, Blue – Neutral, Brown – Live. As the colours of the wires in the mains lead of an appliance may not correspond with the coloured markings identifying the terminals in the plug, proceed as follows. The wire which is coloured green and yellow must be connected to the terminal which is marked with the letter E or by the earth symbol or coloured green or green and yellow. The wire which is coloured blue must be connected to the terminal which is marked with the letter N or coloured black. The wire which is coloured brown must be connected to the terminal which is marked with the letter L or coloured red. If in doubt, consult a qualified electrician.*

The correct rating of fuse must be used as per the manufacturer's instructions.

General

Consider your own safety and that of other people.

Act in a way that prevents incidents becoming accidents.

Use your common sense . . . think before acting.

Tidy workplaces make safer workplaces.

Identify potential hazards.

Observe the rules of safety first.

Never underestimate the possible dangers.

Chapter 4

Basics – electrical

Special note: *Variations in supply systems used in countries other than the UK.*

As detailed in the text in this chapter, various types of earthing systems may be encountered – one of the most popular being the PME system whereby neutral and earth are BONDED (linked) at the supply point to the property. The choice of which supply system (and ultimately which earth system your property has) is a matter for your supply authority. The requirement of a sound earth path however is common to all domestic systems.

For the sake of safety around the home or office, a basic understanding of electricity is essential. Even if you don't intend to carry out any repairs or servicing of your appliances yourself, a sound understanding of household electrical supply will prove invaluable in the long run. Ignorance is no protection against either yours or a third party's errors, whether it be on repairs, servicing or the installation of appliances. It is with this in mind that this chapter has been written. It is not an in-depth study of the subject, there are many books that contain more detailed information for those who want to know more about electricity. In this instance, the aim is to impart a safe knowledge without too much technical data. To be informed is to be enlightened – to be aware of danger helps one to avoid it and to understand how and why certain safety criteria should be adopted.

A simplified, but typical household supply is as follows.

The substation has power supplied to it at very high voltage (400,000V) in three-phase form. This supply is converted at the substation via a transformer, down to 230V single-phase and is then distributed to our homes. Under normal circumstances, current flows from the live supply of the substation's transformer through the electrical items being used in the house and back via the neutral conductor (cable) to the substation transformer's neutral pole (a closed loop). The neutral terminal of the transformer is in turn connected to the ground (earth – meaning in this case, the general mass of the earth).

It is usual to use the armoured sheath of the electricity supply authority's cable in order to provide a low impedance continuous link back to the supply transformer's start point. Various types of earthing can be encountered, connection to the armoured sheath of the authority's supply cable, own earth rod, transformer earth rod via general mass of the earth or the increasingly popular use of the neutral conductor of the authority's supply cable (often called PME protective multiple earthing or TN-C-S system). If with any of the mentioned earth systems a fault should occur between the live conductor and the earth conductor, another loop would be formed. This is called the 'earth loop' for obvious reasons. The earth loop path is designed to encourage current to flow in the event of an earth fault, to enable the protective device in the consumer unit to operate in order to isolate the supply to the circuit. Failure to cause the protective device to operate will result in the appliance remaining 'live' with the consequence that any person touching the appliance will receive a nasty, if not fatal electric shock. For this reason the resistance of the earth loop path must be low enough to allow sufficient fault current to flow to operate the protective fuse or circuit breaker.

It is very important not only to have an earth, but one that has a low resistance/impedance, i.e. perfect earth. The term used for testing for this is earth loop impedance, which means checking to see if the current flow is impeded and if it is, by how much. This test requires a specialised meter giving a resistance figure in ohms. Recommended resistances for the various supply configurations in the IEE Regulations. However, the main criteria is that as low a resistance as possible exists in the earth supply, around 1.1 ohms or less in most instances. **Note:** *An earth loop test cannot be carried out using a low voltage multimeter as a fault may exist that allows the low voltage of say 9V to pass easily (i.e. just one tiny strand of wire poorly connected), but would break down and go high resistance or open circuit if a true fault voltage of 230V at 13A tried to be passed.*

Though low voltage testing will give an indication of earth path, it cannot indicate quality. Only an earth loop impedance meter gives a clearer indication of earth quality under more realistic conditions.

What is an earth fault?

An earth fault is defined as the condition where electricity flows to earth, which, under normal circumstances, it should not do. There are two recognised ways in which this may happen – Direct and Indirect.

Direct – when contact is made directly with the current carrying conductor which is designed to carry that current, i.e. possibly as a result of failure to isolate the supply or by ignoring safety precautions, etc.

Indirect – touching a part or metal casing, etc., that would not normally carry current but is doing so owing to a fault.

Consumer units with MCBs (miniature circuit breakers) with RCDs (residual current devices) provide a much higher degree of protection.

What is a consumer unit?

The consumer unit is the point at which the supply into the house is split into separate circuits, i.e. lights, sockets, etc. It houses a main isolation switch or combined RCD which is used to isolate/remove power to all the circuits in the house. Also housed within the unit are various fuse carriers for cartridge or rewirable fuses or an MCB in place of fuses. Each circuit leading from the consumer unit has its own rating of fuse or MCB and only that fuse rating and no other may be used. **Note:** *Even when switched off, there is still a live supply to the consumer unit. Do not remove the covers of the consumer unit or tackle any inspection or repair to this item without seeking further information. Faults other than fuse renewal are best left to skilled electrical engineers. Although assistance may be available from other publications, extreme care should be exercised. As mentioned earlier, it is not the aim of this book to encourage the repair or maintenance of items that are not fully isolated.*

What does it do?

The consumer unit's function is to divide the incoming supply at a convenient point (though not always easily accessible due to poor design). It also allows all circuits to be allocated a fuse and to conveniently house them in one unit. Isolation of all circuits is possible by a main double-pole switch which is also incorporated within the unit.

Fuses in more detail

Two versions of fuses are to be found. Cartridge and rewirable fuses have been around for sometime now. The rewirable type being difficult and fiddly and the cartridge type, although easier to renew, is often difficult to obtain. Both these systems have drawbacks in being awkward and not very 'user friendly'.

An ordinary fuse is simply a weak link designed to break/rupture at a preset rating. If a circuit is overloaded or a short circuit occurs, the resulting overload will cause the fuse to melt and sever the supply. Unless a direct short circuit occurs, the overload on the fuse may not be enough to cause the fuse to blow as it has a fair degree or leeway over its rating value. It therefore offers only basic safety and will not afford any personal safety as the time taken to break/rupture is generally too long.

Miniature circuit breakers (MCB) are now widely used which avoid all the problems normally associated with ordinary fuses. They are small sophisticated units that afford a much higher degree of protection than the ordinary fuses. They are tamper-proof and are easily identified when one has tripped (switch moves to OFF position). Most importantly, they cannot be reset if the fault still exists which eliminates the practice of putting in the wrong fuse wire or cartridge to get things working – a foolish and most dangerous practice! MCBs are available in similar ratings to ordinary fuses. These units are factory calibrated to extremely accurate tolerances and must not be tampered with or attempts made to readjust.

Unfortunately, neither fuses nor miniature circuit breakers alone can give protection to anyone involved in a 'direct contact' situation and it is quite possible for the same statement to apply in the case of 'indirect contact'. This may sound confusing, but It should be realised that in a 'direct contact' situation a person is literally shorting out Live and Earth whereas in an 'indirect contact' situation, the Live to Earth path is already there because the equipment itself is connected to earth. The reason the fuse hasn't blown or the circuit breaker tripped is because the fault is not large enough to operate them, yet is large enough to be fatal. For instance, a 10A fuse would never blow with an 8A earth fault on the circuit, yet 8A constitutes a very dangerous level of earth fault current.

To afford a higher degree of protection, another device has been developed and is available in various forms:

a) Mounted within the consumer unit to protect all or selected circuits.
b) As individual socket protection.
c) An adapter to be used as portable protection and used where required.

The name given to this device in all its forms is an RCD (Residual Current Device). It may also be called RCCB (Residual Current Circuit Breaker). In the early days of its introduction, it was known as an ELCB (Earth Leakage Circuit Breaker). The primary protection is the integrity of the earthing. RCDs in addition to the earthing, provide a much higher degree of protection depending upon the degree of sensitivity. For personal protection it is recommended that a sensitivity of 30 mA is used.

It is generally considered that an earth fault of 1A or more is a fire risk, 50 mA or more provides a shock risk which can have varying effects upon the human body depending upon the value of earth fault current and the body resistance of the person and of course, their state of health. The heartbeat cycle is about 0.75 second, it is therefore necessary to cut off the fault current in less than one cardiac cycle. The Wiring Regulations stipulate that for Indirect Contact protection isolation must occur within 0.4 second.

How does an RCD work?

An RCD protects by constantly monitoring the current flowing in the live and neutral wires supplying a circuit or an individual item of equipment. Under normal circumstances, the current flowing in the two wires is equal but, when an earth leakage occurs due to the fault or an accident, an imbalance occurs and this is detected by the RCD which automatically cuts off the power within 200 mS.

To be effective, the RCD must operate very quickly and at a low earth leakage current. Those most frequently recommended are designed to detect earth leakage faults in excess of 30 mA (30/1000ths of an amp) and to disconnect the power supply within 200ms (of the rated sensitivity): these limits are well inside the safety margin within which electrocution or fire would not be expected to occur.

It should now be apparent that RCDs are designed to sever mains current should your electrical appliance develop an electrical fault or should you cut through the mains cable of your lawnmower for instance. They are not designed to let you increase the risk to yourself by adopting a cavalier attitude with regard to safety. They are simply a fail safe device and should be used as such. Used correctly they are an invaluable asset to your household.

NOTE: *The use of an RCD must be in addition to and not instead of normal overload protective; i.e. fuses or MCBs. All residual current devices have a test button facility. It is essential that this is pressed regularly to verify that the device operates. For use with adapters or sockets, or for outside use, test before each operation. If failure occurs, i.e. does not trip, or trip appears sluggish or hard to obtain, have the unit tested immediately. This will require an RCD test meter and is best left to a qualified electrician.*

Chapter 5
Plugs and sockets

Problems with electrical appliances may not always be the result of a failure of the item itself but with the electrical supply to it via the socket. A three-pin socket must have a Live supply, a Neutral return and a sound Earth path. When a plug from an appliance is inserted in the socket, a firm contact must be made at all three points. If the live or neutral pins of the plug or connection point within the socket fail to make adequate contact or are free to move, localised heating will occur within the socket. Appliances used from spur outlets must be connected correctly and securely. The spur outlet must also have a double pole isolation switch and great care must be exercised to ensure the outlet is switched OFF prior to disconnecting or working on the appliance. It is good policy and strongly recommended to isolate the spur outlet by both its switch and by removing the relevant fuse (or switching OFF the MCB) supplying that circuit at the consumer unit. Furthermore, confirm the spur has no power by using a non-contact voltage-sensing device like the one shown. DO NOT simply rely on the fact that the appliance connected to the spur outlet does not work, power could still be present. Ensure you check before proceeding.

Problem spotting

Telltale signs of this type of fault often show themselves as:
1 Burn marks around one or both entry points on the socket.
2 Plug hot to the touch after use of appliance in that socket.
3 Pungent smell from socket when appliance is in use.
4 Pitting and burn marks on and around the pins of the plug.
5 Radio interference to nearby equipment caused by internal arcing within the socket creating spurious radio emissions. These may pass along the ring main to hi-fi units, etc.
6 Intermittent or slow operation of the appliance being used.
7 Failure of the fuse in the plug. In this instance, this is not caused by a fault within the appliance but by heat being transferred through the live pin and into the fuse which fails by over-heating.

All these conditions are more likely with appliances such as washing machines,

heaters and kettles, etc., which draw a high current when in use.

Why does it happen?
The reasons for such problems are various and may be caused by one or a combination of any of those listed below:
1 Repeated use of the socket, opening up the contact points within the socket. In other words general wear and tear.
2 Poor quality socket or plug.
3 Loose pins on plug.
4 The use of a double adapter. This can cause a poor connection purely by the weight of cables and plugs pulling the adapter partially out of the wall socket. Worse still is allowing a number of high-current-draw appliances to be run through one socket thus causing overloading. Examples might be a fan heater and kettle or washing machine and tumble dryer. Whenever possible, avoid the use of adapters by provision of an adequate number of sockets and do not exceed 3 kW load on any single socket.
5 Use of a multi-point extension lead when the total load on the trailing socket can easily exceed the 3 kW load of the single socket supply. **Note:** *It is unwise to use a washing machine or similar items via an extension lead. Make provision for a convenient 13A supply socket to accommodate the original length of the appliance cable.*

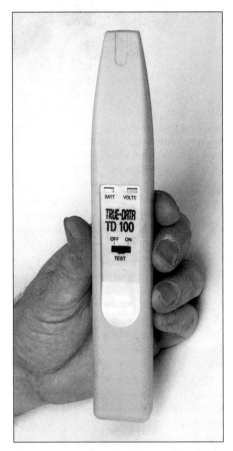

Non-contact voltage testers used to check if a spur or outlet is isolated. This particular type of tester has a self-test facility to maximise safety and emits both audible and visual indication if voltage is detected. The use of neon test screwdrivers should be avoided at all costs

Socket highlighting overheating. Both plug and socket will require replacing

Rectification
Firstly, DO NOT use the socket until the problem has been rectified. If the socket is found to be showing any of the previously described faults, it must be renewed completely. If it is a single socket it may be wise to have a double socket fitted as a replacement. Numerous DIY books describe the renewal of sockets so I won't duplicate the instructions here. Suffice to say that caution should be exercised when tackling socket renewal. When buying a replacement socket, make sure it is a good

Internal view of severe burnout caused by poor connection to terminal. A new plug is required and the cable cut back to sound wire or renewed

Incorrectly fitted plug. Wiring bunched and not trimmed to right lengths. Ensure all plugs are fitted correctly

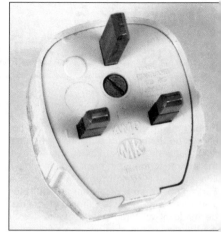

Typical resilient plugs which can stand up to rugged use without cracking

High quality three-pin plug ideal for home appliances

Always look for the ASTA/BS sign when purchasing electrical fittings

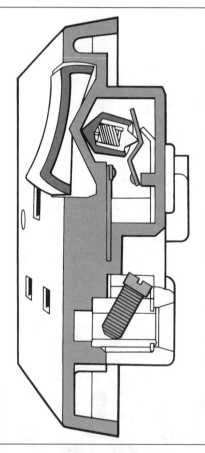

Internal view of 13A socket

British Standards do apply to these items, quality does vary considerably. When buying plugs and sockets, go to outlets that can give advice and that carry a good selection. This will allow you to compare quality and build of the products. Look for the ASTA mark which proves that the design and manufacture has been approved by the Association of Short Circuit Testing Authorities. Replacement fuses should also carry this mark.

The earth

All of the faults mentioned previously relate to the 'live' supply and neutral return on the socket, the plug or both. There is, of course, a third pin. Although it takes no active part in the operation of the appliance, it is, however, the most important connection of all. The function of the earth system is explained in *Basics – electrical*. Products that have three core cable must have the yellow and green earth wire securely connected to the earth pin of the plug or pin marked E.

The earth path of an appliance can be checked easily using a simple test meter (see *Using a meter*). Remember, a path of low resistance is required from all items within the product that are linked into the earth path via the yellow and green cable. **Note:** *The earth path of an appliance from its exposed metal parts to the earth pin of the plug should be a maximum of 1 ohm (BS3456).*

Checking the socket will require the use of an earth loop test meter which needs to be operated correctly. As these meters are expensive and problems could be encountered with distribution boards fitted with an RCCD, it is advisable to have these tests done by a qualified electrical contractor. A simple plug-in tester like the one shown can

quality one as there are many of dubious quality to be found. Price is a good indicator of quality in this field.

It is advisable to renew all plugs that have been used in the faulty socket because damage may have been caused. It is possible, of course, that a faulty plug damaged the socket. To continue using the

old plugs could result in premature failure of your new unit.

As with sockets, plugs can be found in many styles and qualities. While some of the poorer quality plugs may prove to be reliable on low current consumption items like lamps, TV and radios, they may not be so good for washing machines and heaters, etc. Although

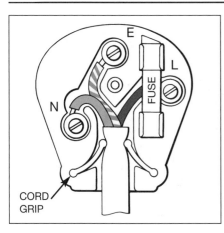

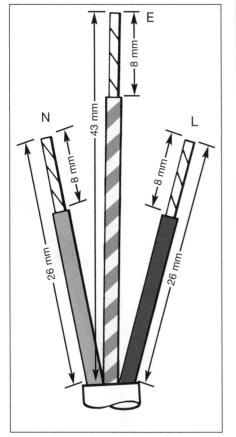

Typical plug in socket tester

slotted through a hole in a work surface, or due to damage), because of its moulded construction, it is not possible to take it off in the normal way. The plug has to be cut off with suitable wire cutters and a new plug fitted correctly as shown.

Warning: *Any moulded plug removed in this way must be disposed of immediately. It is wise to remove the fuse and to bend the pins of the plug as soon as it is removed to make sure that it cannot be inadvertently plugged into a socket. Do not leave it lying about or dispose of it where children can find it and plug it in.*

Make sure a moulded plug removed from an appliance cannot be inadvertently plugged in. Remove the fuse and bend the pins

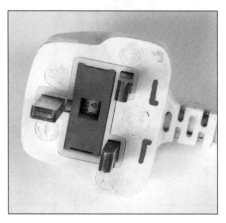

Typical moulded plug

be found in most good electrical shops and DIY outlets. This is most useful for checking the socket for reverse polarity. In other words, it will show if a socket has been incorrectly wired. An incorrectly wired socket can still work and outwardly give no sign of any problem. This type of fault is dangerous and not uncommon. The plug-in tester also indicates if an earth path is present. However, the quality of the earth in the socket is not shown. That is to say, it may have a very high resistance but would still allow the neon of the tester to light. If the earth resistance is high, remember this may result in a failure to blow the fuse which may cause overheating at the high resistance point or allow a flow of

electricity through anything or anyone else that can give a better route to earth.

Plug fitting

The fitting of a plug is often believed to be a straight forward task that needs little or no explanation. On the contrary, this is an area where many problems are to be found and dangers encountered if the fitting is not done correctly. Do not neglect this most important item.

The following text and photo sequences deal specifically with modern 13A flat-pin plugs. If your property has round-pin plugs and sockets, the indication is that the house wiring may be old and it would be wise to have it checked thoroughly by an expert.

When wiring a plug, it is good practice to leave the earth wire (yellow/green) longer than is necessary merely for connection to the earth terminal to be accomplished. The extra length is taken up in a slight loop shape within the plug. Doing this means that, should the appliance flex be pulled hard accidentally and the plug's cable grip fail to hold, the live and neutral wires will detach from the terminal first, leaving the earth loop intact to provide continued safety cover. The photo of the pillar type plug shows how the extra little bit of earth wire is contained inside the plug.

Moulded plugs

Some appliances may be supplied with one-piece moulded 13A plugs fitted to the mains cable. If for any reason this type of plug has to be removed (e.g. to allow the cable to be

Do's and Don'ts

● DO ensure the cable insulation is removed carefully. Use of correct wire strippers is recommended.

● DO make sure that connections are the right way around.

● DO ensure that wires are trimmed to suit plug fixing point and no bunching is present.

● DO make sure that all connections are tight and no strands of wire are left protruding from terminals. To prevent this, twist the strands together, prior to fitting.

● DO make sure that the cord grip is fitted correctly around the outer insulation only.

● DO ensure correct rating of fuse is used to suit appliance.

● DO ensure the plug top/cover fits tightly and securely with no cracks or damage present.

● DO NOT damage the inner core of wires when removing the outer or inner insulation. If you do, cut back and start again.

● DO NOT fit tinned ends of cables into plugs. Some manufacturers tin (dip in solder) the end of the exposed inner conductors.

The tinned/soldered end, if fitted to the plug, will work loose and cause problems associated with loose connections. Although tight when fitted, constant pressure over a long period will compress the soft solder resulting in a loose joint.

A second problem associated with tinned conductors is the excessive length of exposed inner wire which the manufacturer usually provides. This can protrude below the cord clamp bunch within the plug to allow the cord clamp to grip the outer insulation only. Both of these practices are dangerous and must be avoided. Always cut cable lengths to suit the plug. If this poor method of fitting is found on an appliance it must be corrected immediately.

● DO NOT allow strands of wire to protrude from any fixing points.

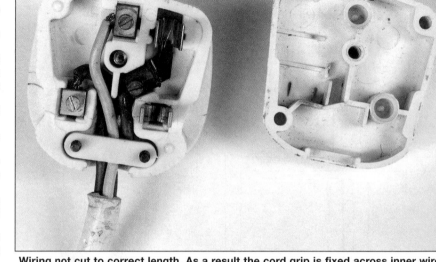

Wiring not cut to correct length. As a result the cord grip is fixed across inner wires, not outer sheath

● DO NOT fit incorrect fuse ratings. Always match fuses to appliances and observe the manufacturer's instructions.

● DO NOT re-use overheated or damaged plugs.

● DO NOT by-pass the internal fuse.

Conductor wire protruding from plug pins

Note: All of the above photographs are used to illustrate the lack of attention to safety to this small but vital component. Always fit plugs correctly and safely. To give further assistance, a step-by-step photo guide for the two types is given on the following pages.

Wiring a plug – pillar type

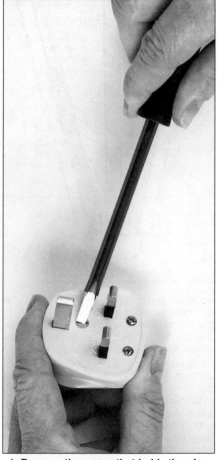

1 Remove the screw that holds the plug top-cover in position, taking care not to lose it

Wiring incorrectly bunched into plug to allow cord grip to hold outer sheath

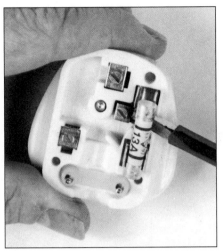

2 Ease the fuse from position (if using a screwdriver, take care not to damage it)

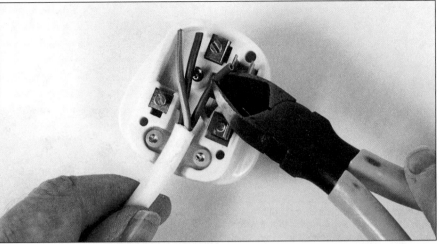

5 Offer the wiring to the plug base with the outer sheath in its correct position resting in the cord clamp area. Next, cut the inner cables as per the manufacturers instructions, if these are not available allowing 13 mm (½ in) past the fixing point. Don't forget to allow a little extra on the earth cable to form a slight loop

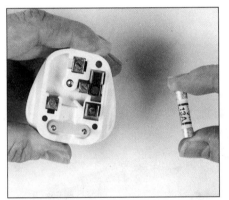

3 Check that the fuse supplied with the plug is of the correct rating for the appliance. Many plugs are supplied with 13A fuse already fitted, but do not be tempted to use it unless it is right. In this instance a 13A fuse was required

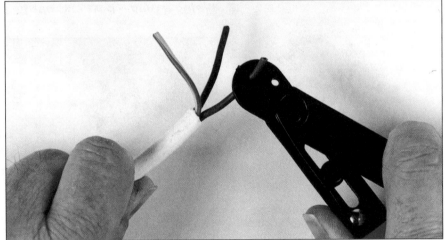

6 Carefully remove 6 mm (¼ in) of insulation from the end of each wire. This must be done with care to avoid damaging or cutting any strands of the conductor

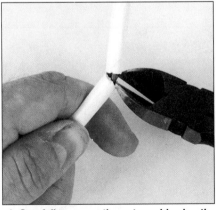

4 Carefully remove the outer cable sheath to expose the inner wires. If damage should occur to the inner wires in the process, cut back and start again

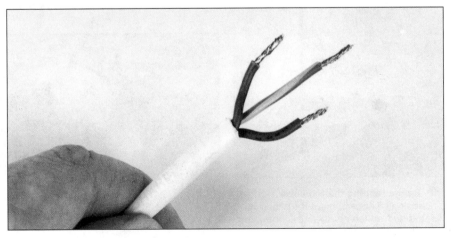

7 Twist the strands of each wire securely together. Make sure there are no loose strands

8 Fit each wire into its correct pillar and tighten each screw ensuring that it grips the conductor firmly (with thin wires it will help if they are folded over on themselves first). Make sure the wire fits up to the insulation shoulder and no wires or strands protrude from the pillar

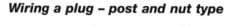

9 Fit the cord clamp over the outer sheath and screw it firmly into position while being careful not to strip the threads of the plastic grip

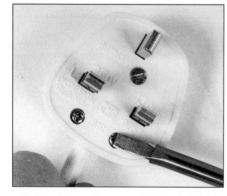

10 Before refitting the top/cover, double check all fixings. Ensure the wiring is seated and routed neatly and is not under stress or bunched. Fit the correct rated fuse, making sure that it is firmly and securely positioned

11 With top/cover refitted tighten the securing screw

Wiring a plug – post and nut type

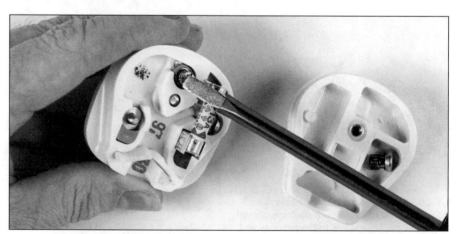

1 Remove the screw that holds plug top/cover in position

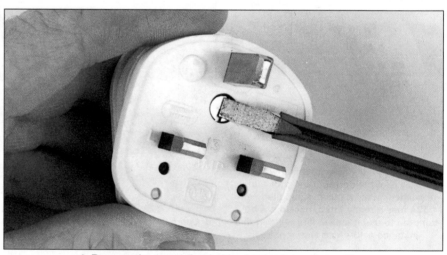

2 Remove the knurled/slotted nuts and place them safely in the top

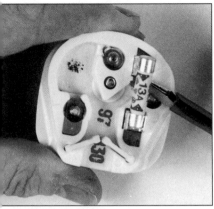

3 With the plug top/cover removed, the fuse can be eased from its position. If using a screwdriver, take care not to damage the fuse

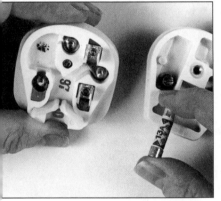

4 Check that the fuse supplied with the plug is of the correct rating for the appliance. Many plugs are supplied with 13A fuse already fitted but do not be tempted to use it unless it is right. In this instance a 13A fuse was required

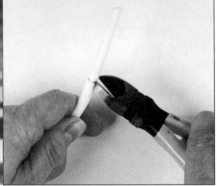

5 Carefully remove 43 mm (1¾ in) of the cable sheath to expose the inner wires. If damage should occur to the inner wires in the process, cut back and start again. Next, cut the inner cables as per the manufacturer's instructions, in this instance trim the live and neutral wires to 34 mm (1⅜ in)

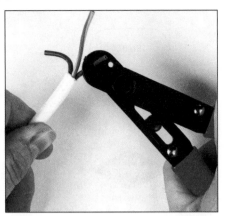

6 Now remove 15 mm (⅝ in) of insulation from the end of each wire. This must be done with care to avoid damaging or cutting any strands of the conductor

7 Twist the strands of each wire securely together. Make sure there are no loose strands

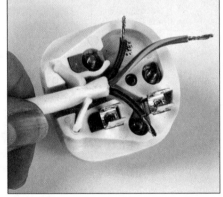

8 The prepared cable can now be inserted into the cord grip ensuring only the outer sheath of the cable is gripped

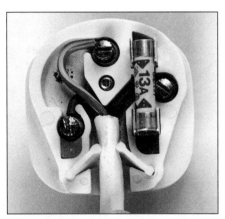

9 Fit each conductor (wire) to its correct terminal. Make sure each is fitted in a clockwise direction otherwise it will be pushed out as the nut is tightened. Ensure only the conductor is gripped and not the outer insulation

10 Securely tighten all three nuts. Ensure that the wire fits up to the insulation shoulder and no wires or strands protrude from the terminal. Before refitting the top/cover, double-check all fixings. Ensure the wiring is seated and routed neatly and is not under stress or bunched. Fit the correct rated fuse, making sure that it is firmly and securely positioned

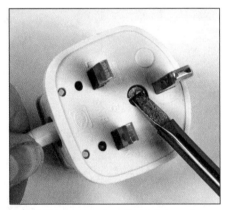

11 With top/cover refitted tighten the securing screw. This type has a captive screw with a shockproof washer to prevent it working loose during use

Plugs and Sockets – flowchart

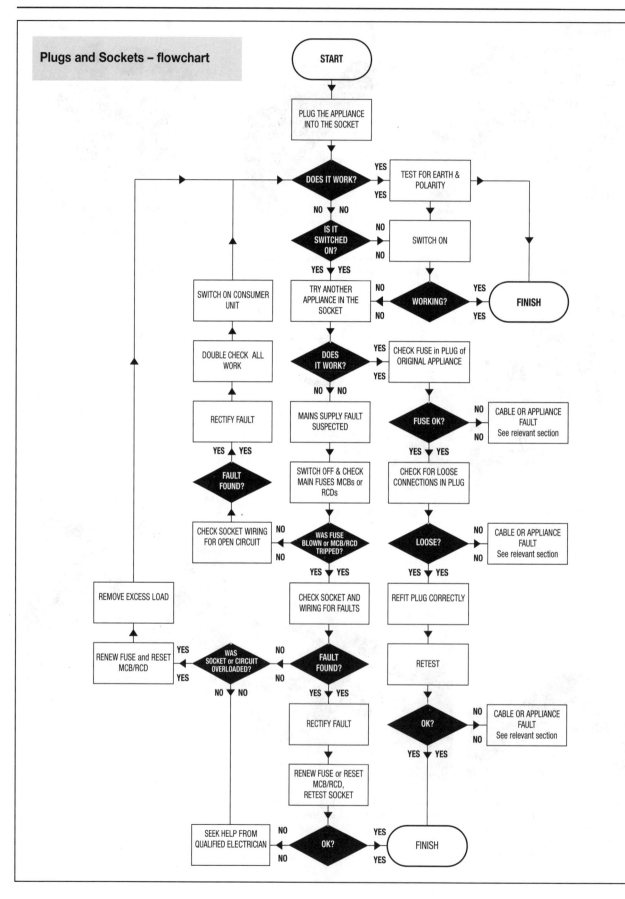

Chapter 6
Using a flowchart

Flowcharts are used throughout the book, and are designed to help you quickly locate the area or areas of trouble, and to show that a step-by-step approach to even the most difficult of faults is by far the best way to ensure they are found and rectified easily.

The use of flowcharts to those with some experience of home computers will need little explanation. To those of you who will be seeing them for the first time, here is how they work.

The diamond

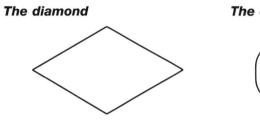

This asks a question, i.e. if the answer to the question in the diamond is yes, then follow the yes line from the diamond. If the answer is no, follow the no line.

The elipse

This is a terminator. When this box is encountered, you either start a new chart or finish one. The text in the box will indicate the action.

How flowcharts work

To the uninitiated, the use of flowcharts may seem a difficult way of fault finding. This is not the case, and will be quite simple if a few small, but important points are remembered. As you will see in the examples, there are only three main types of symbols used. A rectangular box, a diamond and an ellipse. With a little practice, you will become aware how invaluable this method can be in all areas of DIY work. The construction of one's own flowchart before attempting the job in hand will be of help when the time comes to reverse the stripdown procedure, i.e. notes can be made next to the relevant boxes on the flowchart, of what was encountered at that point, i.e. number of screws, positions of wires, etc. Small points – but so vital, and so often forgotten with an unplanned approach.

The rectangular box

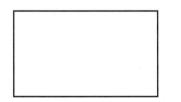

This is a process, i.e. in the box is an instruction. Carry it out and rejoin the flowchart where you left it, travelling in the direction indicated by the arrows.

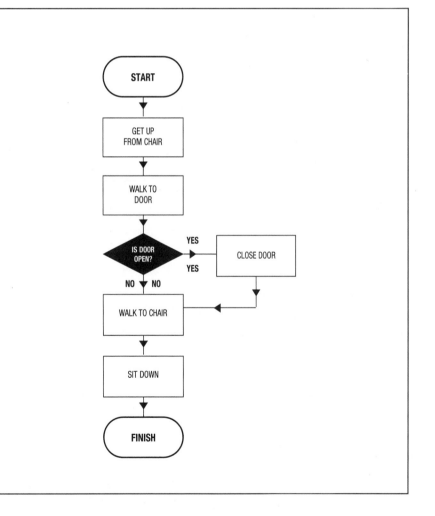

This example flowchart illustrates the steps involved in carrying out the simple task of making sure a door is closed. The arrows indicate the direction to the next step, which guides you through the logical sequence

Chapter 7
Basics – plumbing

Although the machine may have been working correctly in its present position for some time, incorrect installation of a machine may cause faults many months later. Because of this time span, the faults are not associated with bad plumbing and can cause the DIY repairer or engineer to look for other faults, which is very time consuming and annoying. Having said this, it is therefore worth a few minutes examining pipework, and checking the manufacturer's installation details. These details will be found in the manufacturer's booklet that came with the machine. Even if the installation of your machine was left to an 'expert', it is still advisable to read this section, as the chances are that they will not have read the installation details either!

For those of you who cannot find the manufacturer's booklet, what follows is a brief description of plumbing requirements that apply to nearly all automatic washing machines, and the reasons that they should be observed.

If the machine is to be plumbed in 'Hot and Cold', then isolation taps must be fitted. This enables the water supply to be cut off (isolated) between the normal house supply and that of the washer. **Note:** *The rubber hoses connected to the isolation taps should be positioned so that they don't get trapped when the machine is pushed back, or rub against any rough surfaces during the machine's operation. Both of these conditions can cause the pipe to wear, due to the slight movement of the machine when in use. Also ensure that no loops have been formed in the hot inlet hose. In the beginning this will not cause any trouble, but as the pipe gets older and the hot water takes effect, the pipe will soften and a kink will form. This will then cause a restriction or complete stoppage of water to the machine. This can also happen to the cold inlet hose, although it is very rare, due to the increased pressure in the cold system.*

The next thing to do, is check that there is adequate water pressure to operate the hot and cold valves, (see also *Functional testing*). On hot and cold machines, select a hot only fill. The machine should fill to working level within four minutes. The same should apply when a rinse cycle has been selected. This gives a rough indication that the water pressure is adequate to open and close the valves. This is because the valves are pressure operated and 4 p.s.i. minimum is required for their correct operation, (see *Water inlet valves* chapter). The cold pressure is usually governed by the outside mains pressure, but the hot water pressure is governed by the height of the hot water tank or its header tank.

Problems can arise when the tanks are less than eight feet higher than the water valve they are supplying. This is often found in bungalows and some flats. If a slow fill is suspected, check the small filter that can be found inside the hot and cold valves, when the inlet hose is unscrewed. These can be removed and cleaned by simply pulling them out gently with pliers. Care must be taken not to damage the filter or allow any small particles to get past when you remove it. Clean water is normally supplied to the valves, but in many cases old pipework or the limescale deposits from boilers, etc., can collect at these points.

Kinks and loops can also affect the outlet pipe and cause several problems to the wash, rinse and spin programmes.

Some machines may use larger and more specialised inlet hoses - for details of these types of systems, refer to the Chapter: *Water inlet valves*.

Causes of drain and outlet pipe blockages

As the ingredients in modern cleaning or washing products are specifically designed either to break down into harmless waste, or remain in very minute particles that are not large enough to form deposits of any noticeable size, they cannot actually cause a blockage.

Research has shown that blockages are nearly always caused by something becoming trapped in a drain or waste pipe, which acts as a nucleus around which other matter can form. Broken buttons, pins and poorly finished pipe joints are generally the root cause of a problem. This can slow down the passage of waste into drains so that other soil, such as grease from food or a wash load, particles of dirt and lastly a washing product will start to build a deposit, which can lead to a blockage.

Caustic soda is normally very effective at clearing any blockages in waste pipes. Caustic soda should periodically be used down a sink waste pipe if this leads to the same drain as any washing appliances. Great care should be taken when using this substance, which is available from pharmacists and hardware stores.

Do it yourself plumbing in

When a machine is to be fitted in close proximity to an existing sink unit, you can take advantage of the new style SELFBORE taps and outlet systems now available. These simple and effective DIY fittings will save both time and money.

In most cases, the fitting of these taps can be done with only a screwdriver and no soldering is required. You do not even need to drain or turn off the main water system at all.

At this stage I feel it is better to give you some visual help rather than pages of text, The following page shows you how easy the fitting of such units can be!

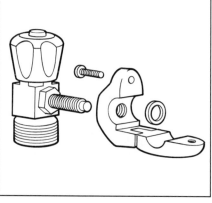

1 First, unscrew tap and open clamp

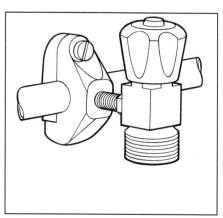

4 Insert tap assembly into clamp. Ensure tap is in off position

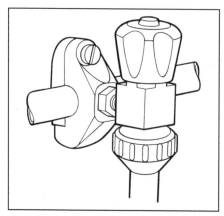

7 The tap is now ready for use. Connect hose to ¾ BSP thread on tap and turn on

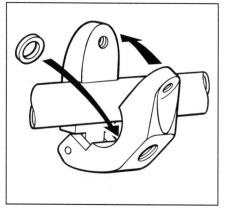

2 Fit clamp around copper pipe in required position. Make sure washer is in position

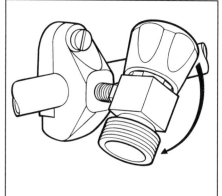

5 Turn clockwise until pipe is penetrated. Set tap to position required

Outlet hose

The outlet hose MUST fit into a pipe larger than itself, thus giving an 'air brake' to eliminate syphoning. The height of the outlet hose is also important if syphoning is to be avoided. Syphoning can occur when the end of the outlet hose is below the level of water in the machine which would result in the machine emptying at the same time as filling, and if the machine were to be turned off, would continue to empty the water from the machine, down to its syphon level.

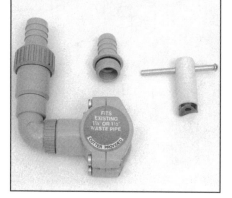

Typical self plumbing out kit

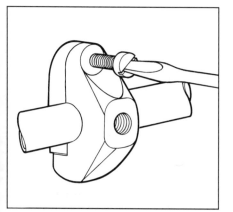

3 Engage screw and tighten until clamp is secure. Do not over tighten

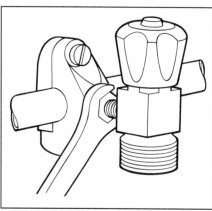

6 Tighten hexagonal nut towards the pipe. This secures tap in position

Do it yourself plumbing out

1 Select the most convenient place in the waste pipe. 31mm (1¼in) or 38mm (1½in) diameter.

2 Disconnect components (as shown). Place saddle around waste pipe, removing saddle inserts if pipe is 38 mm (1½in) diameter. Ensure that 'O' ring is seated in recess. Tighten screws by stages to give an even and maximum pressure on waste pipe.

3 Insert cutting tool and screw home (clockwise) until hole is cut in waste pipe. Repeat to ensure a clean entry.

4 Remove cutter and screw in elbow. Use locking nut (5) to determine final position of elbow and tighten, or screw non-return valve (3) directly into saddle piece.

5 To complete installation choose correct size hose coupling to suit drain hose and secure hose with hose clip (not included).

6 It is important to regularly remove lint and other deposits from non-return valve. Simply unscrew retaining collar (4).

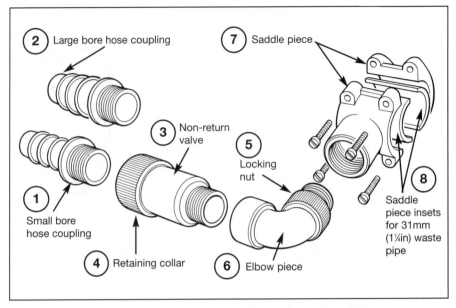

All components can be unscrewed by turning anti-clockwise

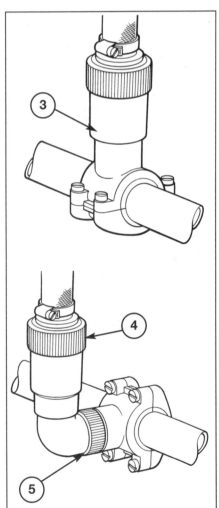

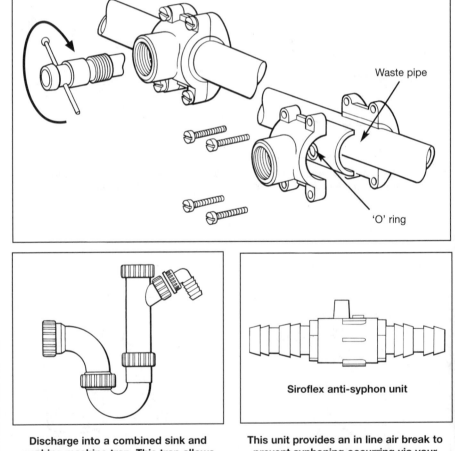

Discharge into a combined sink and washing machine trap. This trap allows water from the sink to drain away as normal but has an extra branch for attaching the washing machine hose

Siroflex anti-syphon unit

This unit provides an in line air break to prevent syphoning occurring via your appliance drain hose. Full fitting instructions are supplied with every unit

Chapter 8

Venting

Many washerdriers and tumbledriers vent the warm moist air which is produced during the drying cycle, into the room in which they are situated. This can amount to several pints of water vapour which will readily condense on the nearest cold surface, i.e. cupboards, windows, etc. Most appliances are situated in the kitchen where a fair amount of moisture is already produced from cooking, so the addition of extra condensation is an unwanted burden resulting in damage to the surrounding areas and also encourages the growth of mould in some situations. Condenser washerdriers and tumbledriers do alleviate this problem although the condenser drier is costly when compared to ordinary vented tumbledriers.

The answer to the problems caused by ordinary vented machines is external venting. This may simply be a case of attaching one end of a flexible hose to the outlet vent of the machine and hanging the other end out of an open window (both front and rear venting machines can be vented in this way). Although this solves the problem of moisture condensing in the room, it has its drawbacks, one of which is that there has to be a window near by which can be left open with the hose hanging through for as long as the machine is in use. As the majority of tumbledriers are used mainly in the autumn and winter, leaving a window open may not be convenient. The machine may also be left unattended or used at night on Economy 7* – either way, it is not wise to leave a window open,

The most convenient way around all these problems is to vent the machine permanently. This is not a difficult procedure, and with the square, through-the-wall vent system as opposed to the large round trunking, fitting can be quite simple. Several variations are available, with ends to fit most popular makes. If a convenient outside wall is not available, the kit can also be used to permanently vent through glass, again avoiding the need to leave windows open. Each kit comes with fitting instructions, but obviously care must be taken to check for hidden pipes or cables prior to making the hole in the masonry.

*Note: *Although the setting of domestic appliances to take advantage of off-peak electricity is commonplace, I have reservations about this practice and advocate the use of a smoke detector placed in the vicinity of any machines that are used in this way, giving added protection should a serious fault develop whilst the machine is unattended.*

A window mounted permanent vent system

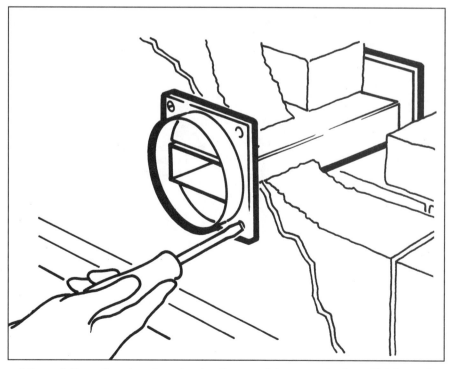

A through the wall vent system showing the new style square ducting which is much easier to fit

Points to remember

Many combined washerdriers which vent to atmosphere have a removable filter fitted within the exhaust tube which should be cleaned regularly. This is often overlooked because of its inaccessibility, i.e. under worktops, etc. If permanently venting this type of machine, do not forget to remove the filter or it will quickly clog and cause problems.

When sliding a machine with a rear fixed vent hose back into position, make sure that the flexible section of the hose does not get flattened between the machine and the wall, thus causing a restriction. Other problems that can occur are if a hose is fitted which is too long, or if it is simply pushed through the hole in the wall without using a proper vent kit, it can kink and form U-bends. If moisture condenses on the inner wall of the hose it will collect at such points and effectively block the hose or severely restrict the normal airflow thus reducing drier efficiency. If pushed through a cavity wall, the soft flexible hose may again form a U-bend, but it could also slip back so that the open end rests within the cavity thus allowing the water vapour expelled during the dry cycle to penetrate the cavity of the wall. All these problems can be avoided by obtaining a suitable kit and installing it correctly.

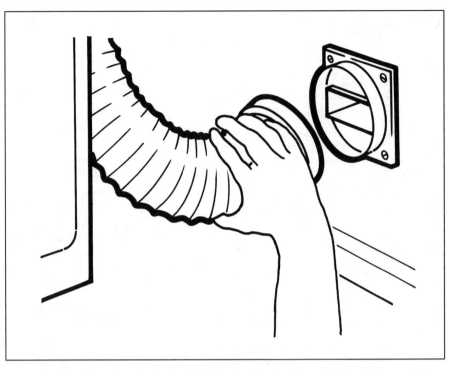

Both through the wall and window fittings take the circular vent hose of the machine and adaptors are available to suit most sizes of hose and machine combinations

If anti-draught cover is fitted, make sure it remains clear by checking it regularly for blockages and fluff build-up

Chapter 9
Functional testing

Throughout the book, reference is made to functional testing to ensure that the action of the machine is correct and installation is suitable. Use this sequence as a guide to ensuring correct operation after installation, repair or servicing. The purpose is to test where practicable, all functions of the machine and plumbing installation in the most efficient manner. The test will suit most types of machines which use mechanical timers/programmers. Some slight modification may be required to suit model variations. Electronically controlled machines, i.e. non-mechanical timers, will normally have selectable self-test programmes similar to this sequence. See *Timers (programmers)* chapter.

A typical installation and functional test

1 With the machine in its correct operating position and levelled correctly, and with all panels fitted, ensure that both hot and cold taps and power supply socket are turned on.
2 Ensure the door is correctly closed and latched.
3 It is not necessary to put a wash load into the machine or detergent in the dispenser for this type of test.
4 Select a hot wash cycle (90-95 degrees). On most machines this will only energise the hot fill valve and therefore test the flow rate/pressure supplied to it. The machine should fill to low level within four minutes if the water pressure is adequate. If the fill time is over this period, check that the hot supply tap is fully on. In most instances little can be done for slow hot filling, (see *Basics – plumbing*) and will in general cause only minor problems such as failing to dispense powders effectively from the drawer. In severe cases either connect solely to cold supply with a Y-joint or, alternatively, the powder could quite simply be sprinkled over the wash load in the drum, (only if the wash is to be started immediately), still allowing the machine to take the hot fill at its reduced rate.
Note: *Some machines can be modified internally. Instruction for this will be given in the accompanying user handbook/installation document supplied with the machine. Follow the instructions given and do not attempt alteration without the detailed instructions of the manufacturer. As with any repair, inspection or maintenance, isolate the machine thoroughly prior to removing any panels.*

5 Check for drum action when machine has filled to low level. Some machines may require the timer to be advanced slightly to avoid a paused heat-only cycle before drum rotation takes place. See *Timers (programmers)* chapter (Thermostop). Check for clockwise and counter clockwise drum action.
6 Check that door interlock operates and that door will not open during this cycle.
7 Switch the machine off and move it to the special treatments (fabric conditioner) position. This will select a higher level fill via the cold valve. Some machines will possess a choice of the positions for this – one before the short or delicates spin and one before the normal or fast spin. Remember that on delicate cycles the machine will normally stop full of water after the special treatments cycle and will only move on to the spin when instructed. Each machine has its own way of impulsing to the spin from this 'hold' position so make yourself aware from your handbook. See also *Machine will not empty* chapter.
7a If you choose the position prior to the normal spin, the machine will fill to its high level using the cold valve and therefore a check of the cold inlet can be made. Wait four minutes maximum for the high level to be reached. As the cold inlet pressure is usually governed by the street mains to the house the pressure is normally well above the minimum required.
8 When the high level is reached check for rotation, again clockwise and counter-clockwise.
9 As the programme of special treatments is short, allow the machine to impulse normally to the pump out stage. (If delicate cycle, use the normal advance mechanism). Check that the machine empties within one minute or thereabouts (verifying that the pump rate and outlet are correct).
10 Allow the machine to impulse on to the spin and through to the off position. Time and spin speeds will differ depending on whether special treatments cycle or spin speed was selected.
11 Check immediately after the OFF position has been reached to see if the interlock correctly inhibits entry to the machine.
12 Time the delay of the interlock, minimum one minute but up to two minutes. Check that after such time the door can be opened correctly. Do not be impatient and force the latch mechanism or handle.
13 Next, select a drying programme. Reference to the manufacturer's instruction booklet will be required as machines differ in the way they are set.
14 During the cycle, check for drum rotation clockwise and counter-clockwise, blower motor operation (background noise), warming up of door glass (do not touch the door glass directly as some makes get extremely hot). On condenser type machines, check also for intermittent pump action. Do not allow the dry sequence to continue for too long without a load in. With vented washerdriers, check the rear vent (or if a vent hose system is fitted check hose) for free flow of warm air.
15 Move the drier timer to the cool tumble position (i.e. five minutes before end of drying programme), and allow the sequence to finish. This allows both drum and heater unit to cool correctly whilst confirming correct operation of dryer timer.

This sequence is likely to take 10-15 minutes. If at any point a fault should occur, the correct action can be implemented.

These simple steps have in effect, confirmed (or otherwise) the operation of both water valves and pressure supplied to them, the pressure system for water level control, hoses and seals, outlet pump and waste outlet, programmer (though not in depth), spin speed, drier blower motor (if fitted), heater and drier timer. However, what this relatively simple test has not shown is whether the wash heater works or if the wash thermostat operates correctly. To confirm this, the time taken to heat up should be noted, also the correct impulse from the thermostat for that particular programme setting. These two items will be tested on the next full wash cycle after the basic functional test proves satisfactory. It is therefore advisable to check both heater and correct temperature advancing on a normal wash cycle.

Chapter 10
Locating a fault

Whenever possible the symptoms of the fault should be confirmed by the operation of the machine up to the point of the suspected fault using the appropriate test sequence, the machine should then be stopped, disconnected from the mains supply and the relevant flowchart or fault sequence followed. For major leaks, blown fuses, etc., this is not practical (more damage may result by repeated operation of the machine). In these cases, the fault is known and further confirmation would be of little benefit. Continuing to use a machine with a known fault may in fact, result in further damage to the machine or its surroundings.

Being able to assess and locate a fault may at first seem a difficult thing to do, but if a few simple procedures are carried out prior to starting the work, they will help cut down on the time spent on the machine. Hopping from one part of the machine to another in a random fashion, hoping that you will come across the fault and subsequently repair it, is hardly the best approach to repair work. This is not the way to tackle any job. Without doubt, the best method of fault finding is to be gained from your own experience of the machine; the fault with it and its location and rectification based on all the available information. Always remember a methodical approach to the work in hand, saves time and effort by eliminating unnecessary replacements based on guesswork.

However there are a few things that can be done before such testing. These will confirm if it is the machine itself that is at fault or if an external/user fault is the source. Indeed, a large percentage of repair calls are not a fault of the machine at all therefore before jumping to conclusions, pause for a moment. You will not only save time and effort, but money as well.

Remember these points when starting a repair.

1 Allow yourself enough time to complete the task in hand.
2 Do not cut corners at the expense of safety.
3 Try to ensure adequate working space wherever possible.
4 Make notes about the position of the part/s to be removed, the colours and position of wires, bolts, etc.

If you can acquire this practice, it will help you in all repairs that you carry out, not only with your washing machine or tumbledrier.

A few simple checks.
a) CHECK – that the machine is turned on at the socket.
b) CHECK – that the fuse in the plug is intact and working. This can be checked by replacing the suspected fuse with one out of a working item of the same rating.
c) CHECK – that the taps are in the ON position.
d) CHECK – that the door is closed correctly, and that a wash cycle is selected and the knob or switch has been pulled/pushed to the ON position.
e) CHECK – that the machine is not on a RINSE HOLD position. This on most machines will cause the machine to stand idle until instructed to do otherwise.

If the fault still remains, the next stop is to determine its true nature, and subsequent repair.

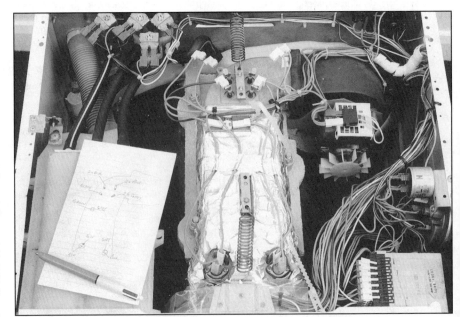

Make notes and drawings as the work progresses

Chapter 11
General care and attention

For many repairs it is best that the machine is laid on its front face or side. Generally it is best to lay the machine on the side opposite the timer. (The timer is located directly behind the main programme knob on models with mechanical programme control.) This is to avoid the tub and drum assembly coming in contact with the timer.

Always ensure that the outer shell of the machine in protected with a suitable cover when attempting to lay the machine down. The machine should be lowered slowly, to avoid excessive movement of the suspension. When lowering the machine, it is a good idea to place a block of polystyrene or similar material under the top edge of the machine, to provide room for the fingers for lifting the machine back into its correct position after the repair,

When laying the machine over, care should be taken to protect oneself from injury. Firstly, ensure that the machine is completely disconnected from the main supply, and that the inlet and outlet hoses are removed. Secondly, before attempting to lay the machine over, decide if you need any help. These machines are very heavy and a little help may prevent a slipped disc! Thirdly, before attempting to move the machine, ensure that the floor is dry. A wet floor has no grip, especially if the water contains detergent.

The correct rating of fuse must be used as per the manufacturer's instructions. As a general guide, the applications for the three main ratings of fuse are listed in the *General safety guide* chapter.

Blockages in the washing machine

Blockages in the washing machine itself cannot be associated with the use of a particular brand or type of washing detergent.

Although many cite detergents as the cause of the problem extensive research was undertaken to establish the actual cause of the problem. The results showed conclusively that blockages are not linked to the use of powders or liquids. What was found was that internal blockages are associated with calcium salts and grease residues that have detached from the inside of the machine. In some cases these residues can form a blockage in the narrow tube that leads to the pressure chamber.

A build-up of calcium and grease residue is usually caused by underdosing the washing detergent (even slightly) over a long period of time, and a problem can arise when a change of detergent, such as from a powder to a liquid, means that the recommended dosage is used. This extra detergent can loosen deposits inside the machine and then it is possible for a blockage to occur.

The recommended dosage of detergent, as stated on the pack, should always be used, and extra detergent should be added if items are heavily soiled or stained.

A 'maintenance wash' should be carried out 2 or 3 times a year (this is often recommended by machine manufacturers in the machine instruction booklet). The procedure involves running the machine through without any clothes in the drum, on the hottest wash possible, with the normal dosage of powder containing a bleaching agent, such as Persil Performance powder, Radion powder or Surf powder. This process will emulsify any grease deposits, which have built up, and the detergent will specifically be working on cleaning the machine rather than cleaning soiled clothes.

Regular inspection points

A regular internal inspection of your machines may enable you to identify a part that may not be working correctly, or find a perished hose before a leak occurs. It is recommended that the following points be checked regularly.

Inspect	When	Special notes
Pump filter (if fitted)	Weekly	As per manufacturer's manual. Often depends on usage.
Vent filter (if fitted)	After every dry cycle	Must be kept clean for efficient drying.
Valve filters (hot & cold)	6 months	If dirty, pull out carefully with pliers and wash.
Door seal	6 months	If seal is tacky to the touch it may need to be renewed soon.
Door glass		Remove sticky fluff or scale deposits from door glass inner surface with non-abrasive 'Scotchbrite' pad. Check inlet duct for cracking.
All hoses	6 months	Ensure that all corrugations in all hoses are checked thoroughly.
Pump and sump hose catch pot	6 months	Check for items that may have collected in or at these points. Remove as necessary.
Condenser unit (if fitted)	6 months or as required	Check for fluff build-up in fan chamber and ducting. Some makes are more prone than others to problems. Also dependent on usage.
Suspension	6 months	Check suspension mounts on tub and body of machine. If slide type, see *Suspension* chapter.
Motor brushes (if fitted)	6 months or yearly	Check for wear and/or sticking in slides. Renew if below half normal length.
Belt tension	6 months or yearly	Check and adjust belt tension if necessary. See *Belts* chapter.
Level machine	Yearly/after every repair	Check that the machine is standing firmly on the floor and does not rock. Adjust by unscrewing adjustable feet or packing under the wheels.
Check plug and connectors	Before and after every repair	After repair look for poor connections in the plug and socket. Also look for any cracks or other damage. Renew as necessary.
Taps and washers	Before and after every repair	Check taps for free movement, corrosion and/or leaks.

Note: *For inspection points on tumbledriers, see chapter on Dry-only machines.*

Chapter 12
Determining the fault

Throughout the manual, flowcharts are used to aid the fault finding process. The location of faults will become much easier as you become more conversant with your machine.

Selecting the correct flowchart or fault guide for the job will be made easier if it is remembered that faults fall into three main categories, mechanical, electrical and chemical.

Mechanical faults will normally become apparent by a change in the usual operational noise level of the machine. For instance a faulty suspension may cause a banging or bumping noise. A broken or slipping belt (incorrect tension) may give rise to excessive noise during the spin cycle or little or no drum rotation. This may also indicate a drum or motor bearing fault. Read all sections of the book thoroughly to help in understanding the way in which items function together. Full comprehension of all aspects will assist you greatly in determining the cause of the trouble from the symptoms displayed by the faulty appliance.

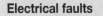

Electrical faults

Electrical faults fall into two major categories

Impulse path faults

A fault is classed as an impulse fault when an internal, pre-determined instruction has failed, e.g. thermostat does not close or open at the required temperature, or the timer fails to move on after a given time sequence. This constitutes an impulse path fault. Simply, this is the failure of the machine to move correctly through its selected programme. An instance of this type of fault is explained here:

The timer supplies power to the heater, but due to a fault in the thermostat circuit, the timer is not supplied with the information that the correct temperature has been reached. Because of this the timer does not move on, but remains on the heat position and exceeds the selected temperature. It should be noted that there is no fault in the timer, just in one of its impulse paths. A similar fault would arise even if the thermostat circuit was OK, the thermostat closed at the correct temperature, but the timer failed to move on after the correct time had elapsed. This would be a fault of the timer's internal impulse path via its timing mechanism, and would constitute a component fault, e.g., timer coil, thermostop or complete timer unit. See *Timers (programmers)*.

Component faults

A fault is classed as a component fault when a complete unit has failed. If, for instance, the pump, heater or motor should fail, the fault is said to be a component fault. Not all component faults are readily apparent. For instance, a failure in the coil of the water valve supplying the condenser unit would manifest itself as a failure of the machine to dry the clothes. The wash cycles would be unaffected and all obvious functions of the dry cycle such as heating up, circulation of air (noise of motor) etc., would appear to be OK, but with no water to cool the condenser, drying could not take place.

Chemical faults

These are normally associated with the detergent being used and will create such problems as poor washing, scaling problems, blocking, etc. A comprehensive guide to washing problems and useful hints will be found at the rear of this manual, in the chapter *Common causes of poor washing results*.

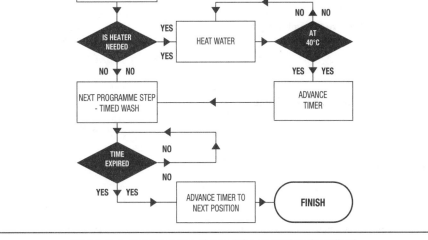

Shown is a simplified flowchart of the operation described

Fault finding guide – wash cycle

Machine will not work at all

Basics – electrical
Locating a fault
Door switches (interlocks)

Machine leaks

Emergency procedures
Locating a fault
Leaks fault finding flowchart
Water level control
Pumps
Motors
Water inlet valves
Suspension

Machine will not empty

Emergency procedures
Locating a fault
Pumps
Basics – plumbing
Wiring and harness faults

Machine washes but no spin

Locating a fault
Door switches (interlocks)
Pumps
Motors

Machine will not turn drum

Belts
Motors
Door switches (interlocks)

Machine spins on all positions

Locating a fault
Module control (Motors chapter)
Motors
Timers (programmers)

Machine will not fill/take powder

Basics – plumbing
Locating a fault
Water inlet valves

Machine does not wash clean

Locating a fault
Belts
Common causes of poor wash results
Basics – plumbing
Pumps

Machine is noisy

Noise faults (this chapter)
Bearings
Motors
Suspension

Machine won't move through programme

Basics – plumbing
Temperature control
Heaters
Water inlet valve
Timers (programmers)

Machine sticks through programme

Locating a fault
Basics – plumbing
Pumps
Timers (programmers)

Machine blows fuses

Emergency procedures
General safety guide
Basics – electrical
Low insulation

The lists below the main fault headings indicate the chapter sequence with which they should be examined.

Fault finding guide – dry cycle

No drying cycle

Check for correct setting
(own instruction booklet)
Basics – electrical
Basics – plumbing
Door switches (interlocks)
Wiring and harness faults

Poor drying of clothes

Check load size (own instruction booklet) (Introduction
and Dry-only machines chapters)
Basics – electrical
Basics – plumbing
Drying components – faults
Air ducts, motors, i.e. main wash, pump and fan
Heaters (airflow type)
Thermostats
Timers – both main and auxiliary (drier)
Harness faults

No heat at all on dry cycle

Air ducts (blockages). See Drying components
chapter
Heaters (airflow type)
Thermostats and TOCs
Timers

Heat too high

Check setting (own instruction booklet)
Air ducts (blockages)
Motors (fan motor)
Thermostats
Harness connections
Timer (drier)

Noise faults

Noise can be one of the first signs that something is going wrong with your washing machine. Noise faults are easily ignored, subsequently over a length of time they can be accepted as the norm, because of this it is important that noise faults be examined immediately.

As with other faults, noise faults become easier to locate the more familiar that you become with your machine.

Noises and their most common locations

A loud grating or rumbling noise would indicate a main drum bearing fault. See the *Bearings* chapter.

A loud high-pitched noise would indicate a main motor bearing or pump bearing fault. See the chapters on *Motors* and *Pumps*.

A noise just before and after spin would indicate wear or water penetration of the suspension mounts. See the chapter on *Suspension.*

A squeaking noise mainly during the wash cycle would indicate a poorly adjusted drive belt. Instructions on how to adjust the drive belt appear in the chapter on *Belts*.

Noise on the dry cycle may indicate a blockage in the fan housing, perhaps a build up of fluff or distortion of the plastic moulding, etc. See: *Drying components* chapter. A more metallic or grating noise could denote a failure of one or both bearings of the fan motor. Such faults may be accompanied by intermittent operation of the motor due to jamming, poor/lengthy drying or too high a temperature during the dry cycle caused by a reduction in air flow as the fan rotates slowly, See *Motors* chapter.

A rather unusual though not uncommon fault can be found on machines with cast aluminium pulleys. If a crack or break develops in one leg/spoke of the pulley, a noise very similar to that of main drum bearing failure can be heard. Check such pulleys closely for this type of defect and also for a tight fit on shaft of drum. These should not be a loose fit. See *Bearings* chapter. This type of fault may be apparent on wash, spin and dry cycles alike.

Coin damage

Coins and other metal items are easily trapped in the machine, and can cause a great deal of damage. They can become trapped between the inner drum and outer tub, and should be removed before damage to the drum occurs.

Coin damage can be identified by small

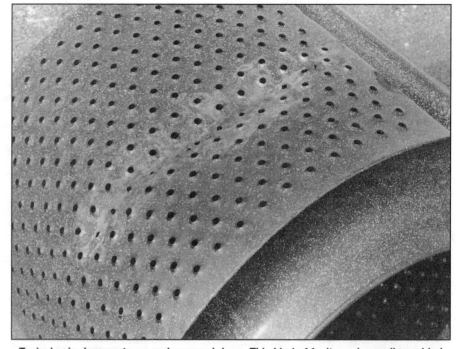

Typical coin damage to an early enamel drum. This kind of fault can be easily avoided by careful checking of pockets, etc., prior to loading the washer. If this type of damage has been caused, the only cure is to carry out a complete drum renewal

Typical damage caused by coin damage to an enamel outer tub. Although this does not seem as bad as the damage to the previous drum photograph, the chips on the enamel will cause corrosion. To cure this type of damage, treat the affected areas with an anti-corrosion compound. This is readily available in motorists' shops and is generally used for minor car bodywork repairs. When applying the above compound, please ensure that the manufacturer's instructions are followed carefully, and that the compound does not come into contact with rubber hoses or seals, etc. Always use this type of substance in a well ventilated area bumps on the inner drum or a rattling noise when spinning. On early enamel drums, this may be accompanied by small flakes of enamel in the wash load. It is not uncommon on machines with stainless steel drums for the drum to be torn open by coin damage. Take care when checking the drum interior for this kind of damage as the torn metal edges can be extremely sharp. In such instances the inner drum will need to be renewed, as a repair is not possible. On drums with plastic paddles, small pips of plastic found in the wash load may indicate the presence of a coin or similar item trapped between the inner and outer tub. This is a result of the coin (or similar item) chipping off the plastic rivets securing the paddles.

Where there is no damage to the drum or outer tub, it may be possible to avoid a full stripdown by extracting the coin from the drum/tub gap by removing the heater, see *Heaters*. The offending item can either be removed via this opening, or manoeuvred into the sump hose, where it can be extracted easily. **Note:** *Any large items such as bra wires or keys can be removed via the heater opening avoiding the sharp 90 degree angle into the sump hose. All such problems could of course be avoided by first removing all items from pockets before washing. This simple action can save a lot of time and money in the long run.*

Damage caused by a coin on a stainless steel drum. Avoid this type of expensive problem by checking pockets before washing clothes

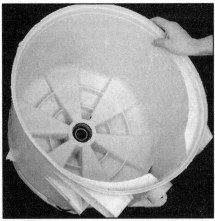

Plastic outer tubs are generally more resistant to coin damage

Modern plastic outer tubs can be cracked by coin impact. Check the tub closely for faults if the inner stainless steel drum shows signs of impact damage. Close inspection for hairline cracks is recommended

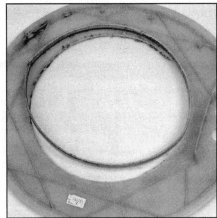

The plastic front of this tub unit was badly damaged by excessive bearing wear and drum movement

Chapter 13
Leaks fault finding flowchart

The leaks described in this chapter relate equally to wash-only machines, vented washerdriers and condenser washerdriers. Additional problems can be found with the extra hoses, connections and seals found in condenser machines, and reference to the *Drying components* chapter will be required. Specific problem areas on such systems are:

1 Poor positioning of hoses resulting in chafing.

2 Poor connection of rubber hoses to moulded plastic condenser units resulting in difficult to isolate leak faults.

3 Lack of heat resistant sealant (from earlier repairs) in areas such as heat duct to door seal inlet, fan chamber to both heat duct and condenser unit. This latter fault can give rise to vapour leaks that condense within the appliance. The result from this can lead to serious electrical problems and component failure.

Ensure all connections are secure and correctly positioned and all the protective covers and sleeves are in good condition. Seal hose connections and condenser mouldings and ducts with the correct sealants, see *Useful tips and information* and *Drying components* chapters.

With the above in mind, the flowchart can be followed. At first it may seem obvious where the leak is coming from, but it would still be wise to follow the flowchart through.

If the machine still leaks after these checks, please refer to the following chapters, *Basics – Plumbing* and *Motors* (speed control).

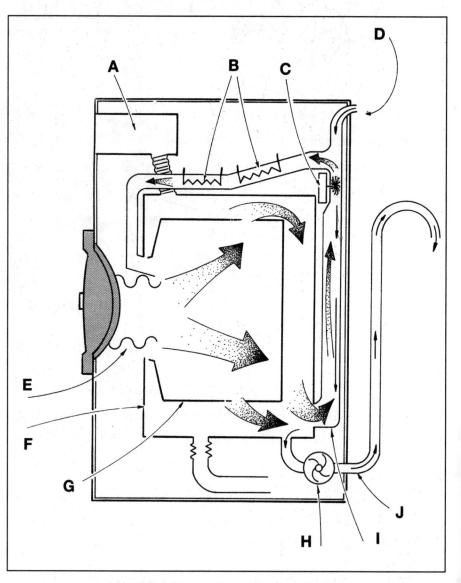

A simplified diagram of a combined washerdrier

A Soap dispenser
B Heaters housed in heater ducting
C Fan and motor for air circulation
D Cold water inlet to condenser unit
E Door seal with inlet for heat duct.
F Outer tub unit
G Inner drum
H Outlet pump
I Condenser unit
J Outlet hose

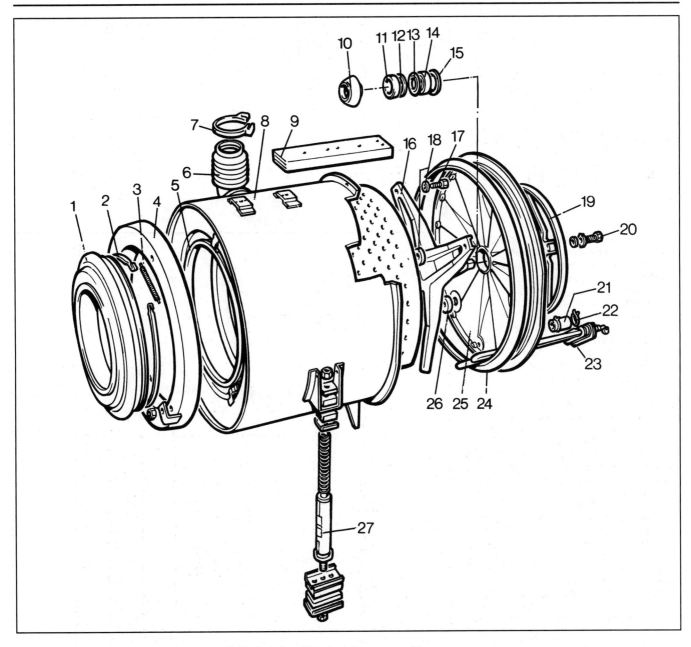

Exploded view of typical drum assembly

1 Door seal (door boot).
2 Clamp band.
3 Spring fastening for clamp band
 (could be bolt or rubber garter type).
4 Front tub weight size and position
 may vary.
5 Tub lip for door seal to locate onto.
6 Dispenser hose.
7 Dispenser hose clip.
8 Outer tub. Position of tub weights vary.
9 Top tub weights. Locations vary.
10 Carbon face seal for main bearing.
11 Front drum bearings
 (ball bearing type).
12 Front bearing spacer.
13 Rear bearing spacer.

14 Rear bearing (ball bearing type).
15 Securing clip (spring type).
16 Drum spider (detachable version).
17 Spider fixing bolt.
18 Spider washer and spacer.
19 Drum pulley.
20 Drum pulley fixing bolt and
 locking tab.
21 Pressure vessel hose.
22 Pressure vessel hose clip
 (spring corbin clips).
23 Heater.
24 Rear tub seal (back half seal).
25 Backhalf casting.
26 Thermostat grommet.
27 Suspension unit (spring damper type).

Box 1

The smallest of holes in the door boot (door seal) can be the cause of the biggest leaks. The seal should also be checked and replaced if any holes are found or if it feels sticky or tacky to the touch. The contact between the door glass and the seal should be a good one, with no scaling or fluff adhering to the door glass, If any scale, etc., is found on the glass it can be easily removed by rubbing gently with a non-abrasive Scotchbrite scouring pad. Details of door seal replacement can be found in the chapter on *Door seals*.

Box 2

The clamp band that secures the door seal to the tub front should be checked for tightness. Details of different types of clamp bands can be found in the chapter *Door seals*.

Box 3

The dispenser hose is located at the base of the soap dispenser, and forms the flexible connection with the tub. Again, thorough inspection of this hose is advised, as most of the water that the machine uses passes via this hose, and can therefore lead to some quite large leaks. This hose is usually a grommet type fitting, and should be checked for tightness, i.e. it should not rotate. A sign of a bad fit is scaling/powder marks running down the outer tub at the fitting point. If the hose feels sticky or tacky to the touch, it should be replaced. **Note:** *If this hose has leaked, the water would have contained detergent. If the water has come into contact with the suspension legs it may cause a loud squeaking/grinding noise just before and after the spin. (This fault is more pronounced on early Hoover automatics.) This is because the suspension works its hardest at this time. Please refer to the chapter on Suspension. Some soap dispensers avoid the use of flexible dispenser hoses and use a rigid duct to feed the water from the dispenser in to the drum via an aperture in the door seal.*

If your make of washer has a hose connected between the outer tub and the rear of the machine, this is called an air vent hose or tube. This in itself cannot leak as no water passes through it, although it may be used if the machine overfoamed, overfilled or has spun whilst still full of water. This type of hose is normally of the grommet fitting type, and should be checked for perishing as before. Most modern machines use the soap dispenser as the air vent as well as the water inlet, thus eliminating an extra grommet fitting hose in manufacture.

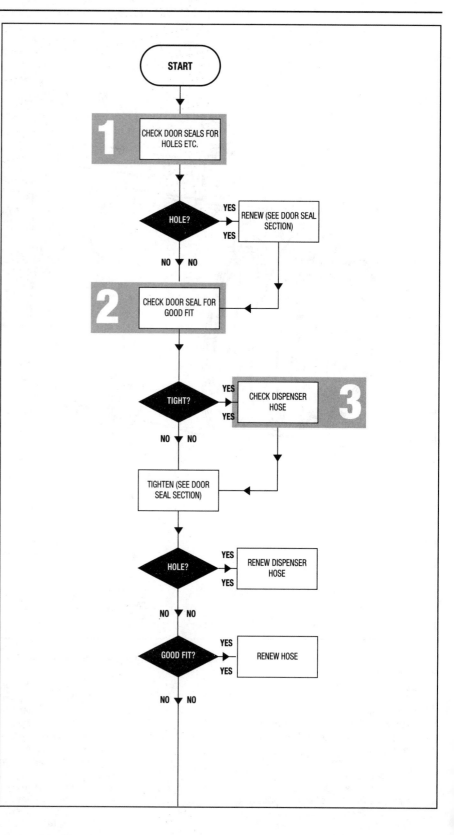

Box 4

The sump hose is the flexible hose located at the bottom of the machine. Depending on the make and model of your appliance, this will be in one of two configurations.
a) Linking the pump and the tub
b) Linking the filter and tub, with a separate hose linking the filter and pump, thus creating a trap for any foreign objects to prevent them reaching the pump.

Again this should be checked for perishing and replaced if found to be tacky or sticky. The grommet fittings should also be checked, as explained in Box 3, and the clips should be checked for tightness as explained in the *Pumps* chapter. If the machine is the type with a filter fitted, all hoses to and from the filter housing and the filter seal should be checked for defects. At this point it would be advisable to thoroughly check the pump as detailed in the *Pumps* chapter.

Box 5

The location of the heater, and thermostat seal depends on the make and model of the machine. Front servicing models will have the thermostat, heater and pressure vessel located on the front of the outer tub, directly behind the front cover panel. Access to these components is gained by the removal of the front panel of the machine. Alternatively these components may be located at the rear of the machine and access gained by removal of the back panel. Details of both versions of machine appear throughout this book.

If the heater seal is found to be leaking, it can sometimes be stopped by tightening the centre nut. This increases the width of the rubber seal by squashing it 'vice like'. If the leak persists at this point, the heater will have to be changed completely, as the seal is not available as a separate item. Avoid over tightening the bolt as this will bend the internal metal plate and make subsequent removal of the heater extremely difficult.

Box 6

The connections between the pressure switches and the tub should be checked now, as detailed in the *Water level control* chapter.

Box 7

The hoses and clips on the inlet valves should now be checked in conjunction with the *Water inlet valves* chapter. On some valves there is a slight chance that the top of the valve can split (often the result of freezing).

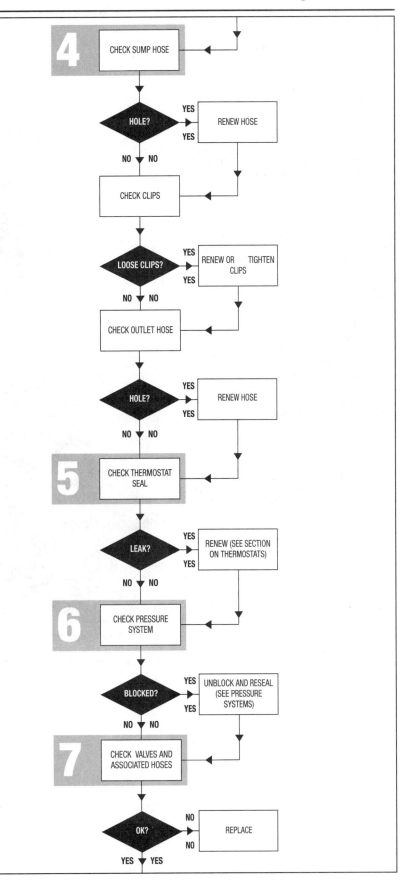

Box 8

The tub seal and grommets are to be checked now. This means the seal or seals that fit between the separate parts of the main tub assembly. In addition to these seals, small rubber grommets may be found. These will have been fitted to block 'machine holes' that are used in the manufacture of the machine. If these come out or leak, they should be replaced or have sealant applied to them. If the large tub seals leak they should also be renewed. This type of repair is described in the *Bearings* chapter.

Box 9

Any corrosion or flaking of the enamel covering of the outer tub can be treated with a good brand of rust inhibitor, taking care that it does not come into contact with any of the internal rubber hoses, seals, etc., and is used in conjunction with the manufacturer's instructions. Places to note are where the brackets for the motor and the suspension are welded on to the outer tub. These are stress points where the enamel may crack and flake, allowing rust to form. By the time a leak has started at these points, it is too late to save the outer tub and it must be renewed completely if a lasting repair is to be made. Check plastic outer tubs closely for cracks. It is felt that the occurrence of tub renewal on today's modern automatics is very rare, therefore, the need for a lengthy section in this book would be unnecessary. Also, the cost of such items and all the relevant seals and parts necessary to complete such a repair may not be cost effective.

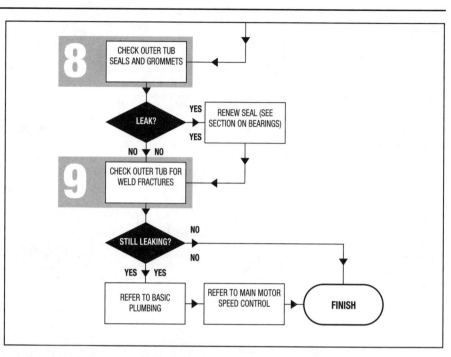

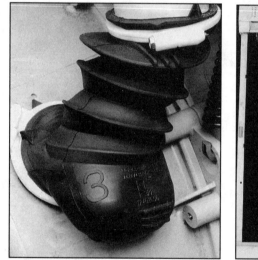

This type of split tub construction is popular in a wide range of makes including Zanussi, Bendix, Electrolux and many more

Removable front plate systems are becoming much more popular and can be found in many makes including Hoover, Hotpoint, Creda, etc.

Chapter 14
Machine will not empty

Of all the faults reported, this must be one of the most common. Often this fault and the 'leak' fault are one and the same. The reason for this being that on many machines there is no 'spin inhibit system'. This is especially true of older machines. If there is no spin inhibit system, it means that if for any reason the machine cannot empty, it will still try to spin. The consequences of this action is that the increased drum speed pressurises the tub, causing leaks from soap dispensers, air vent hoses and door seals. This one fault can cause several problems. On most later machines and many of the machines currently produced in Britain, the level switch inhibits (stops) the machine before the spin if a level of water is detected. This means that if there is water in the machine, the pressure causes the switch to move to the OFF position, therefore not allowing the machine to spin. For a more detailed description of the pressure switch, please refer to the *Water level control* chapter.

The 'not emptying' fault can fall into three main categories, blockage, mechanical fault or electrical fault.

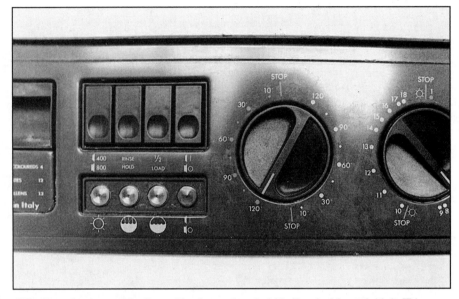

This vented type combined machine has a rinse hold button 2nd from the left. This may be correctly causing a spin inhibit and retention of water, check your instruction booklet for correct operation and use

Box 1

Follow the emergency procedure for removing the water already trapped inside the machine.

Box 2

Check the outlet and sump hoses, as well as the outlet filter (if fitted). If a blockage or a kink is found, remove it and refit the pipe(s) and filter.

Box 3

The pump is located at the machine end of the outlet hose, and junction of the sump hose. The small chamber should be checked for blockages. Pumps driven by shaded pole motor should have the impeller checked for free rotation, and that it hasn't come adrift from its mounting to the pump motor shaft. If the impeller is adrift from the shaft, no water would be pumped although the motor itself would run. A quick way to check the connection of the shaft and impeller is to hold the shaft whilst trying to turn the impeller. If all is well, they should only turn in unison. Remember to turn counter-clockwise, otherwise on most pumps the impeller will unscrew from the shaft. If a fault or an alternative type pump motor is found at this point, refer to the *Pumps* chapter.

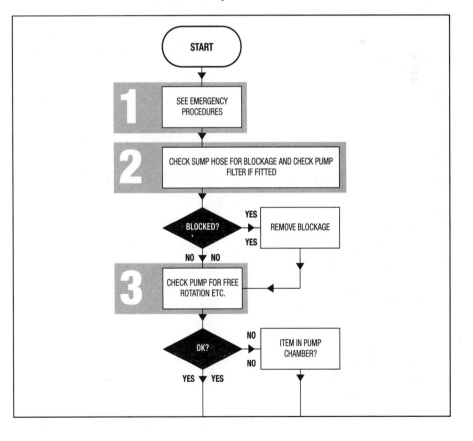

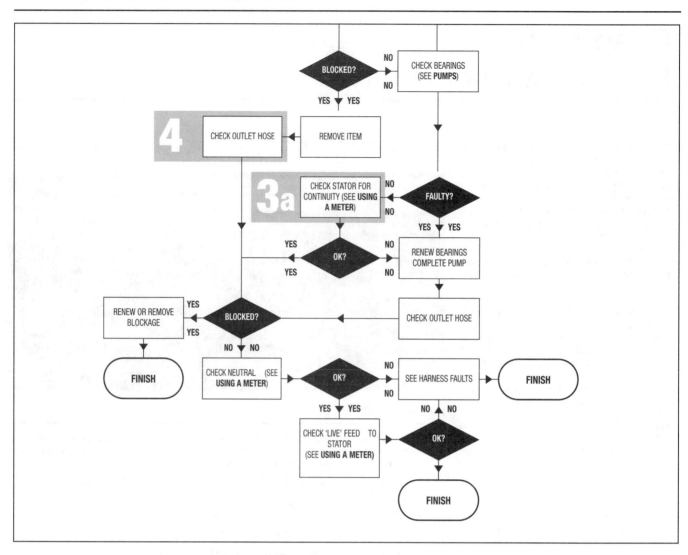

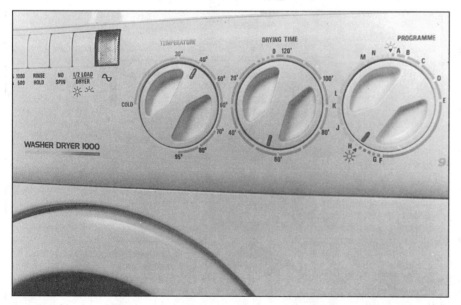

This combined condenser washerdrier machine clearly indicates the no spin option 3rd button from the left. However, errors in setting can still occur, always double check.

Box 3A

If no blockage is found in the section above, and the bearings are not suspected, the stator continuity of the pump windings must be checked. Please refer to the *Using a meter* chapter.

Box 4

At this point, the outlet hose should be checked again. An internal blockage such as a coin or button can act as a valve and be very difficult to locate. The best method of checking a hose for a fault is to connect the hose to a standard tap, observing the flow of water. Alternatively, raise one end of the hose and pop a small marble in, the marble should easily run through the hose if no blockages are present.

Box 5

The final step is to check the wiring harness connections. Please refer to the *Wiring and harness faults* chapter.

Chapter 15
Door seals

Door seal fitting – helpful hints

There are many types of door seal to be found, depending on the make, model and the age of your machine. The removal and fitting of four typical door seals (without heater ducting connections) is shown. The models used in this example are Hoover, early Bendix, Hotpoint and the Zanussi range including late Bendix and Electrolux types. They are used to illustrate principles which can be found on most modern machines. Door seals used on combined washerdrier machines may have the addition of a heater duct entry point connection. This will be dependent on make and model of your machine. See photographs of various types of door seal and ducting. The door seal bridges the gap between the outer tub and the shell of the appliance, and in most washerdriers is used as a convenient entry point for the air inlet duct (although not always so). The flexible rubber seal provides access to the inner drum via the door opening for loading the machine and inlet point for the heater duct during the drying cycle (on some machines), whilst also giving a watertight seal to the door glass. The seal should be renewed if found to be perished or holed at any point, paying special attention to the folds and mounting of the door seal. The air inlet duct rubber moulding (if fitted) should be inspected closely for signs of cracking and hardening due to heat damage, and check also that it is correctly seated and sealed with the correct sealant (if required).

There are three ways that a door seal is secured to the outer tub, all very similar in concept. On the outer tub there is a formed lip. When the rubber seal is located onto this lip, it is then held in position by a large clamp band, and pressure exerted by the band to create a watertight seal. There are several versions of clamp bands used in today's machines – four of the most common are described below. The majority of machines will have one or a combination of those listed, whereas the others may have a variation of one of those described. Use this list to help identify the type used in your machine.

1 A simple metal band secured by a bolt, which when tightened reduces the diameter of the band.
2 As (1), but the open ends of the band are secured by a spring.
3 This method is best described as a large

rubber band or spring joined together to form an expanding ring. Both types are called garter rings. When fitted correctly, the ring rests in a recess in the door seal, which in turn rests in the recess of the tub lip, therefore creating the watertight seal. Unlike the previous two methods, this band cannot be slackened by the loosening of a bolt or spring, and is best removed by prising the garter ring from its position in the seal recess by using a flat-bladed screwdriver to lift it over the lip. The best way to refit a rubber or spring garter ring is to locate the bottom of The ring in the recess of the fitted door seal slowly working the ring inside the recess in an upward direction with both hands meeting at the top. This can be likened to fitting a tyre onto a bicycle wheel after mending a puncture.
4 A slightly unusual fastening may be encountered where both ends of a wire band are joined by a small metal plate. The ends of the wire band are linked into two holes in the metal plate. The plate has a larger hole/slot in it and if a small screwdriver is inserted into this slot and forms a tight fit, when turned, a 'cam' action occurs which reduces or increases the overall circumference. Only a small movement is required, approximately a quarter turn between open and closed. When closed correctly, the plate will lock into position. Access to the plate can be gained through the door latch hole after first removing the two interlock fixing screws. This type of fixing is mainly found on machines in the Colston/Ariston range. The reason for this type of clamp band is that access to the more usual clamp band would be impossible due to a close front fitting circular concrete tub weight which surrounds the door seal tub lip. **Note:** *To aid the fitting of a door seal, a little washing up liquid may be applied to the tub lip or the door seal tub lip moulding. (Not on the front shell lip.) This will allow the rubber to slip more easily into position on the metal or plastic lip of the outer tub.*

As described earlier, many modern washerdrier machines vent the warm air into the drum of the machine via a preformed extension of the door seal which fits around the lower portion of the heating duct. It is essential that the door seal is positioned correctly on the tub lip in order to allow the duct and seal to fit neatly without any distortion. It is most important that this union is correctly fitted and sealed to avoid the possible leak of water or vapour. Various

fixings can be found which secure the door seal to the heater duct. Sealant is often applied in the manufacturing process to help fit parts together and to fill in any gaps left between the door seal and any irregularities that may be present. If your machine had sealant used in manufacture, it is essential that it is renewed whenever the door seal is renewed or whenever the ducting is removed or stripped down for any reason. Only the correct heat resistant sealant should be used, see: *Useful tips and information* chapter. Do not use the general purpose sealant which is used for watertight seals on hoses and pressure systems. The fitting of the door seal to the shell of the machine is similar to the tub lip system in that three major variations are found:
a) The most straightforward seal simply grips the shell lip with no other added support other than the elasticity of the door seal itself on early machines. For safety reasons modern machines now use various methods of secondary fixing to prevent the door seal being easily removed or dislodged from the shell lip. It is essential that such fixings are replaced if they have been removed for any reason.
b) This type also uses the shell lip, with the aid of a clamp band. A recess is formed on the outer edge of the seal for a clamp band or clamp wire to be inserted. This ensures a firm grip on the shell lip. As with the inner tub lip, many variations can be found.
c) The third method involves a plastic flange that is screwed on to the outside of the shell. The screws that hold this flange pass through a recess in the outer front lip of the door seal therefore securing it firmly to the front panel.

Variations on both of the later clamps can be found on modern machines. All are fitted as a safety measure to restrict access to the inner of the machine. It is essential that any such fixing is replaced correctly if it has been removed for any reason. Before removing the old door seal a simple examination of the old seal and a note of its correct positioning will aid the subsequent repair and renewal as the new seal will need to fit in exactly the same position. Some door seals have a definite top and bottom, or pre-shaped sections for door hinges or catches, etc., and will fit no other way. **Note:** *It is easier to line up the seal before fitting rather than trying to adjust the seal when the clamp bands have been fitted.*

Some machines have one or more of their tub weights mounted on the front section of the outer tub, encircling the door seal and tub clamp fitting, leaving little or no access to the clamp or tub lip. However, do not remove the front tub weight to aid door seal fitting as it is not necessary for most machines, e.g. Creda, Zanussi, Electrolux, Ariston and Bendix, etc., even though some have front tub weights surrounding the tub clamp bands. The Zanussi and Creda seals can be changed through the door opening in the front panel of the machine, without removing the top at all. (Having said this, removing the top of the machine will provide more light, – remove if necessary). The way in which the door seal of washerdrier machines fits to both outer tub and shell are identical to wash-only machines i.e. lip and clamp. Various types of fitting will be found from clamp plate to clamp spring. Refitting therefore will be a reversal of the removal process.

Removal of typical door seal (Hoover)

1 Check door glass inner for scale deposit ridge and clean off with non-abrasive pad

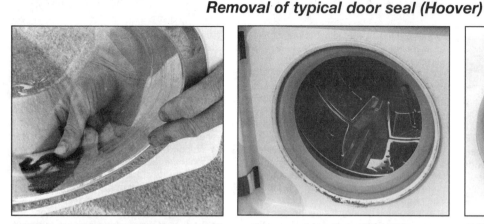

4 Free complete door seal from the front lip and allow seal to rest on inner side of front panel

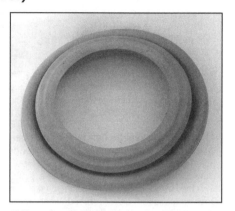

7 New door seal of type to be fitted to the machine shown

2 Grasp door seal firmly and pull downwards to free from shell lip. Some machines may have clamp band on front lip. Remove this first

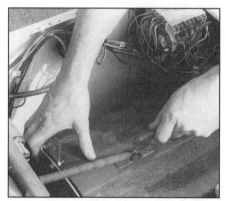

5 With top removed, free the top support springs or tie, and lean outer tub unit back as far as possible

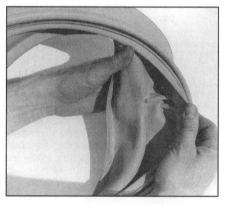

8 View showing inner lip moulding and ridge. The ridge is fitted at the 9 o'clock position when viewed from the front of the machine

3 When freed from lip, continue pulling in a downward direction

6 With position of clamp band and bolt in view proceed to remove band. Free seal from the clip as shown above

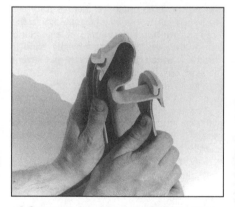

9 Cutaway view of a typical door seal to show intricate moulding and positioning of tub and shell lips of the seal

Removal of an early Bendix door seal

1 Remove the plastic flanges around the door seal front

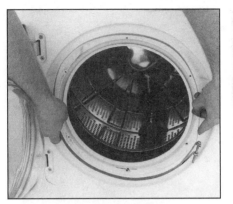

4 Picture showing the orientation of the band inside the machine. Must be refitted in the same position

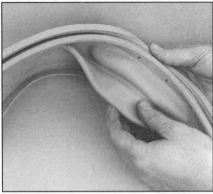

7 New door seal checked prior to fitting and seared with a little washing up liquid to help slide it into position. (Inner lip only)

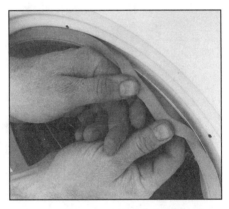

2 Remove the door seal from the front lip

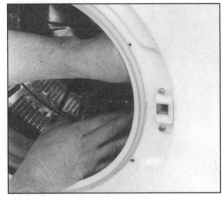

5 Slacken off tub clamp band bolt and remove old door seal

8 Ensure that the three drain holes on the door seal are fitted at the bottom of the tub lip

3 Showing the position of the clamp band with the top of the machine removed

6 View showing the tub lip and weight block gap. (Clean off any scale and/or deposit on the tub lip before fitting the new seal)

Removal of a Hotpoint front loader door seal

1 Remove outer plastic surround screws, and top and bottom section

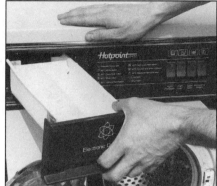

4 Pull out the soap dispenser drawer completely and remove the front facia fixing screws

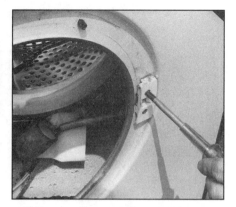

7 Remove door switch assembly and pressure switch bracket

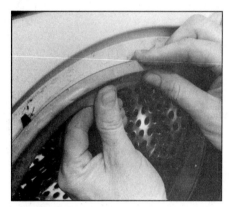

2 Pull seal to release from shell lip, hinge and catch

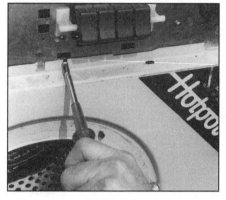

5 With the front facia removed, remove the screws securing the front panel of the machine

8 With front panel removed, the clamp band can easily be removed

3 Unscrew the timer knob centre and remove the timer knob. Also remove the **two** front facia fixing screws found behind the timer knob

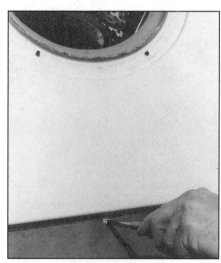

6 Four hexagonal headed screws secure the front panel under the bottom edge. (On later machines, three Philips headed screws will be found)

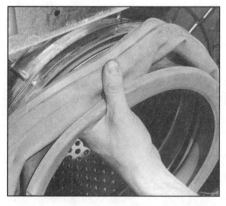

9 Note the position of hinge and catch mouldings The door seal can then be pulled free from the tub lip

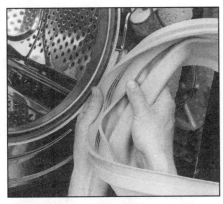

10 When fitting a new seal to the tub lip the tub gap can be adjusted slightly. *(Note: the inner lip of the door seal is ribbed)*

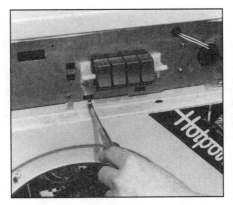

13 Refit front panel, door catch and all front panel fixings

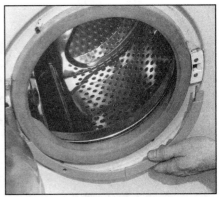

16 Refit plastic surround and ensure that the ends locate correctly. The plastic pips can be moved to aid fitting. The machine is now ready for the functional test

11 When the new seal is fitted in this position, check that the inner drum rotates without fouling the door seal inner. Adjust if necessary to obtain the smallest gap possible before refitting

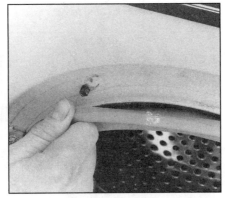

14 With front panel secured fit the door seal to the front panel lip

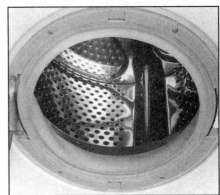

17 When fitted, the new seal should not have undue kinks or twists. It is essential that this is correctly fitted

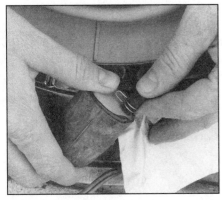

12 With new door seal in this position it is wise to check that all of the leads, hoses and pressure vessel are correct before refitting the front panel

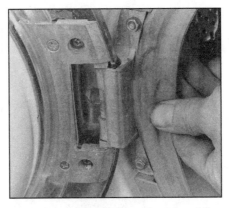

15 Lubricate the hinge and catch points with a little washing up liquid, and ease into position

Removal of a spring clamp band door seal (Zanussi, late Bendix, Electrolux, etc.)

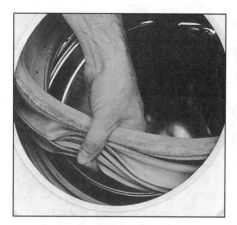

1 To remove a spring type inner clamp band you will need access to both the inner and outer edges of the inner tub lip so do not place the front of the seal in the drum. Press firmly on the inside of the seal at the bottom and using your fingers or a flat bladed screwdriver ease the seal free from the tub lip (this may require a degree of force). Place your forefinger through the gap created and meet up with your thumb on the outside of the seal. Ensure you have both the seal and spring encircled and simply pull the seal and spring free

2 When fitting the new seal ensure it is correctly orientated and placed within the tub and shell gap

3 With one hand on the inner surface and the other on the outer use your fingers to correctly locate the seal recess to the tub lip starting at the bottom. Work around the tub lip until fitted

4 Press firmly around the perimeter to check that the seal is correctly positioned and seated on to the tub lip

5 When satisfied that the seal is located on the lip, invert the front section into the drum. This will allow better access for fitting the spring clamp band

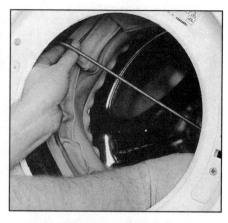

6 Place the spring in the bottom of its recess and with both hands work upwards allowing the spring to slip into the securing recess like fitting a bicycle tyre

7 Refit the front of the door seal to the shell lip

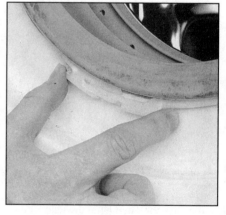

8 Ensure the front clamp band is refitted

Door seal deterioration

Rubber is a relatively unstable substance, and does have a limited life before it starts to perish. This process cannot be prevented but deterioration can be slowed down by the addition of stabilising ingredients to the rubber before it is moulded.

Washing products themselves do not cause the rubber to deteriorate more quickly, but the speed at which deterioration occurs can be affected by a number of other important factors.

1 Frequency of machine use. The life of a gasket will obviously vary depending on how often the machine is used. Some people use the machine every day, whilst others only use their machine occasionally.

2 High temperature programmes. Most chemical reactions tend to happen faster at higher temperatures, so the life of a rubber gasket would be likely to be shorter on a machine where the 'boil wash' programme is used regularly.

3 Type of washload. Certain types of soiling can affect deterioration of rubber gaskets. Oils, fats, and heavy grease soiling on clothes can be deposited on the gasket during the wash process and increase the rate of deterioration.

4 The presence of copper in the wash water. Copper may be present in the water supply through the installing of new pipes and some occupations involve work clothes coming into contact with metal compounds.

Preventative measures

To prolong the life of a rubber porthole gasket:

1 Always use the recommended dosage of washing product; taking into account the size of the washload, the amount of soiling on articles, and water hardness.

2 If soiling is particularly heavy use the pre-wash facility, and increase the dosage of detergent, dividing it between the pre and main wash.

3 Always wipe the porthole gasket dry after the machine has been used, and leave the door open to allow a free circulation of air.

Warning: *It is possible for small children to climb into washing machines and injure themselves – ensure measures are taken to avoid this.*

washerdrier door seals with heater duct inlet protrusions

Fagor

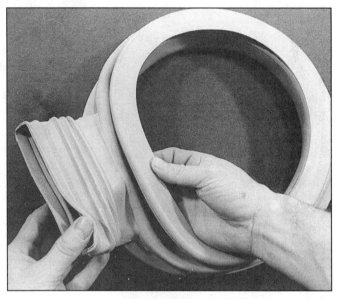

Hoover

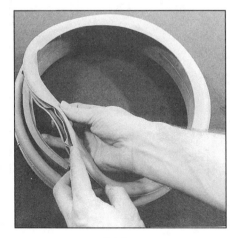

Ariston

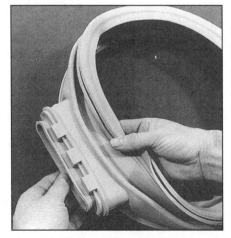

Candy (with removable integral duct seal)

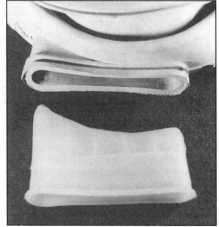

Candy seal detailing duct seal

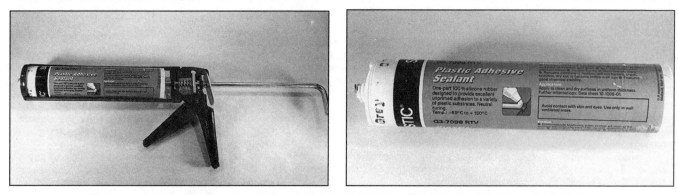

Types of sealant sometimes used to secure door seal to heater duct inlet. If originally used, it must be renewed if disturbed or when fitting a new door seal, etc.

Not all washerdrier machines use the door seal for the heater duct entry point. This early Hotpoint machine has a normal door seal, air inlet is via a fixed outer tub fitment

Access to the door seal from the top of the machine may be limited in many combined washerdriers such as this Philips/Whirlpool machine. With a little thought and planning, however, fitting can be easily carried out

When removed from the shell of the machine this Zanussi washerdrier tub assembly clearly shows the large tub weight completely encircling the door seal. This type of seal is held in place by a garter spring. Removal and refitting of both seal and securing band can be carried out with the unit *in situ*. The unit is shown removed from the machine for photographic purposes only

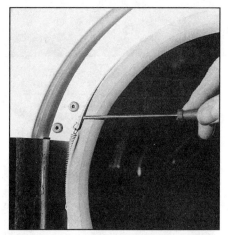

The front lip of this door seal is secured by a wire and spring type fixing. Carefully insert a flat-bladed screwdriver to ease fixing from its position as shown (shown with door removed for photographic purposes only)

Chapter 16
Water inlet valves

In this chapter we deal with several of the most common reported faults such as not taking powder, not filling at all, not filling in certain parts of the programme and condenser water supply.

Many configurations of water valve can be found from single hot or cold to much larger units consisting of three or more individually operated valves grouped together to control the flow to several outlets from one inlet. All inlet point threads are the same size ¾ B.S.P., but outlet hose connections from the valve may differ. A wide variety of fixing brackets are also used, outlet angles can be in-line (classed as 180 degree valves) or angles downwards (classed as 90 degree valves). Operation of the electro-mechanical action follows and covers the general operation of all such valves regardless of size or fixing styles, etc.

A solenoid coil of some 3-5000 ohms (3-5kΩ) resistance when energised (i.e. supplied with power), creates a strong magnetic field at its centre. This field attracts a soft iron rod or plunger up into the coil and will hold it in that position as long as power is supplied to the coil.

When power is removed (de-energised) from the coil, a spring at the top of the plunger recess returns it to its resting position.

How does it work?

Shown here in detail are the two states of the water valve. With no power supplied to the solenoid coil (A) the soft iron core (B) is pressed firmly onto the centre hole of the flexible diaphragm by spring (C). As chamber (D) is only at atmospheric pressure and the water is at least 4 p.s.i. (somewhat higher), pressure is exerted on the top of the diaphragm*, effectively closing it tight. The greater the water pressure the greater the closing effect of the valve therefore no water will flow.

When power is supplied to the solenoid coil, the resulting magnetic attraction of the coil overcomes the power of the spring (C) and pulls the plunger up into the coil centre. This allows an imbalance of pressure to occur by exposing the centre hole of the diaphragm. The imbalance lifts the flexible diaphragm and allows water to flow into chamber (D), thus water flow is achieved.

It is easier for the water to lift the diaphragm than to balance the pressure by flowing through the very small bleed hole. Any enlargement or blockage of this vital bleed hole will render the valve inoperative.

*The pressure on top of the diaphragm is

via a small bleed hole marked (E). It is essential that this very small hole is not obstructed. Though very small, it is a major factor in the correct operation of these types of pressure operated valves.

Main benefits of such valves

1 The higher the pressure supplied to it the tighter the valve will close
2 Cost is relatively low
3 Very reliable
4 Simple to change if faulty

Typical faults to watch for

1 As with ordinary house taps, the valve seat may wear and allow a small trickle of water to pass even when de-energised. This will cause the machine to fill when not in use if the taps are left turned on over a long period of time and the machine will over-fill, resulting in a possible flood.
2 The valve, when de-energised, may fail to allow the plunger to return to its normal resting/closed position. This problem will cause severe overfill and flooding. **Note:** *Turning off the machine will not stop the over filling in such cases. Complete isolation of*

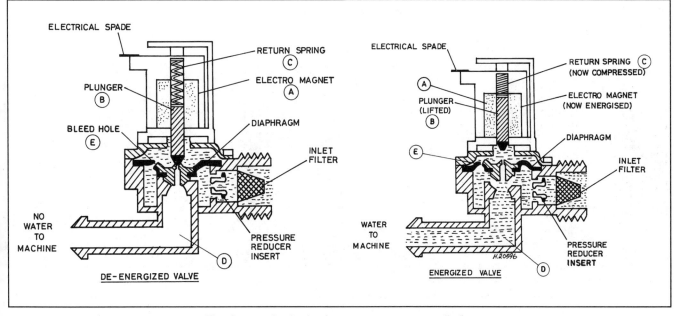

The de-energised valve (at rest – no power supplied)

both power and water supply is required and, as with step 1, complete renewal will be necessary.

3 The valve fails to allow water to flow due to open circuit in the winding of the solenoid coil. See *Using a Meter* chapter.

4 The valve fails to allow water to flow due to a blocked filter on its inlet. Carefully remove and clean. Do not allow any particle, no matter how small, to escape past the filter as it could block the bleed hole.

Water valves come in many sizes and an assortment of shapes, from single valves, double valves and triple valves or a combination of all three. On the double and triple valves, each solenoid operates one outlet from a common inlet. Unfortunately, a fault on one coil or one outlet will generally mean a complete renewal of the whole valve assembly, as individual spare parts are not

available. **Note:** *On condenser machines with double or triple valves, a restrictor will be fitted to one of the valve outlets. It is important that any replacement valve has this internal restrictor fitted. The valve with the restrictor is for water supply to the condenser unit, as it requires a slow trickle of water to operate correctly. See* Drying components *chapter, faults confined to condenser machines only.*

The condenser washerdrier machines and some condenser dry-only machines appear to be somewhat unusual in that they require a cold water supply during the dry cycle. However, without this water supply, the machine will not dry. The flow of water from the valve during the drying sequence is restricted to slow it to around 0.35 litres per minute. Restriction of the water flow is by means of a plastic insert in either the valve

outlet to the condenser or at the receiving end within the condenser unit itself. The restrictor is simply a plastic insert with small holes through which the water can pass at a given rate. If the restrictor gets blocked for any reason, the water flow will become too slow for the condensing action to take place. Blocking of the small holes in the restrictor is not uncommon, especially in machines having restrictors or spray points mounted in the condenser unit. Such problems are often related to water hardness. If the restrictor is removed, cracked or moves out of position, the flow of water could become too great thus preventing drying. This woud be as a result of a water build up within the machine between the periodic pump action or water droplets being picked up by the air flow and deposited on the clothes.

As the machine uses a separate valve, i.e. one for normal cold inlet for pre-wash, wash and rinsing, and the other restricted for dry cycle only, the machine may fill correctly for wash cycles, but fail to dry when this option is selected if the fault lies within the restricted valve used to supply the condenser unit. When obtaining replacement valves, make sure that if the original valve had a restrictor, the new one must also have a corresponding restrictor fitted to the correct outlet. In common with all valves and hose connections, make sure that they are a secure and water-tight fit.

This is especially so with machines that are fitted with restrictors at or within the condenser as pressure can build up within the supply hose (valve to condenser unit) and if not securely fitted, may blow off or weep.

Further details of the condenser unit, its components and specific fault guide can be found in the *Drying components* chapter.

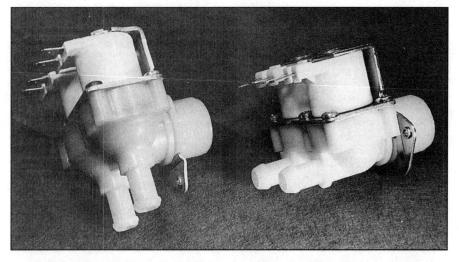

Double valves 90 degrees and 180 degrees outlet respectively. Typical use on a combined washerdrier would be one side for wash/rinse cycles, the other for restricted condenser supply

Triple valve configuration typical use on a combined washerdrier would be pre-wash, main wash and restricted condenser supply

Double valve clearly showing restrictor in left-hand outlet used for condenser unit supply

Single valve: Red for hot supply. White for cold supply

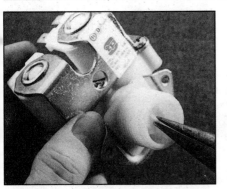

Cleaning of the valve inlet filter can be carried out by carefully removing the filter with pliers. Ensure the filter is not damaged and that no debris gets past during removal

With the filter removed, carefully clean and inspect it (if damaged or if you suspect that dirt may have entered the valve, renew the unit). This procedure can be carried out without removing the valve(s) from the machine. Here, it is shown removed for photographic purposes only

Verify the suspected fault

In this theoretical instance, the machine was loaded and a programme selected but failed to fill. Moving the timer/control to a pump out position confirmed that power was being supplied and that the door interlock was working. See *Door switches (interlocks)* chapter.

Box 1

Reselect wash programme to confirm that machine was originally set and turned on correctly.

Box 2

With the machine correctly set, this confirms that although the machine has electrical supply, no water is entering to begin the filling/washing action.

Box 3

This may seem too obvious to mention, but many an engineer has been called out to find the taps were in the off position. This normally brings the comment that the taps are 'never turned off', and in this case it must have been some other devious member of the family or innocent plumber that has done the dirty deed! This comment brings in the cardinal rule that all automatic washing machines and dishwashers should be turned off at their isolation taps when the appliance is not in use. This may seem a quite pointless task, but the objective is simple. If an inlet pipe should split, or an inlet valve fails to close correctly, a quite disastrous flood could occur. However, if the taps were turned off between each use of the machine this could not happen.

Box 4

By unscrewing the hose from the valve, the water supply can be easily checked by turning the tap to which it is connected on and off, ensuring that the free end of the hose is held in a suitable container. Failure of water flow could be a clue to a faulty tap or tap shaft or an internal fault of the supply hose. Some makers of machines supply rubber inlet hose seals which have a metal or gauze filter moulded into them, it is recommended in the manufacturer's instruction booklet that the two washers supplied with the filters are fitted at the isolation tap end of the supply hose as a first line filter for the valves. Check if such filter washers were used during the original installation by unscrewing the supply hose from the isolation tap. Clean or renew as required.

Box 5

Checking of the water valve inlet filter can be carried out while the hose is removed for Step 4. Take care not to allow any particles to escape past the fine mesh filter and into the valve. Carefully clean the filter of all scale and debris, etc., and refit. **Note:** *The filter can be removed by gently gripping the centre with pliers and pulling it free of the main valve body.*

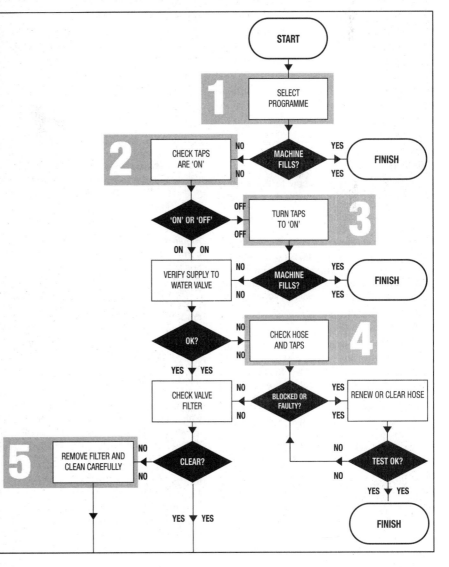

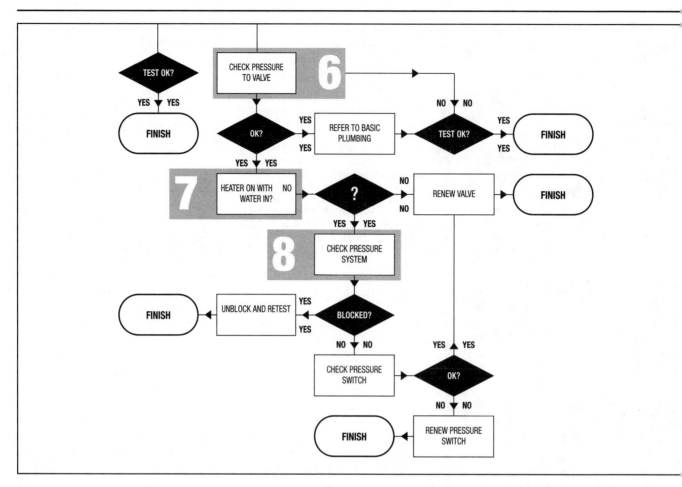

Box 6

Ensure that the water supply to the valve is adequate to operate the valve. See *Basics – plumbing* chapter.

Box 7 & 8

If the heater is found to be on when there is no water in the machine, a pressure system fault is indicated and should be checked. Details of this process will be found in the *Water Level Control* chapter. If the heater is in the off position when there is no water in the machine, the valve would appear to be suspect. The valve is easily changed by removing the fixing screws and detaching the internal hose/s from the valve. Making a note of the wiring and hose connections that are on the valve, remove them and replace with a new valve assembly by simply reconnecting the hoses and wires in a reverse sequence.

Water valves come in many sizes and an assortment of shapes – single valves, double valves and triple valves or a combination of all three. On the double and triple valves, each solenoid operates one outlet from a common inlet. Unfortunately, a fault on one coil or one outlet will generally mean a complete renewal of the whole valve assembly, as individual spare parts are not normally available. **Note:**

Condenser machines with double or triple valves will normally have a restrictor fitted to one of the valve outlets. It is important that any replacement valve has this internal restrictor fitted. The valve with the restrictor is for water supply to the condenser unit, as it requires a slow trickle of water to operate correctly. See Drying components *chapter, faults confined to condenser machines only.*

The condenser washerdrier machines and some condenser dry-only machines appear to be somewhat unusual in that they require a cold water supply during the dry cycle. However, without this water supply, the machine will not dry. The flow of water from the valve during the drying sequence is restricted to slow it to around 0.35 litres per minute. Restriction of the water flow is by means of a plastic insert in either the valve outlet to the condenser or at the receiving end within the condenser unit itself. The restrictor is simply a plastic insert with small holes through which the water can pass at a given rate. If the restrictor gets blocked for any reason, the water flow will become too slow for the condensing action to take place. Blocking of the small holes in the restrictor is not uncommon, especially in machines having restrictors or spray points mounted in the condenser unit. Such problems are often related to water hardness. If the restrictor is

removed, cracked or moves out of position, the flow of water could become too great thus preventing drying. This would be as a result of a water build-up within the machine between the periodic pump action or water droplets being picked up by the air flow and deposited on the clothes.

As the machine uses a separate valve, i.e. one for normal cold inlet for pre-wash, wash and rinsing, and the other restricted for dry cycle only, the machine may fill correctly for wash cycles, but fail to dry when this option is selected if the fault lies within the restricted valve used to supply the condenser unit. When obtaining replacement valves, make sure that if the original valve had a restrictor the new one must also have a corresponding restrictor fitted to the correct outlet. In common with all valves and hose connections, make sure that they are a secure and water tight fit.

This is especially so with machines that are fitted with restrictors at or within the condenser as pressure can build up within the supply hose (valve to condenser unit) and if not securely fitted, may blow off or weep.

Further details of the condenser unit, its components and specific fault guide can be found in the *Drying components* chapter.

Anti-flood inlet hoses

Most automatic washing machines are supplied with standard hot and cold inlet hoses normally 1.5 m in length with ³/₄ B.S.P. threaded connections, to help with awkward plumbing situations 2.5 m hoses are available. However, alternative flood protection hoses are to be found on some models. A description of the two most popular types is as follows.

Water block inlet hose – pressure activated

The water block hose is a mechanical protection system primarily to reduce the chance of flooding should a fill hose split or leak. The water block hose consists of several layers making a hose within a hose configuration. Only the inner hose carries the water from the valve to the appliance. If the inner hose should perish or leak, the pressure will be trapped within the next layer and used to close a mechanical valve situated at the inlet end of the hose. Most hoses have a means of indicating that the safety valve has been activated, for obvious reasons once tripped this device cannot be reset. If required this type of hose can be used to replace ordinary fill hoses to increase the level of protection. **Note:** *On most machines this type of hose can be fitted in place of a standard inlet hose.*

Water block inlet hose – electrical/mechanical

This system consists of a special one-piece inlet hose and inlet valve combination often referred to as an 'Aquastop' hose. It can be activated in two ways either electrically or mechanically via pressure (similar to the water block hose). On some versions safety is further improved by the use of a water inlet valve with a two-solenoid configuration i.e. two valves in series. The valve(s) and solenoid(s) are housed in a large protective container at the water entry point of the fill hose with the valve screwing directly on to the isolation tap connection. The power supply for the water valve solenoid(s) and the hose from the valve outlet to the appliance run through a bulky corrugated plastic cover. The reason for this configuration is to alleviate the constant pressure carried by conventional flexible inlet hoses where the inlet valve is situated at the machine end. The fill hose consists of several layers with the inner hose carrying the water from the inlet valve to the appliance. Should the inner hose leak the pressure will be contained within the next layer and used to close a mechanical inlet valve, refer to *Water block inlet hose* for details. For obvious reasons once tripped this device cannot be reset.

Note: *In essence the 'Aquastop' system alleviates the potential for leakage problems that may not be covered by the appliances internal overfill protection system. However,*

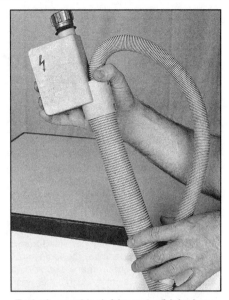

Typical water block ('Aquastop') inlet hose

the hose is bulky and the large end connection can be difficult to connect unless the correct plumbing requirements are in place. Additionally simple valve failure will result in a complete new 'Aquastop' hose being fitted which can be expensive. These points should be weighed against the incidence/failure rate of conventional inlet hoses, which are often and unwisely left under pressure (ideally the isolation tap(s) should be turned off after each wash cycle).

Chapter 17
Water level control

Modern automatic washing and combined washerdrier machines have several fill levels each of which corresponds to the type of wash cycle selected, e.g. high level fill for delicate programmes and lower level for the more robust wash programmes. There may also be the facility for an intermediate level option if a half load selection is available to the programme. Some modern machines use very small volumes of water circulated from a reservoir situated beneath the outer tub. Water is pumped from the reservoir and sprayed over the clothes during the wash cycle. To dilute the detergent during rinsing, normal levels of water are used. Irrespective of which type of machine you have the way in which the amount of water used for any type of system or programme is ultimately governed by a pressure system.

What is a pressure system?

The pressure system governs the level of water in the machine.

Where is it located?

The pressure switch has no standard fixture location, but is usually to be found at the top of the machine. It can be identified as the large circular switch that has several wires and a plastic or rubber tube attached to it leading to a pressure vessel. Several variations of pressure vessel are available. It may be an integral part of the plastic filter housing located behind the front face of the machine's shell, alternatively it may be an independent unit located to the rear or front of the outer tub. There are also pressure hoses that function in the same way as the rigid pressure vessel. These hoses will either be grommet fitted to the lower part of the outer tub, or directly moulded to the sump hose. Machines that have moulded plastic outer tubs normally have provision for a rigid pressure vessel to be mounted on the lower section. Although the position and style of the switch and pressure vessels vary, the basic way in which they operate does not.

How does it work?

The pressure switch does not actually come into contact with water, but uses air pressure trapped within the pressure vessel or pressure hose. When water enters the tub and the level rises, it traps a given amount of air in the pressure vessel. As the water in the tub rises, this increases the pressure of the trapped air within the pressure vessel. This pressure is then transferred to a pressure sensitive switch via the small-bore flexible tube.

The pressure switch is a large circular device that houses a thin rubber diaphragm, which is expanded by the corresponding pressure exerted on it. The diaphragm rests alongside a bank of up to three or more switches, each of which is set to operate at a different level of pressure. Operating in this way the switch is totally isolated from the water ensuring maximum safety.

Pressure switches may also have the electrical connections in an 'in-line' configuration as in this example. The operation of the switching action remains the same but allows for block rather than single wire connections.

Possible faults in the pressure system

To create the highest pressure in the chamber of the pressure vessel, the vessel must be positioned as low as possible in the machine. Unfortunately, any sediment that forms in the

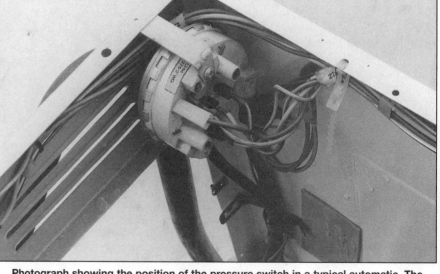

This Zanussi machine has a rigid pressure vessel (left-hand side of picture) connected to the sump hose

Photograph showing the position of the pressure switch in a typical automatic. The positions may vary with makes, but all will be found as high in the machine as possible

Pressure switches may also have the electrical connections in an 'in-line' configuration as in this example. The operation of the switching action remains the same but allows for block rather than single wire connections

Showing the pressure vessel used on machines such as Hoover, Creda and Servis

A typical pressure system

Typical double level switch

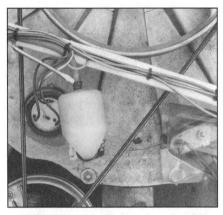

Any loose connections on the pressure system will allow the pressure to drop. This will cause overfilling. Ensure a good seal

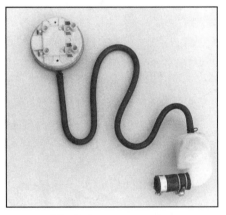

Single level switch

Typical triple level switch, which is more common on machines with plastic tubs or plastic drum paddles

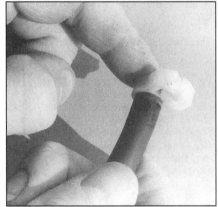

Check the pressure tube for chafing and small porous cracks. Renew if suspect

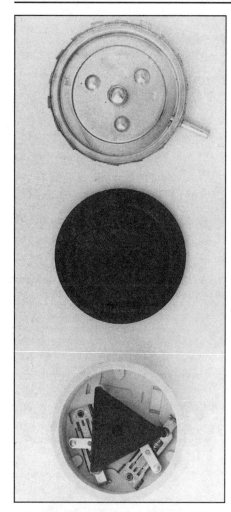

An internal view of a pressure switch, showing the diaphragm and switches. This pressure switch was faulty due to a small hole appearing in the internal diaphragm. Operation would appear correct, although the pressure would decrease during the wash, and the machine would overfill. If the first functional test was rushed, this type of fault could be overlooked. The switch in the picture was stripped down to confirm the fault only. These switches require replacement when faulty, as they cannot be repaired

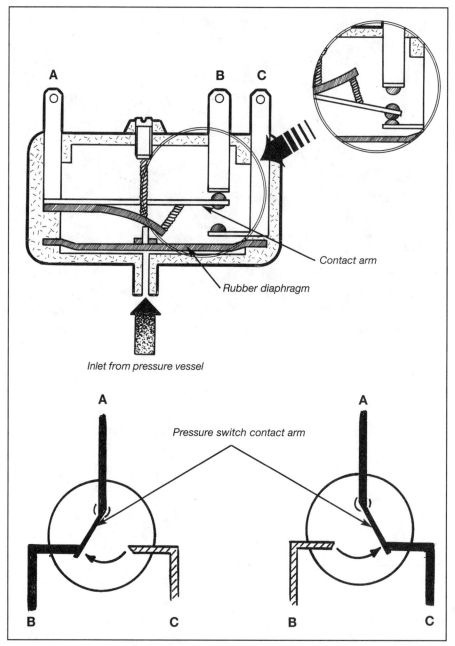

These diagrams illustrate the theoretical operation of a single level pressure switch. A being the live supply. Point B is the empty position of the pressure switch, and in this position power supplied to A via the programme timer would be allowed to flow to the fill valve via B. When the preset level of water is reached, the diaphragm of the pressure switch pushes the contact arm across to contact C. Power to the fill valve is therefore stopped and transferred to connection C which in turn could supply the main motor and heater

machine is liable to collect at this point and can therefore easily block the entrance to the vessel. Similarly, because of its very small internal diameter, the pressure tube can also block. The pressure that this device creates is very small, and can easily be blocked by a very small obstruction, such as a lump of detergent, sediment deposits or the growth of algae.

The seals and hoses of the system are also of great importance. These should be checked for air leaks and blockages. Any puncture or blockage would create a loss of pressure, resulting in the incorrect operation of the switches, i.e. if the air pressure in the pressure vessel were to leak out, the vessel would fill with water. Indicating that the machine was empty, the water valves would be re-energised, thus filling an already full machine. The results would be obvious.

The above example assumed that the air was prevented from actuating the pressure switch. If a blockage occurred whilst the switch was pressurised, the machine would work as normal until the machine emptied. The next time a programme was started the pressure switch would already be pressurised. Therefore the machine would not take any water, but proceed to turn the heater on. Although most heaters are now fitted with a TOC (thermal overload cut-out – see

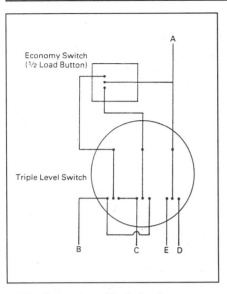

Economy Switch
(½ Load Button)

Triple Level Switch

A

B   C   E D

The figure above illustrates the way a 3 level switch is used in conjunction with an economy switch, to give an alternative level as an economy feature

Jargon), this may not act until some damage has been done to the clothes inside the drum or worse.

Points to note

a) The pressure system should be checked at yearly or half-yearly intervals, depending on the water hardness in your area.

b) Any hoses or tubes that have been disturbed must be resealed, and any clips tightened.

c) Blowing down the accessible end of the pressure tube may seem an easy solution to remove a blockage, but this may only be a temporary cure. Also, water may enter the pressure vessel before you can push the end of the tube back onto the pressure switch. This will render the pressure system inaccurate, if not useless.

d) The use of a quality low lather detergent specifically formulated for use in automatic machines is essential. Failure to use the correct detergent will result in foam entering the pressure system and rendering it, at best, inaccurate.

A pressure switch should only be suspected when the system has been thoroughly cleaned, checked, sealed and re-tested.

Checking a pressure switch

Blowing into the switch via the pressure tube, the audible 'clicks' of the switches should be heard. This should also happen when the pressure is released. If your machine uses a single level of water, one click will be heard. Two levels of water will produce two clicks. If your machine has an economy button, a third faint click will also be heard. **Note:** *Do not blow too hard as this may damage the switch. Remember the pressure they operate on is very low.*

Many machines have overfill level detection system which will activate the outlet pump should excess water enter the machine for any reason. Several systems use the third or fourth switch of the existing pressure switch bank, operated by the increased pressure caused by the overfill.

Unfortunately, systems that use the same pressure vessel for both normal and abnormal water level detection may fail to detect overfilling if it is caused by a blocked pressure vessel or hose fault that allows the pressure to escape.

Systems using a separate pressure vessel and a separate pressure switch for detecting overfilling are much less prone to failures of this nature. Nevertheless, they still require cleaning and checking frequently.

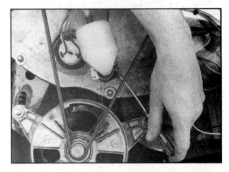

1 Note and remove all connections to the pressure switch. Remove the complete system from machine

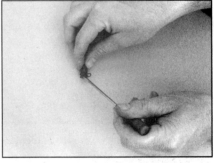

2 Check connecting hose for blockages at both ends and blow down tube to check for air leaks and to clear any obstructions

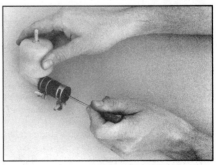

3 Clean inlet to pressure vessel and check hose for leaks and/or perishing

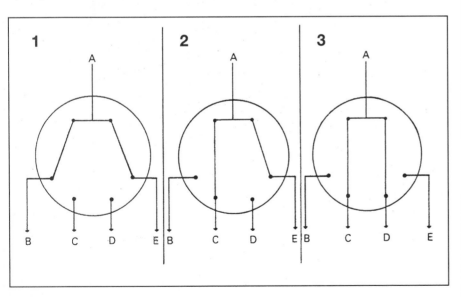

1   2   3

A   A   A

B   C   D   E B   C   D   E B   C   D   E

The diagram above illustrates the theoretical operation of a double level pressure switch. Fig. 1 shows the machine filling with water. If B and E are taken as hot and cold valves respectively, it can be seen that the machine is filling with both hot and cold water. In Fig. 2 the lowest level of water is reached. The pressure breaks the connection with the hot valve (B), and remakes it with the heater switch (C). The cold valve (E) continues filling. Fig. 3 shows the highest level, with the cold fill stopping, switching in the motor (D)

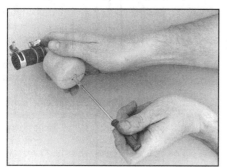

4 Carefully check outlet of pressure vessel for any build-up of sludge

5 Wash out pressure vessel thoroughly to remove any loose particles and sludge

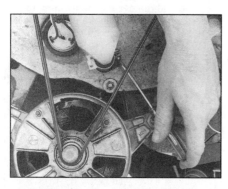

6 Check the pressure tube and any rubber hose connections for wear (ie rubbing on pulley, belt or clips)

Main faults within the pressure switch

a) When the diaphragm becomes 'holed' or porous. The switch can be operated and clicks heard, but will click back again without being de-pressurised.

b) The contact points inside the switch may 'weld' themselves together which would not be uncommon if an item such as a heater were to short circuit and blow a fuse. This would alter the number of clicks heard, as one or more switches may be inoperative. Movement of the unit can often free the contact points, although this will not be a lasting repair, as the switch will inevitably fail again due to contact point damage.

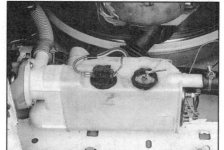

This large plastic moulding houses the filter, heater, thermostats and pressure vessel. It also has connections for the outlet pump and a second pump for circulating water during the wash and rinse cycles. It is located beneath the tub unit and is a part of a 'Jet Wash System'. Check this type of system for scaling and blockages, especially in hard water areas. Several manufacturers now use water circulation systems similar to this one

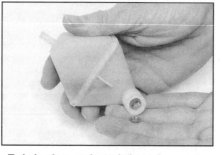

To help clean awkward shaped pressure vessels pop one or two small nuts into the inlet, add a little water, cover the inlet and shake the vessel

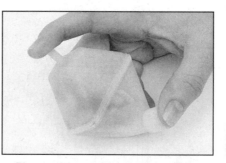

Rinse and repeat this process until the water runs clean. Ensure you use nuts that will fit easily into the vessel and ensure they are removed before refitting to the machine

Any of the above faults require the fitting of a new switch. The make, model and serial number of the machine should be stated when ordering, as pressure switches are internally pre-set for specific machines, although the external appearance is similar. Fitting is a simple direct exchange between the old and new.

Pressure vessel variations

When refitting check the pressure tube and any rubber hose connections for wear (i.e. rubbing on pulley, belt or clips).

A similar procedure should be followed for all types of pressure vessel and care should be taken to re-seal all hose connections that are removed. Remember to wash clear all loose particles, etc., as even the smallest of blockages in this system will cause trouble.

A front fitting pressure vessel of the type used for Hotpoint machines

A grommet fit pressure hose

Pressure hose fitting on the under side of the outer tub. The grommet fitting to the tub can leak, so ensure that the good seal is maintained should the hose be removed for cleaning

Chapter 18
Pumps

Most washing machines have just one pump, which is used to drain the water from the machine when required. However, some makes and models may have a second pump to circulate the water and detergent mixture during the wash cycle. The most popular of these circulation systems is the Zanussi 'Jet System', although similar systems are used by other manufacturers. The function of a circulation system is essentially very simple. The following information relates mainly to drain pumps but is equally applicable to circulation pumps. Both types of pumps can be found in shade pole or permanent magnet versions. **Note:** *For details of the motors used to power the pump, see* Motors *chapter.*

Leaks from the pump may not be apparent, but the resulting pool of water usually is. So here are a few points to look out for.

Firstly check all clips on the hoses to and from the pump and tighten if they are loose.

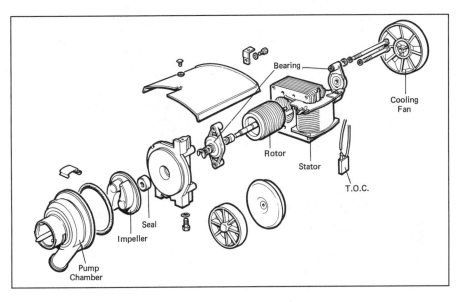

Shaded pole pumps

If the leak remains and the pump uses a shaded pole drive motor the shaft seal should be checked. This is the seal that forms a watertight barrier on the rotating shaft of the motor directly between the impeller, and the front motor bearing. The seal can be broken by a collection of fluff/lint forming between the seal and the impeller itself, thus distorting the rubber seal. To check if this is happening, remove the pump chamber by removing its securing clips or screws, and whilst securing the rotor of the pump motor, turn the impeller clockwise to undo it from the shaft (impeller and rotor are often left-hand threaded). Having done this, remove any objects

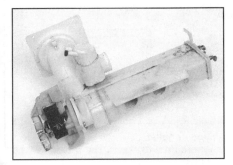

This large moulding is the reservoir chamber for a 'Jet System' washing machine and has connections for an outlet pump and a circulation pump

adhering to the shaft and refit, ensuring the pump chamber seal is in position. If the seal still leaks, it will be because it is worn or the seal has softened. On most machines, this means the complete renewal of the pump, not as costly as you may think, as many genuine and 'patterned' pumps of good quality are now available at very low cost. This may seem drastic for such a small seal, but the fact that water containing detergent would have been entering the front pump bearing, long before the leak was bad enough to see, means the pump will probably be damaged itself and next in line to cause trouble.

Other leaks can be attributable to the pump, due for example to impeller damage, that is to say blades of impeller broken off or badly worn away by a solid object lodged in the pump at sometime, e.g. small coin or tight bearings causing slow running of motor.

Both of the above will result in poor water discharge, i.e. slow draining which can be detected by functional testing. This in turn may cause the machine to spin whilst some water still remains, thus causing other hoses, etc., on the machine to leak or the machine to fill to too high a level, as some machines have a timed rinse fill action. On other machines slow drainage may mean that the machine does not spin at all. This is due to the pressure switch detecting the presence of water in the machine which the slow pump failed to discharge in its allotted time, therefore not allowing a spin to take place by either missing out the spin completely or stopping the wash cycle at the spin positions.

This may occur on the intermediate spin half way through the rinse sequence on many machines. On models with pressure actuated door interlocks, failure to fully empty the machine will result in not being able to open the door of the machine at the end of the cycle. See *Door switches and interlocks* for further details.

Checking the impeller and bearings can be done at the same time as checking the seal.

Similar faults on condenser drying machines may give rise to poor drying due to the failure to discharge the condensate and water used/produced in the drying process quickly enough. This leads to a build-up within the outer tub, which may be sufficient enough to wet the clothes but not high enough to be visible to the user. Ensure the correct pump out rate by using a functional test sequence. The pump on a condenser machine is operated periodically or continuously (depending on make and model) during the drying sequence to discharge the condensate and water. Failure due to wear is more common on condenser washerdrier machines although some manufacturers do fit more robust pumps to compensate for this. Always fit the correct replacement pump and make sure it has a TOC. To avoid premature failure, a good quality pump must be fitted and the machine should be serviced regularly.

Shown is a simple illustration of the outlet pump chamber and impeller. Water from the sump hose enters from the front. The rotation of the impeller lifts the water in the direction of the narrower outlet hose. Some machines are fitted with a non-return valve system on the outlet hose, watch out for blockages at this point. There are two types of impeller. One is simply a paddle type and more prone to blockages, the other type is like the one illustrated below and is called a vortex pump. This type of impeller is more of a flat etched disc that allows a gap between itself and the pump chamber. This gap lets particles pass through easier than the bladed impeller version. The vortex impeller applies lift to the water as shown in the diagram below. The action is similar to the rotating vortex created when a bath or sink empties.

Permanent magnet pump

The construction of the permanent magnet drive motor helps alleviate the problem of shaft seal leaks and bearing failure which are common to shaded pole versions. However, water ingress into the sealed rotor chamber can cause the rotor to pop out of its chamber. This occurs when the water that has entered the sealed rotor chamber heats up and expands forcing the rotor out of position. This fault is often accompanied by a chattering noise when the pump is energised and tries to run. The pump may work but inefficiently.

Access to typical sump hose filter or catch pot. As can be seen from photographs A and B, pump positions vary between makes but the basic operation is the same

Typical pump replacement

Note: *Ensure that the machine is isolated before attempting any repair on your washing machine.*

A Pump mounted lower left-hand side Philips washerdrier connected to accessible front filter unit

The machine was leaking badly when inspected, but was in fact still working. When questioned the user admitted that the

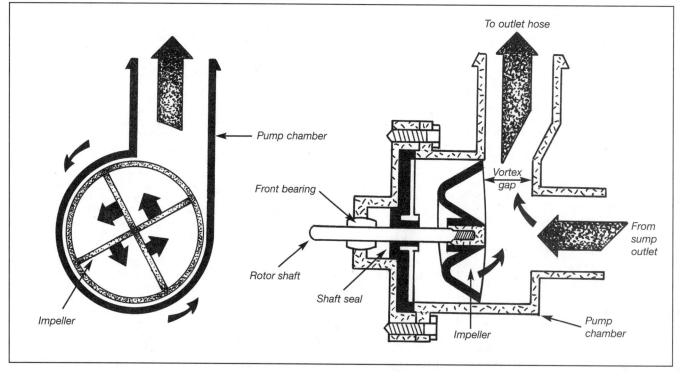

Vortex style pump. Dynamic force exerted on the water in the direction of outlet.
Above is a simple illustration of the outlet pump chamber and impeller. Water from the sump enters from the front. The rotation of the impeller lifts the water in the direction of the narrower outlet hose

B Pump mounted right-hand side directly to sump hose with internal filter only accessible during routine servicing

machine had been leaking for some considerable time, but now more water seemed to be leaking out than ever before. As you may see, this is obvious in pictures 3 & 4, by the degree of corrosion to both pump and the shell of the machine. (This level of corrosion would have been avoided by earlier detection/report of the initial much smaller leak.)

Shown in pictures 5 & 6 are variations of pumps that may be encountered on this type of machine. Pictures 7 to 12 show the further

1 Ensure that machine is isolated and remove rear panel

stripdown of the pump. In this case, it was thought best to renew the pump completely because of the amount of water and detergent damage to both the bearings and metal laminations of the stator. Again, this could have been avoided if the earlier leak had been dealt with sooner. **Note:** *In most modern machines, wash-only and washerdriers, the pump has to be changed as a complete unit for even the smallest of problems.*

The complete pump of the type shown in picture 6 was fitted, and the shell and mounts were coated with anti-rust compound prior to the fitting of the pump. The anti-corrosion coat mentioned can be one of several types available from DIY car centres and hardware shops. Use it as per the manufacturer's instructions only, taking care not to allow any contact with rubber hoses or plastics. When

2 Machine face protected and carefully laid over. Position of pump now clearly visible

3 Note and remove the hose clips and connections. Corrosion may be found on the mounting; treat with anti-rust compound prior to refitting

using anti-corrosion gel or rubber sealant indoors, care should be taken to protect the floor from spillage, and ensure that adequate ventilation is available.

After replacing all hoses and connections, (a simple reversal of the removal procedure) the machine was moved back into its correct working position and reconnected to the water and power supply. All connections and work was double checked prior to a short rinse programme being selected to ensure that the new pump functioned correctly, that the re-positioned clips were watertight and that no other leaks were present, prior to a full functional test via an RCD protected supply.

At this point, the user was advised of the unnecessary danger (and damage in this case) caused by using the machine whilst ignoring a very obvious fault.

This new type of pump uses a permanent magnet rotor and avoids many of the problems associated with early pumps. It is becoming popular with many manufacturers. A description of how the motor works is given in the *Motors* chapter

Typical electric pump with sump hose and outlet hose of the type found on many of the leading makes. The main differences with electric pumps are the pump chamber mouldings. All pumps empty at about 6 to 8 gallons per minute

4 Shown are two types of early Hoover pump that may be found. (Different styles of impeller and stator)

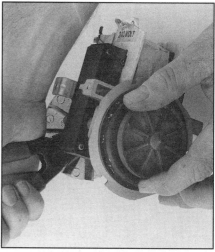

9 Whilst holding rear shaft securely, turn impeller clockwise and remove (LH thread)

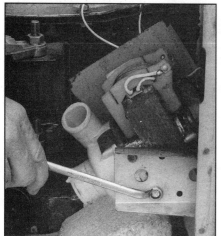

5 Support pump whilst removing securing bolts and withdraw pump from machine

7 Lever small clips loose using small bladed screwdriver. Hold clip lightly to prevent it springing off. Screws may be found in place of clips

10 Rear seal exposed. In this case it is badly worn by a build-up of lint upon shaft

6 This type of 'pattern' pump will fit Hoover, Creda, Servis and Hotpoint. Many other styles are available for other machines

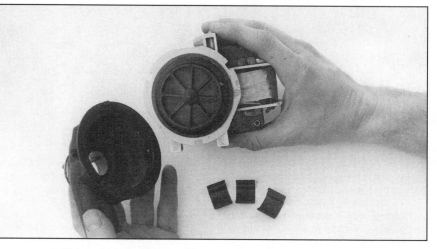

8 Note pump chamber position and remove to expose impeller

11 Seal removed and front bearing checked for wear and damage. Also check rear bearing

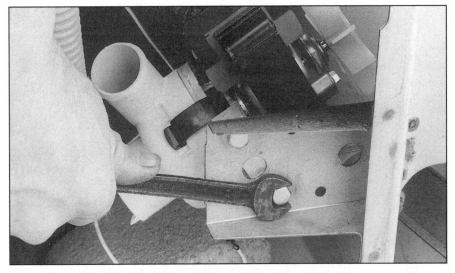

14 Secure pump firmly into position

12 Rear view of seal showing extensive wear

15 Reconnect the terminals. If the pump has an earth tag, ensure that it is a good fit, as with all connections

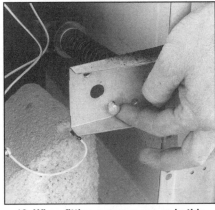

13 When fitting a new pump as in this instance, check the bolt hole sizes of the mounting plate. On some occasions they may need enlarging

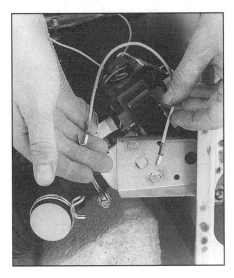

16 If the new pump has a plastic mounting plate and the original was metal, the metal stator laminations may need to be linked to the machine earth path – as in this instance. Make a short lead to connect the earth tag on the pump to the fixing bolt and secure firmly.

Note: *Not all pumps will require this procedure, those that do will have an earth tag connection like that shown. Permanent magnet replacements for original shaded pole versions do not normally require an earth path connection, if in doubt ask the supplier of the replacement part.*

When the hoses and clips have been refitted, the machine is ready for testing on the rinse cycle. Ensure all panels are refitted before commencing functional testing.

Chapter 19
Door switches (interlocks)

What is an interlock?

The name interlock is given to an electrical switch/mechanism behind or near the main door latching device of washing machines and is designed to give a time delay of up to two minutes, before the door can be opened. The delay time differs between the makes and models of different machines.

General safety

Although failure of an interlock or door latching system, which allows the door of the machine to be opened mid cycle, is thankfully not too common, such failure can and does occur. It is strongly recommended that the correct locking action of the door mechanism and interlock are carefully checked on a regular basis throughout

New style interlock with pressure lock included. This works in conjunction with the pressure switch, and does not allow the door to open if any water remains in the machine

the life of the product. In addition young children should be discouraged from playing with or near working machines. Impatient adults should not attempt to open the door of their machine until the interlock mechanism has had time to correctly de-latch. Unless this is in the course of carefully testing the integrity of the latch and interlock under a controlled situation i.e. exercising great care and not in the presence of children.

What are the different types?

A machine with a push/pull timer knob action may also have a manual interlock thus giving double protection. The manual interlock system is quite straightforward, bolting or unbolting the door with a push/pull action of the timer knob, via a latching mechanism. The mechanical interlock acts in much the same way as the electrical version in preventing entry via the door if the machine is turned on except that there is no time delay. Such mechanical interlocks are always in addition to electrical interlocks which incorporate a delay to entry.

A more recent version of interlock also incorporates a pressure switch type of system, that will not allow the door to open if there is any water remaining in the machine. This again is a mechanical operation and will work even when the machine is unplugged. The door can only be opened when the water has been drained out. This must be remembered in the case of a pump failure or blockage. The system is easily recognisable by the pressure tube leading to the door interlock. Such systems may use a separate pressure vessel or a T junction arrangement from the water level pressure switch tube. Whichever system is used faults similar to those described in the water level

Typical dry-only door safety switch. Note the operating arms. As the switch carries all the power it is liable to overhearing problems due to poor connections or contacts

control section will be encountered, e.g. blockages, air leaks, etc.

Some washerdrier machines may also include a simple microswitch attached to the door interlock forming one unit. The microswitch is in circuit during the dry cycle and operates directly via the door latch and slide action of the interlock. Such microswitches and interlock combinations are used on machines when the two minute delay facility during the dry cycle is not used. This arrangement allows the door to be opened if required, but the microswitch would open circuit and interrupt the cycle. **Note:** *Great care must be exercised with combined washerdriers as the door glass can reach extremely high temperatures. Take care to keep children out of reach when the machine is in use. Adults should also be made aware of such dangers.*

On basic tumbledry only machines, a simple microswitch actuated by the door latch pecker or hinge movement is used. No delay action is available and simply opening and closing the door stops and restarts the programme. Details of this system is given later in this chapter.

Zanussi 3DB style interlock

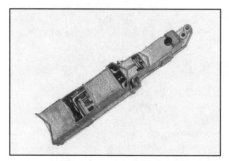

This large metal bodied interlock houses a solenoid operated door interlock and switch

Washerdrier interlock with integral microswitch to rear. Note how access was gained via door seal front lip by removal of front clamp band. See Door seal chapter

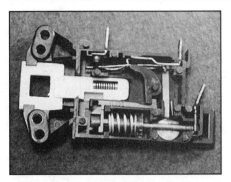

Internal view of interlock which uses the oil filled piston arrangement in place of a bi-metal strip. The piston can be seen in the lower section of the interlock running through its large return spring on the left and supported on the right by the heater pod

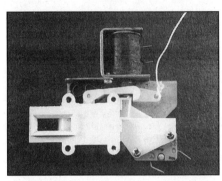

Solenoid operated interlock as used on many computer controlled machines. The microswitch is clearly visible as is the cord for manual actuation of the interlock in the event of power failure/fault

A mechanical pecker system mounted on the main wash motor

Mechanical pecker interlocks

As the name implies this is a mechanical interlock although it can be found combined with any of the other electrical versions detailed in this chapter. The essence of this type of system is to physically detect movement in one of three key areas:

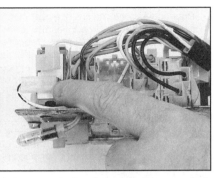

This simple Candy interlock is mounted directly behind the door-opening button on the main switch bank

drum, belt or motor shaft. Only when movement in the area being checked has ceased can the door be opened. The area checked for movement will differ between makes and models, however the principle of operation is similar whichever area is used. A device called a pecker unit is used to detect movement of the belt, motor or drum. The pecker unit is linked to the door interlock mechanism by a bowden cable (similar to bicycle brake cable). The pecker unit consists of a spring-loaded arm with 'the pecker' mounted on a larger pivot arm. The principle of operation is as follows. The pivot arm and pecker are positioned close to but not touching the item to be checked for movement (belt drum or motor shaft). When the user attempts to open the door the bowden cable is tensioned. This transfers movement to the pecker unit and pushes the peck into contact with the motor shaft, belt or drum pulley. If the area being checked (pecked) is moving (in either direction) the pecker will be deflected and the unit will absorb the slack in the bowden cable. However, if the check area is stationary the pecker is pushed directly onto the check area and no deflection occurs. When no deflection occurs the bowden cable remains taught and allows the interlock mechanism to unlatch the door. Correct alignment and adjustment are crucial to the correct operation of the system. Cable adjustment can be made but settings and tolerances differ between manufacturers and models. The main problem areas are: wear often caused by impatient users trying to open the door of the machine while it is still in motion after the spin, damage to the pecker unit often caused by out of balance spinning and incorrect adjustment/position of components.

Coil operated interlocks

This type of interlock uses a solenoid coil to lock the latching mechanism. When energised the solenoid coil magnetically attracts a soft iron core to its centre (similar to the action of a water valve) to lock the latching mechanism. In addition to locking the mechanism the movement of the core slowly expels air from a small chamber. When de-

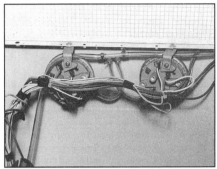

Double pressure switch system with T junction and tube to the right leading down to a pressure operated interlock

A typical microswitch from the tumble dry only machine. The switch is a simple ON/OFF function with no delay or locking action

The 'Rold' interlock is becoming increasingly popular with today's manufacturers. Shown is the Fagor variant. Also found in Indesit machines

energised the return of the soft iron core to its rest position is damped (slowed down) as air slowly re-enters the air chamber through a very small hole. The damping action of the air chamber creates both a smooth locking action and the required delay at the end of the cycle.

The interlock also houses a mechanical switch, which is actuated by the door latch pecker. This type of interlock may be combined with other systems. Due to its simplicity this type of interlock is fairly reliable. However, one common problem is that of excessive noise. This normally takes the form of a buzzing noise, which is magnified by the metal shell of the appliance. Pressing the door or holding the door handle (if fitted) often reduces the noise level. The noise originates in the interlock and is magnified by the shell of the appliance in a similar way an alarm clock can be made louder if placed on an empty metal tin. The noise is caused by excessive lateral movement of the soft iron core, which oscillates in the alternating magnetic field produced by the coil. The noise does not affect the operation of the interlock but can be very annoying to those in the vicinity of the machine. To remedy the problem a new interlock will be required, unfortunately even new interlocks have been known to exhibit this problem. **Note:** *There are two reasons why the noise can be alleviated by pressing on the door or holding door catch/handle. Simply pressing on the door or shell of the appliance damps the vibrations of the metal shell. Holding the door handle or catch partially operates the latch slide within the interlock; the slide is pushed onto the core, which in turn prevents it from vibrating.*

Computer controlled machines

Computer-controlled machines (as opposed to mechanically controlled) may have similar electro-mechanical interlocks to those described in the previous paragraphs. Alternatively, depending on make and model, they could be completely different both in the way the door is opened and the way that access is restricted via the door until the programme has finished and the machine is completely empty of water. A breakdown of basic operation is as follows though it does not typify any specific make as manufacturers will incorporate subtle differences to create individuality of product.

Door opening is by means of a push button action that actuates a simple electrical switch which then makes contact and supplies power to a solenoid operated catch mounted within the machine in place of the door interlock. With power supplied to the solenoid in this way the door latch is released and the door opens. To avoid continuous supply to the solenoid, a microswitch is incorporated within the unit to open circuit the solenoid coil as soon as the door latch pecker is released. The opening operation of the door depends on:

1 Power being supplied to the machine and the machine being turned on.
2 No programme is currently operating.
3 No motor action or drum rotation is taking place.
4 Any water in the machine is below the lowest detectable level of the pressure switch, i.e. all switches in rest position.
5 Door open button is pressed.

The requirements of steps 2-5 are monitored continuously by the micro-processor within the electronically-controlled timer. With condition 1, a power supply is necessary for the door solenoid to operate. However, in power failure or fault situations, many machines have means of de-latching the door mechanism manually; reference should be made to the appliance handbook for further information. Before carrying out mechanical actuation of the latch, ensure the machine is unplugged (isolated) and that the water level is below the door level, see *Emergency procedures* chapter.

Several machines use an LED (light emitting diode) or display to indicate when door opening can be activated.

The use of a micro-processor within such

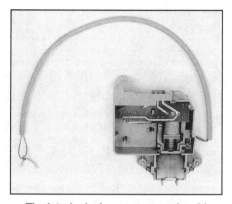

The interlock shown uses a solenoid operated locking mechanism

machines allows for greater interaction and sensing to be carried out. Due to the larger memory size of the chips used, more variable programming is possible. The way in which the programme is written enables it to react to variations within the circuit of the machine which in turn gives rise to a greater number of criteria being monitored to ensure compliance with safety, etc. The micro-processor board also includes a clock chip which can help in controlling programme times and functions accurately. The timing function can also be used to time a delay to the door open switch if required by the manufacturer of the machine.

How does a basic electrical interlock work?

Because manufacturers prefer to have their own version of interlock, it is impossible to illustrate all of the different types. Because of

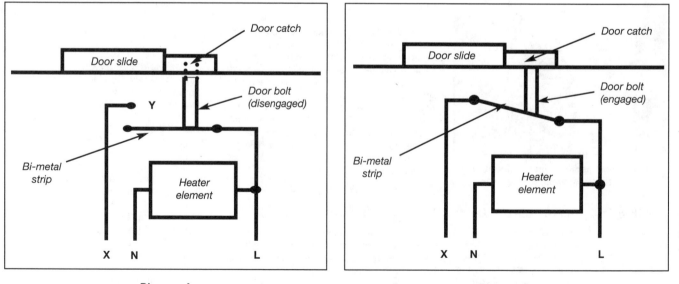

Diagram A

Diagram B

this, the Klixon (3DB) type of switch is used to illustrate the internal workings and theory.

Diagram A shows the state of the interlock before power at L. It can be seen that the door bolt is disengaged and the bi-metal strip is in its 'rest' position. Because of this, there is no connection at point Y. Therefore no power is transmitted to X.

Diagram B shows the state of the interlock when power is applied to point L. The heater is activated, therefore heating the bi-metal strip. This then bends, engaging the door bolt and making the connection at Y, allowing power to flow to X. When the power is disconnected, the heater is allowed to cool and the bi-metal strip then bends back to its rest position. This action can take up to two minutes, thus creating the delay. The delay time (cooling of heater and bi-metal) will vary according to the ambient temperature, style of interlock and position of the appliance. Some makes and variations of interlocks use a small oil filled piston arrangement in place of the bimetal strip. When heated, the oil expands and the resulting piston movement is used to actuate the interlock. As with the bi-metal system described, cooling allows the piston to retract and de-latch the interlock. **Note:** *The heater referred to in this part of the manual is not the large heater in the drum, but is of minute proportions and is only used to heat the bi-metal strip.*

Modern machines tend to link the interlock to all of the other functions of the machines, so if the interlock should fail, power to the rest of the machine would be severed and the machine would then be totally inoperable. With older machines interlock failure would only result in no motor action throughout a normal programme.

A two tag interlock (1DB) is called a straight through interlock as, although locking occurs, switching does not.

Tumbledry only machines

Most tumbledry only machines do not incorporate a time delay system and access to the load compartment is therefore not restricted by time. There will be, however a microswitch actuated when the door is opened which will open circuit and sever power to the motor to stop drum rotation. As the rotation is slow on dry-only machines the drum will quickly stop when the motor is turned off by the microswitch. On some machines, only the motor is open circuited by the opening of the door, leaving the heater still in circuit. The motor used to rotate the drum usually rotates the fan which circulates the air, therefore in such machines, if only the motor

is stopped when the door is opened, the heater temperature will quickly rise and open circuit its TOC. If the door is left open for long periods, cycling of the TOC will occur with the possibility of damage to both TOC and heater. **Note:** *This will only occur if the timer is still on the heat section and will only cycle until the remaining heat time runs out, i.e completes its preset time. Continuous opening and closing the door is not recommended. To avoid such problems many machines now use the door microswitch to open circuit supply to all components. Make yourself aware of the system used in your machine.*

Computer-controlled tumbledry only machines use a system similar to that described in the previous section. Dry programmes on such machines, once interrupted, will not restart by simply closing the door but require the re-pressing of the start button.

Similar systems can be found on the higher specification mechanically-timed machines. These machines use a relay start once normal operation has been interrupted, i.e. by door opening. The remaining portion of the drying time cannot commence until the start button is pressed. This type of system is much safer than the simple microswitch only operation which will restart the drum rotating as soon as the door is closed.

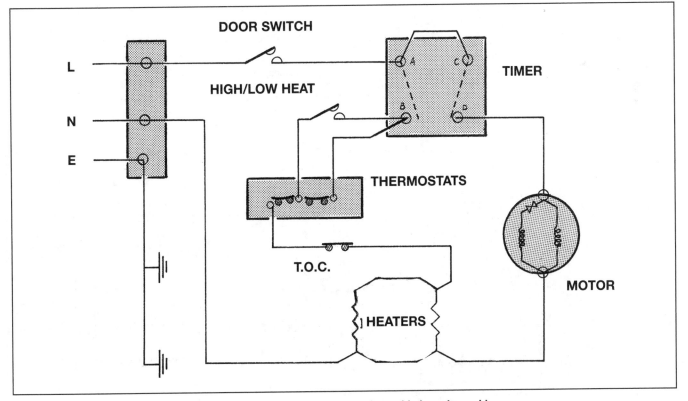

Schematic wiring diagram of a simple tumbledry only machine

Chapter 20
Heaters

Heating elements come in a variety of shapes and sizes, but the elements used in washerdriers and tumbledriers are usually one of two basic types:

1 Exposed single wire elements used exclusively in dry-only machines.

2 Metal sheathed elements found in washerdriers, for heating the air flow (mounted in a special duct on combined washerdriers) and for heating the wash water (immersion type). The solid/sheathed element is also used in many dry-only machines to heat the air flow.

The former type is simply an exposed length of conductor which heats up when a current is passed through it owing to the resistance properties of wire. Being an exposed conductor means that it must be housed and supported in such a way as to avoid accidental contact which could cause electric shock or burns. It must also be housed in such a way that it can dissipate the heat generated and be supported by heat resistant insulators at regular intervals.

Metal covered (shrouded) elements can be found in all three types of machines, vented washerdrier, condenser washerdrier and dry-only. The way in which it is insulated and supported by its solid outer sheath allows it to be bent and shaped into any one of thousands of configurations to suit any situation. This however, can only be done at manufacture and no modification or bending should be done to old or new elements.

The way in which they work is the same as written previously, when a current is passed through the element its resistance gives rise to heating. The element is housed within a tube and surrounded by an insulating material (magnesium oxide) allowing heat to be transferred to the outer sheath, but not the current. Outer sheaths are made of various types of metal to suit the particular requirements and conditions. Some are for use with the external portion of the element submerged in water, whereas others are used within the machine to heat the air flow during the drying cycle.

The design of both exposed and sheathed elements vary enormously from product to product, but the way in which they work remains the same. As with motors, a TOC is normally present to avoid overheating. The TOC is a common area of fault and replacements must be identical to the original. To avoid overheating, make sure of a good airflow over the element, i.e. check that fluff etc., does not block the air intake.

Main faults with heaters

One of the most common faults with heaters, both exposed and sheathed versions, is that of open circuit, i.e. no current flows through the heater, therefore no heat is produced. This can simply be due to a broken or loose connection to one of the heater terminals. This then overheats, leaving an obvious discoloration of the connection or terminal,

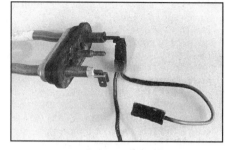

Overheated terminal due to loose connection on live supply

resulting in a break of the circuit at that point. Alternatively, the break in the circuit can occur within the element itself. Heaters can easily be tested for continuity as described in the *Using a Meter* chapter.

Another fault that can occur is that of low insulation. In this case, please refer to the chapter on *Low Insulation*. Accompanying the low insulation fault is that of short circuiting of the heater caused by either a complete breakdown of insulation of sheathed elements or the breaking of exposed elements/mounts allowing the exposed element to touch the earthed metal heat shield or housing. This results in the appliance blowing fuses or earth tripping if an RCD is in circuit.

Wash water heater is clearly visible on the lower right-hand side of the outer tub back half of this condenser washerdrier machine

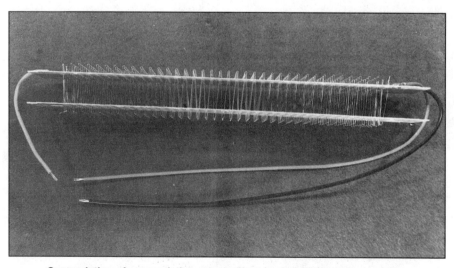

One variation of exposed element used in many tumbledry only machines

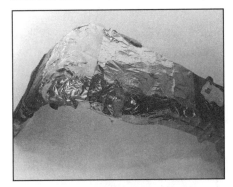

Heater duct of a Philips washerdrier machine (condenser type)

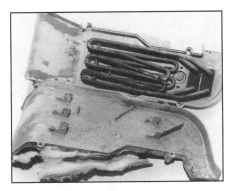

Typical configuration of airflow heaters housed in the ducting of a combined machine

Should any of the above faults occur, a complete replacement of the component(s) is required. **Note:** *Broken exposed style elements that touch an earthed metal heat shield will only blow wired fuses if the remaining element circuit is short and resistance low. It is possible for the remaining length of element to work using the earth as its neutral return. This type of fault results in poor drying through the reduced size and heat output of element. Check exposed elements and their mounts closely for this type of problem. If this fault does occur on an RCD protected circuit, i.e. household supply or via adaptor type during functional test, etc., the RCD would trip preventing further use of the machine until the fault is rectified.*

Where is the wash water heater located?

The wash water heater is usually located in the lower part of the tub assembly, and can be either fitted through the back half of the tub, through an aperture in the tub base or located in the front of the outer tub directly below the door seal. Access is gained by removing the relevant panel of the machine. Details of this are to be found in the *Door Seals* chapter.

Removal and refitting of a heater

After making a note of the connections and removing them, the heater can be withdrawn from its position by slackening, but not removing, the centre nut, and tapping it to release the tension then gently easing the rubber grommet free from its position with a large flat-bladed screwdriver. Refitting is a reversal of these instructions, although a little sealant should be applied to both surfaces of the grommet fitting. Care should be taken that the centre nut is not over-tightened, as this would cause a distortion of the inner metal plate. On most automatic washing machines, the inner of the outer tub has a raised flange or cover plate that engages the curved section at the end of the heater. It is important that this is located correctly when refitting the heater. Check that it is located and held correctly by pressing firmly but carefully downwards on the terminals of the heater whilst slowly rotating the inner drum. If the heater is not located correctly it will pivot on the grommet mounting and allow the element to come into contact with the drum, resulting in a grating noise and vibration. If such a noise is experienced during this simple test, slacken the heater clamp centre nut, remove the heater completely and relocate it correctly then try again. **Note:** *Do not exert excessive pressure on the terminals of the heater. Try to press down on the exposed outer sheath.*

Machines that have plastic or nylon outer tubs are fitted with overheat protectors.

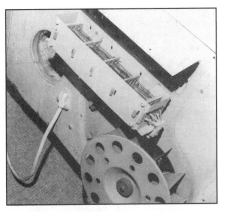

With the large rear cover removed from this Philips tumbledry only machine the heater assembly and fan are easily accessible for cleaning, etc.

This wash water element shows signs of scaling and fluff contamination

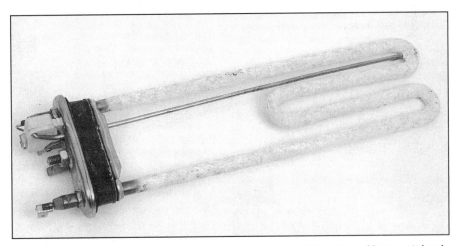

This wash heater has an external safety overheat microswitch actuated by a metal rod that protrudes through the rubber seal and is fixed to the far end of the heater. If the heater comes on with little or no water in the tub the heater will expand beyond its normal size. This expansion pulls the rod forward and in doing so open circuits the switch and turns the heater off. Once pulled through the rubber seal the rod will not self reset the microswitch even when the heater has cooled down. However, on some versions the switch can be reset by easing the rod back into position. Note: *This must only be done when the original fault has been traced and rectified. If in doubt fit a new heater ensuring it also has overheat protection. There are versions that have a double rod and switch system for increased overheat protection*

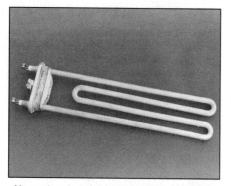

Normal style heater. (Do not fit to plastic tub machines)

Heater with overheat detector (arrowed). This is found on machines with plastic outer tubs

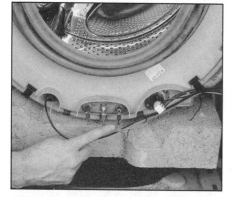

This wash heater has an internal thermal fuse. Although a normal heater will fit the aperture, it is essential that any replacement fitted to the machine also has thermal protection

These are essential and are linked in-line with the live feed to the heater. They are fitted for safety reasons, for if a pressure switch or pressure system were to fail, it is possible for the heater to be engaged with no water in the tub. This would be most unwelcome in a machine with a metal tub, although only minor damage would be caused to the clothes. If this type of fault were to happen in a plastic/nylon tub, the result would be extremely dangerous. **Note:** *Under no circumstances should the overheat protection device be removed or bypassed.*

The overheat protector that is used on early Philips machines was an integral part of the heater and is similar to a capillary thermostat switch. However, on later machines, a simple thermostat is used to open circuit the heater if overheat occurs. On the latest machines the thermostat is connected in the live supply between the door interlock to the pressure switch. If overheat occurs the thermostat goes open circuit and cuts power to all other components apart from the door interlock. Hotpoint use a separate thermal fuse heater protector for boil dry protection of their plastic outer tub machines and this item along with the late Philips thermostat are available separately. Some types of heater have the thermal protector built into the sheath of the element (normally recognised by metal capped terminal).

If such items are found to be faulty, the result would be failure to heat the wash water or failure to move through the programme. If any type of protector is found to be open circuit, it is essential that the cause is identified and rectified prior to renewal. Thoroughly check the pressure system and switch. For more detailed information on thermal fuses and protection devices see the following chapter. Always ensure that a replacement heater is of the same specification as that originally fitted, if the original had an internal protector then so must the replacement.

Airflow heaters

Metal sheathed type

Sheathed elements of similar construction to the water heaters described previously are found in both washerdrier and tumble dry only heating units. Because of the restriction of available space in the combined washerdrier, the elements used in washerdrier heating units are of a compact configuration very similar to their water heating counterparts. On the other hand, dedicated dry-only machines, which use solid sheathed elements, have much longer (often circular) elements. Due to the similarity in construction, the faults encountered will again be open circuit, low

insulation and short circuit. Reference to these relevant sections will be required. Details of the various heating units on both washerdrier machines and dry-only appliances are given elsewhere.

The large bubble on the top of this plastic moulding was caused when the heater came on with little or no water in the system. Blockages within the pressure system led to severe overheating within this combined remote heating, filter and pressure vessel unit

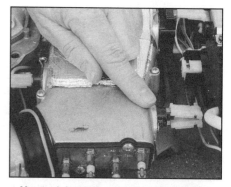

Heater inlet duct with two thermostats and a microtemp thermal fuse

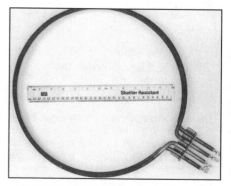

This compact tumbledrier heater unit uses sheathed elements

Exposed type

This type of heating element is used predominantly in tumbledry only machines. As can be seen from the accompanying photographs on page 74 and 75, they are easily distinguishable from the sheathed type of heater. Although several variations and configurations of exposed element are used, they all fall into two basic categories;

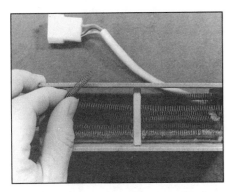

This Zanussi unit displays a typical broken element fault. A complete unit replacement is required in this instance

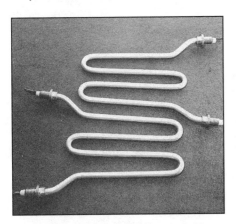

Sheathed airflow heaters are used in combined machines. Shown are Newpol type

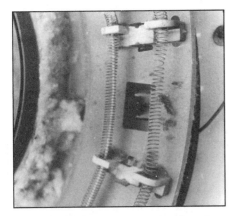

Exposed heater element (spiral type) supported on ceramic mounts (type 1)

1 Simple spiral (spring like) elements, stretched and supported on ceramic holders either in a large circular configuration or a compact box mount system.
2 Single strand element woven into or onto a ceramic or mica support.

It is essential that whatever type is used, it should be correctly supported, free from fluff build-up and all ceramic or mica supports intact. Check closely for any sagging of the element between the supports as this could lead to short circuit between elements on compact heaters and to shorting to earth on the larger circular heaters. Take care when cleaning or removing any fluff as both the supports and the elements themselves become brittle with use and are easily damaged. As with the sheathed elements described earlier, two elements are usually used to allow a high/low heat selection

Do not make twisted joints to repair a broken element. A faulty element should always be renewed along with any broken, cracked or charred support or insulation. The compact types of heater unit are available only as

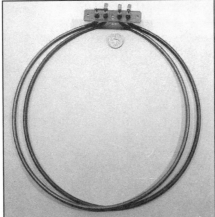

Sheathed elements can also be found in tumbledry only machines. They are normally in a large circular single or double configuration as shown. They can be mounted to the front or rear of the machine depending on make and model

complete units – details of which can be found in the section on *Dry only machines*. The large spiral elements like the ones shown in the photograph on page 75 can be renewed individually and details of this procedure will also be found in the *Dry-only machines* chapter. On machines with large spiral elements a support cord will be found running through the centre of each element, the purpose of which is to prevent the element from shorting to the metal heat shield in the event of it (the element) stretching or breaking. It is essential that the support cord is intact and correctly positioned in order to support the element if breaking or sagging should occur.

On early machines, the support cord was often made of asbestos, and consequently with use the cord itself became powdery and broke. Take care if this type of support cord is found during repair or servicing as the dust can be harmful if inhaled. Moisten the work area to reduce dust and dispose of the waste carefully. The support cord used now is of glass fibre, which is less prone to deterioration and should be used to replace the old type of asbestos element support.

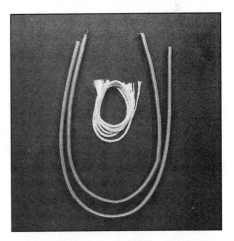

Spiral element kit for Hoover tumbledry only machine. Note new glass fibre support cords. When fitting, measure fixing length required using a piece of string and pre-stretch new element before fitting it to the machine. Keep stretching along the whole length evenly otherwise hot spots will form

78

Chapter 21
Temperature control

Fixed thermostats

A thermostat is an automatic device for monitoring temperature. This can be water temperature, the direct heat of the heating element (in which case, acting like a TOC. See *Heaters* chapter), or airflow temperature of combined or dry-only machines. The thermostat (stat) will either 'make' or 'break' a circuit at a predetermined temperature. Temperature ratings of fixed thermostats are usually marked around the metal perimeter on the back of the stat and are marked NO or NC, i.e. normally open contact (closing and making a circuit at given temperature) or normally closed (opening at given temperature). Some thermostats can and do contain both variants. Some manufacturers use coloured dots to differentiate and identify the thermostats used in their product. Unfortunately each manufacturer appears to use a colour code unique to them and therefore reference to the relevant technical data will be required to ensure a correct replacement is obtained. Problems will also be encountered when the coloured dot is missing or the thermostat is burnt or damaged.

Where are they located?

Positioning of each thermostat depends on the job it has to do. The wash temperature thermostats are most often located on the back half or the underside of the outer tub depending on the make and model of the machine.

Exceptions to this are machines designed for front servicing, where the thermostat,

heater and pressure vessel are located on the front of the outer tub, directly below the door seal. Access to these components is gained by the removal of the front panel of the machine. Details of this are to be found in the *Door seals* fitting chapter.

Thermostats used to control/monitor drying temperatures will be located at a strategic point of the airflow, whereas the thermostats used for overheat protection are located in or near the heater ducting (on combined machines) or heat shields (on dry-only machines).

How a fixed thermostat works

Diagram A shows a typical fixed (non-variable) thermostat which can have one, two, three or more settings.

Variable thermostat showing the switches, capillary tube and pod

Fixed thermostat of the types used in tumbledry only machines for temperature control and overheat safety (TOC)

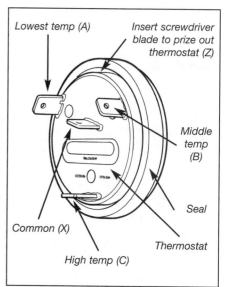

Diagram A

Single thermostat

Double thermostat

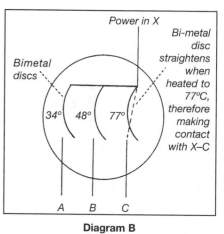

Diagram B

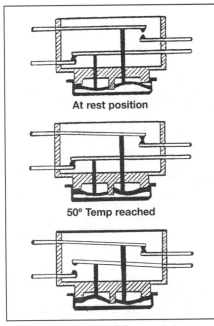

A typical fixed thermostat

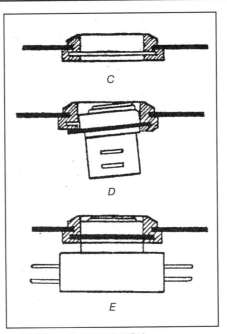

Thermostat fitting

Diagram B illustrates how a three position thermostat works. The power enters the switch at X, but cannot proceed as there is no contact. As the temperature rises and each preset temperature is reached, the bi-metal disc set to that temperature bends, making one of the three possible contacts.

The diagram above shows an alternative style of fixed thermostat, in this instance a 50°C (NO) normally open contact and a 85°C (NC) normally closed contact. The latter is a safety thermostat, which operates if overheating should occur within the machine.

The diagram illustrates the position of the thermostat at rest. Bi-metal discs are mounted directly behind the metal front cover of the stat and are preset to distort at given temperature (in this instance, 50°C and 85°C). They are linked to contact switches by push rods. Any corresponding distortions of the discs, either make or break the corresponding contacts as shown.

When removed from the machine, the thermostat's operation can be tested by placing the metal cover in contact with a known heat source, e.g. radiator, hot water, etc., which matches or slightly exceeds the required temperature. Allow a little time for the heat to warm the stat and bi-metal discs. Testing for closing or opening of the thermostat can now be carried out as shown in the *Using a meter* chapter.

Check temperature with a household thermometer and allow a few degrees either way of the marked temperature on the outer rim of the stat, and remember to check if the stat is normally NO or NC. When cool, check that the stat returns to its normal position as indicated on the rim, i.e. NO or NC.

Removing and refitting a standard washing machine thermostat

Note: *Before the removal or repair of any component from the machine, isolate the machine from the main electrical supply by removing the plug from the wall socket.*

Make a note of the position, orientation and connections of the thermostat and then disconnect the wires. For thermostats fitted in rubber grommets insert a small flat-bladed screwdriver between the inner rubber lip and the metal front plate of the stat and prise the stat from the grommet. Care will be required if sealant has previously been used as this will have glued the stat into position. When refitting, it is advisable to smear a little sealant on the grommet to aid fitting and avoid leaks. Refitting is a reversal of the removal process.

To refit locate the metal lip in the grommet recess (C) and with the aid of a flat-bladed screwdriver ease the outer lip over the metal lip of the stat (D). Sealant will help locate and seal the thermostat into position, (E). Ensure that the thermostat is securely located into the grommet and that the outer lip is not trapped.

Thermostats may also be held in position by metal clips or clamps, and again, make sure of a good seal and check that the clips or clamps do not trap or touch any wires or connectors.

Thermostats on combined washerdrier heating ducts and most tumbledry only machines are secured in place by screws or clips and removal and refitting is therefore a straightforward process.

Variable thermostats

How a variable thermostat works

Diagram F shows a pod type thermostat. This is found on machines that have a variable wash temperature control. Diagram G is a schematic diagram of the internal workings. This consists of an oil or gel filled pod which is connected to the switch by a capillary tube. When the oil/gel in the pod is heated it expands within the sealed system and pushes a diaphragm. The diaphragm acts on the switch gear thus 'breaking' one circuit and 'making' the other.

When the oil/gel cools it contracts, pulling the switch in the opposite direction. The switch is then in its original position and the process repeats if necessary.

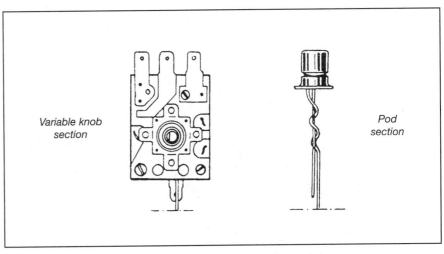

Variable knob section

Pod section

Diagram F – Typical pod type thermostat

Removing and refitting a pod type thermostat

The pod which is located at the base of the capillary tube must be eased from its rubber grommet gently, taking care not to unduly kink or pull on the capillary tube itself. **Note:** *When fitting this form of thermostat, the capillary tube must not come into contact with any electrical contacts such as the heater terminals or moving parts such as the main drive belt. When fitted, the tube should be checked along its entire length for any possible contact with these items. Also, a coiled section of at least two large turns should be left at a convenient position to absorb the movement of the tub assembly.*

Testing a thermostat

The standard thermostat can be subjected to a known temperature (e.g. radiator, kettle, etc.) and be checked with a small test meter for continuity. This process is shown in the chapter *Using a Meter*. The pod thermostat can be tested as above, ensuring that only the pod itself is immersed in water. **Note:** *Whilst at room temperature, the state of the thermostat should be determined. On pod thermostats, the lowest and highest setting should be selected. During testing, ensure that switch actuates both on rise and fall of temperature, see* Using a Meter *chapter.*

Thermostat operation flowchart

Using the flowchart opposite, trace the sequence of events:
1 The machine is turned on.
2 The timer impulses, fills the machine with cold water and turns the heater on.
3-4 The thermostat 'waits' until the water is heated to 40°C.
5-6 When the thermostat closes (i.e. the water has reached 40°C), the timer washes for two minutes. (At this point the heater is still engaged.)
7-8 The above operation is repeated, again with the heater engaged. When the two minute wash has ended, the water will be at 45°C due to the extra four minutes heating.
9-11 The timer then moves to the next position, which disengages the heater, and is then ready for the programme to continue as required.
12 For the purpose of this flowchart, the wash will end here as we are only concerned with the operation of the thermostat at this time.

Note: *This is only used as an example to illustrate the use of the thermostat, and does not actually represent the way in which a wash is formed. For further information regarding the timer, see the chapter* Timers (programmers).

This way of using preset thermostats can give a greater variation in wash temperatures. A combination of preset and variable thermostats is common in order to give protection to the cooler washes, i.e. should the variable thermostat be accidentally left at 90°C and a delicate wash has been selected, the preset stat would override the variable stat, therefore giving some protection to the wash.

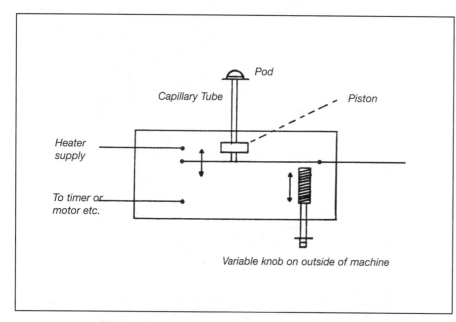

Diagram G – Internal workings of pod type thermostat

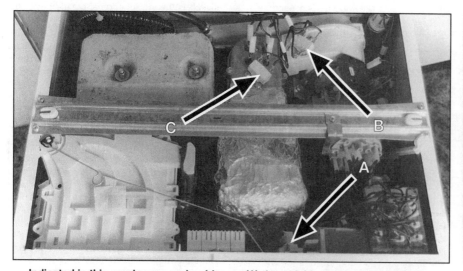

Indicated in this condenser washerdrier are (A) the variable temperature wash stat control, (B) dual fixed temperature air duct stat and (C) fixed temperature stat being used as a TOC to open circuit the air duct heater in the event of overheating

The fixed wash temperature stat (D) and pod for the variable stat (E) are shown in position on the rear of the outer tub

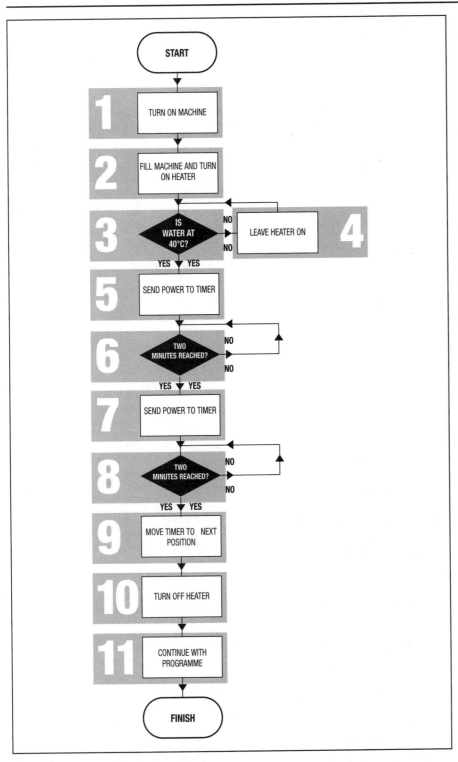

```
START
  ↓
1  TURN ON MACHINE
  ↓
2  FILL MACHINE AND TURN
   ON HEATER
  ↓
3  IS WATER AT 40°C?  → NO / NO →  4  LEAVE HEATER ON
  YES / YES ↓
5  SEND POWER TO TIMER
  ↓
6  TWO MINUTES REACHED?  → NO / NO →
  YES / YES ↓
7  SEND POWER TO TIMER
  ↓
8  TWO MINUTES REACHED?  → NO / NO →
  YES / YES ↓
9  MOVE TIMER TO NEXT POSITION
  ↓
10 TURN OFF HEATER
  ↓
11 CONTINUE WITH PROGRAMME
  ↓
FINISH
```

Typical solid state thermistor

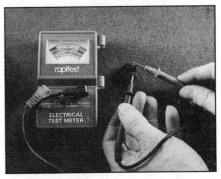

Continuity testing a thermistor with a low voltage battery test meter

Where is it located?

Like all temperature sensing devices, it must come into direct or indirect contact with the substance (air/water) or item that needs monitoring. Its location is therefore similar to the other thermostats but methods of fixings will differ.

How does it work?

Unlike other temperature control devices the thermistor cannot work alone. It is an electrical resistor, the resistance of which varies in relation to its temperature. There are two ways in which its resistance varies depending on manufacturer, and the requirements of the finished product. Thermistors can be positive or negative temperature coefficient. In simple terms, this means a positive coefficient thermistor's resistance increases as its temperature increases and conversely, a negative coefficient thermistor's resistance decreases as its temperature increases. Thermistors are therefore rated as PTC or NTC respectively. The NTC type of thermistor is the version most often used in temperature sensing circuitry in automatic washing machines, e.g. Hoover, Servis, Hotpoint, etc., a theoretical operation of this is given below. It is essential that only the correct variation of thermistor is used which conforms to the rating requirements of the machine and its circuitry.

The variation in resistance to temperature change forms part of an electronic circuit, the output of which controls the advancement of the selected wash programme, in either mechanically or electronically controlled

Thermistors

What is a thermistor?

A thermistor is a solid state device used in place of a fixed or variable thermostat. The thermistors' particular properties allow them to be used as infinitely variable temperature sensors that have no moving parts. They are also incapable of going out of calibration, i.e. giving incorrect temperature resistance values, but occasionally they can and do go 'open circuit', or connections to and from them may short circuit. Both are faults which will inevitably give rise to temperature sensing problems.

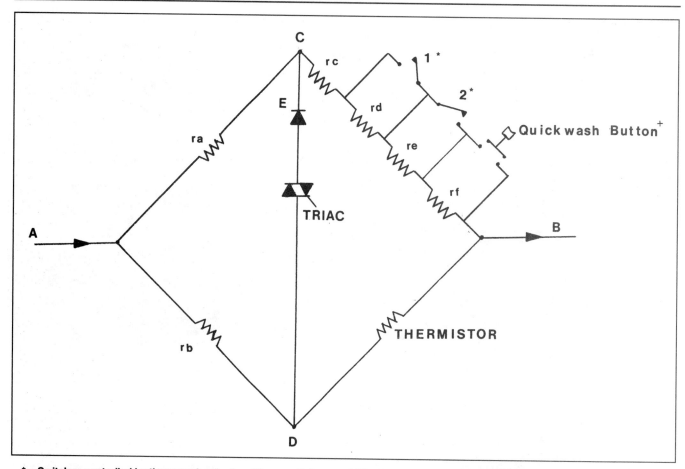

* = Switches controlled by timer wash selection. These switches would be electronic not mechanical on computer controlled machines
+ = Button on facia of machine which is a user selectable option

machines. On electronically controlled machines, i.e. those without mechanical timers, the resistance of the thermistor is monitored directly by the main programme circuit board or sub-module, see *Timers (programmers)*. However, thermistors can be found on machines with mechanical timers/programmers and the way in which they work in this instance is as follows. The resistance of the thermistor forms part of a temperature control circuit. There may be a separate module solely for this purpose or it may form part of the motor control module as in some Hotpoint machines. A theoretical operation of such a system follows.

In this instance the output voltage at D & C are used to control a triac (an electrical component within the circuit). The triac in turn switches the thermostop coil on a mechanical timer or impulse to control panel of a computer control machine. See *Timers (programmers)* chapter.

Being an electronic circuit in either mechanical or computer controlled machines, the operating voltage within this portion of circuit will be low (5V DC). Therefore, any electrical testing of the thermistor must be with a low voltage test meter, as voltages of over 9V will damage the thermistor or module circuitry.

The two resistors Ra and Rb are of the same value. A 5V DC voltage supplied to point A will take one of two routes depending on the resistance opposing it, i.e. A.C.B. or A.D.B. Route A.C.D. has within it four resistors each of which can be switched in and out of the circuit in relation to the programme selected and temperature required for that wash cycle. The diode at point E eliminates reverse supply to the triac. The route A.D.C. contains the thermistor in its second leg D.B. If we assume that the water within the machine is cold, then the thermistor resistance will be high. This will allow a current flow from D to C thus energising the thermostop or holding the programme on the heat cycle until the predetermined temperature (governed by the switchable resistors) is attained. Releasing of the thermostop or impulse of programme is as follows. As the water temperature increases, the resistance of the thermistor decreases (NTC). At some point the resistance in both sides of the circuit will be equal and at this point, no current will flow between D & C and the triac will switch off. This in turn will release the thermostop on mechanical timers or allow impulse to the next stage of the programme on electronically controlled machines. Variations in temperature are gained by switching in or

out the required resistors in the C.B. leg of the circuit, thus altering the point at which equilibrium is reached within the circuit. All switches open = all resistors in circuit rc + rd + re + rf would result in high resistance, therefore a cooler wash of say 30°C is achieved. Quick wash switch closed = resistor rf bypassed, i.e. lower total resistance gives wash of say 40°C. Switch 1 closed = two resistors in circuit rc & re may relate to 50°C with option of quick wash switch to further reduce temperature (and time) if required by user. Switch 2 closed – three resistors rc, rd, rf in circuit may relate to 90°C with option of quick wash switch to further reduce temperature (and time) if required by user. All switches closed = this will leave only rc in circuit at this point, and a high temperature of say 90°C would be achieved, again with option if required.

Note: *The option to alter the temperature selected by the set programme, i.e. by pressing a quick wash or short wash option button on the control panel, may be bypassed itself by the timer on some programmes. This means that although in the theoretical operation detailed above, each setting could be further affected by the quick wash switch, in reality, this may not be the case as a quick wash may not be suitable for certain types of wash loads.*

Thermistors and temperature controlled filling

In addition to basic temperature control the ability of thermistors to react to any temperature change is used to the full in some computer and hybrid timer controlled models. For instance as the machine fills with water the thermistors resistance will be proportional to the temperature of the water entering the tub. This known value can be used by the processor to fill the machine (when circumstance permits) with the ideal starting temperature for that particular wash cycle. This is accomplished by energising only the hot valve and allowing the processor to cycle the cold valve as required to achieve the preferred starting temperature. This is very much like when we want to fill a bowl of water to wash, we dip our fingers in the water and if it is too hot we turn the cold tap on until we achieve the temperature we want. It may seem a simple task but when this ability is added to a washing machine it can equate to a significant saving in energy.

Regulations

Manufacturers of modern tumbledriers have by law to produce machines that maintain full overheat protection in the event that a normal control thermostat fails in the closed circuit position or a reverse polarity connection is made. Such measures are in addition to the normal component protection systems. This means that overheat protection devices should not be able to automatically reset themselves while the heating element(s) are in circuit. There are many devices used in manufacture and details of four of the most popular devices follows. Most machines will use a combination of normal thermostats and Thermal Overload Cut-outs (TOCs).

TOCs

The term TOC is an abbreviation for thermal overload cut-out. In simple terms, if the item the TOC is attached to or is in proximity with, gets too hot (over a predetermined temperature) the TOC will operate and open circuit the supply. The way in which it works is very similar to the thermostat, both of which use the bimetal strip system. Thermostats are in fact used on some machines as TOCs to open circuit for instance the heater if an overheat fault occurs. However, the term TOC generally relates to the smaller devices that are embedded within or on top of motor winding coil of all types, and above the heaters of many makes of tumbledriers.

There are several variations in style and size, each of which being matched to its particular use and position within the appliance or apparatus. It is therefore essential that only the correct style and temperature rating is used

when renewing a TOC. Those that are used to protect motors, pumps, wash motors, tumbledrier motors, etc., are rarely renewable and usually form part of the original winding or moulding. If a TOC had gone open circuit, it will have done so for a particular reason, therefore this safety item must not be bypassed. Always ensure that any replacement component contains a TOC. Some pattern spares may miss out this fundamental safety device in order to cut production costs, so take note that such an omission could be unsafe.

Although designs and ratings of TOCs vary, there are four basic types of operation, e.g.

a) The self-setting TOC. This is like a thermostat and resets when a normal working temperature returns This may result in a cycling of the fault, i.e. if a tumbledrier outlet or filter is blocked, the heater element will overheat due to a reduced air flow. A safety TOC will open circuit the heater supply. Unfortunately, on early machines, when the heater cools, the TOC also cools and in doing so returns power to the heater and the cycle could then carry on until either the pre-set drying time expired or the element or TOC failed.

b) The manual reset TOC. The action of this type of TOC is identical to that described above except for one main difference. Once tripped, it cannot reset itself and has to be reset manually usually by simply pressing a button or rod. **Note:** *This must be done with the machine isolated, i.e. unplugged, and only after the cause of the tripping has been eliminated.*

c) The one-shot TOC. This type of bladed TOC is very similar in appearance to a and b, however, once tripped it will not reset itself nor can it be manually reset. No attempt must be made to reset or bypass this fail-safe device. Identify and correct the problem that caused the device to trip and then renew the one-shot TOC.

d) Details of this particular PTCR device follow later in this chapter.

Some washerdrier machines incorporate both self-setting TOC for low temperature fault levels but a manual reset or one-shot if a cycling fault should occur or if the self-setting component should fail (in the closed position). Tripping of both self-setting and manual/one-shot TOCs are common in both washerdriers and tumbledriers if there is a build up of fluff, the airflow is restricted or the air circulation motor fails. Filters must always be kept clear and any tripping of the safety devices should be immediately investigated and the cause rectified. A delay of up to four minutes (sometimes more) is possible before a manually re-settable TOC can be reset. Modern tumbledriers from 1990 onwards now incorporate a manual reset/one-shot TOCs as standard. Machines that have the reset facility will have a reset button accessible on the outer casing, the position of which will vary from make to make. Before resetting, ensure all possible causes of faults have been eliminated/rectified.

Two variations of bladed self-resetting TOCs widely used to protect elements in tumbledry only machines from overheat. They are available in a wide range of temperature settings

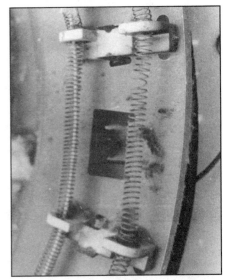

Bladed self-setting TOC in position between the spiral elements of a Hoover tumbledry only machine (centre of photo)

The button of manual reset TOC is located on the rear of this tumbledry only machine. Manual reset TOCs can also be found in some combined machines

Thermal fuses

Many small appliances now have this type of overheat protection device. It can also be found in many makes of washerdrier and tumbledrier machines. It is essentially a failsafe device which when actuated by a predetermined temperature goes open circuit. Once open circuit, it cannot self-set or be manually reset, therefore renewal of the thermal fuse is required once the device has gone open circuit. Renew the thermal fuse only when the fault which caused it to operate has been corrected.

It is a solid-state device and as such contains no moving parts or contacts that may in themselves fail. Thermal fuses alleviate the possibility of fault cycling, are cheap and in most instances easy to fit. They are small but easily recognisable and are often housed in protective sheaths or mouldings.

There is a wide variety of temperature ratings available to suit the various applications, so great care must be taken when replacing the device to match the original rating. The rating is usually printed on the outer casing of the device. **Note:** *The metal outer is not insulated and will be at mains voltage when in use, therefore ensure that all mounts, fixings and covers are correctly replaced.*

One-shot thermostat TOCs

One-shot thermostats appear very similar to the fixed thermostats described previously. However, they have one major difference, just like the thermal fuse and one-shot bladed TOCs they operate only once and cannot be reset. They are, as the name implies another type of one-shot TOC. They can be found in both large and small 'button' versions on a wide range of tumbledriers including Creda, Hotpoint and Zanussi. From the rear they look similar to self-setting thermostats but the metal front plate is normally open and the internal bi-metal disc can be seen. The state of the

thermostat can be checked both visually and by simple continuity testing. If the thermostat is OK then the disc will be convex and therefore continuity will exist between the terminals. Conversely if the disc is concave it has tripped and will be open circuit between the terminals. When handling or inspecting a good thermostat (i.e. not tripped) DO NOT be tempted to touch the disc as slight pressure can actuate the device and render it useless. Locate and rectify the problem before replacing thermostats that have tripped. DO NOT attempt to reset or bypass these or any other safety-related device.

TOCs with PTCR locking

This is yet another bi-metallic device designed to go open circuit when its rated temperature has been exceeded. However, unlike the plain TOC this type has the ability to remain tripped in the open position as long as the item it is protecting is still being supplied with power. The way in which this is achieved is as follows. The PTCR TOC is located in the heater's neutral return with the normal control thermostat in the live supply to the heater. Within the TOC is a PTCR (a positive temperature coefficient resistor) capsule. When the bi-metallic blade is tripped by an overheat situation (blocked filter, broken fan belt, etc.) it open circuits the heaters normal neutral path and directs the current through the resistor PTCR capsule which heats up. With the PTCR in circuit the main drier heater fails to operate and cools. However the bi-metal will not reset as it is now heated by the PTCR and the PTCR capsule which remains heated as long as the heater is supplied with power. Even when power is removed from the heater circuit (machine turned/reset or cool down period reached) it will take at least 6 minutes for the device to automatically reset.

Note: *This system of operation is very similar to the bi-metallic door interlock system.*

Some models combine a neon light on the front panel to indicate when the device has operated. This may take the form of a light telling user to check/clean the filter, etc. DO NOT rely on such devices nor allow them to operate frequently, check and clean the lint/fluff filter every other dry cycle. **NOTE:** *A photograph and explanation of an alternative wash heater TOC system based on expansion is shown in the previous chapter on heaters.*

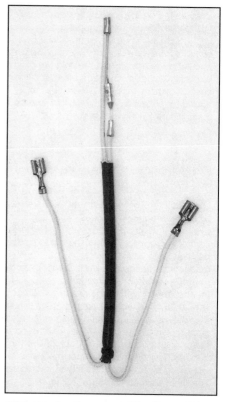

With the sheath removed the thermal fuse can be clearly seen.

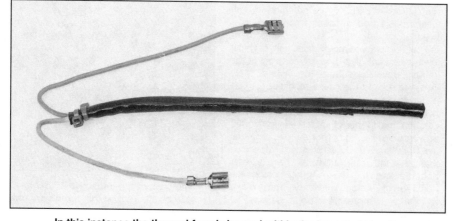

In this instance the thermal fuse is housed within the insulated sheath.

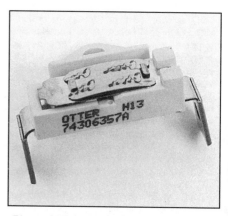

Bi metal TOC with PTCR system, refer to text for details of this device

Chapter 22
Drying components (washerdriers)

As previously stated in the book, combined washerdriers, both condenser and vented versions, are largely based on their wash-only predecessors. The aim of this section of the book is to look at the components that turn the ordinary automatic washing machine into a washerdrier. The additional parts are often referred to as the 'drying group' or 'ventilation group'. Each part will be looked at independently and as a whole. Reference to other sections within the book, e.g. thermostats, heaters, motors, etc., will also be necessary. Although there are numerous variations in design and positioning of the components in the combination washerdriers, they are all based on the two basic types.
a) vented types which draw air in from the surrounding atmosphere, heat it, circulate it through the previously spun wash load and vent the resulting moisture laden air from the machine (similar operation to simple dry-only machines).
b) condenser types which use a sealed warm air circulation system combined with a condenser unit to remove the resulting moisture from the airflow.

As the diagram and photo sequences show, both systems have many parts in common with one another. For instance both systems have a common configuration of fan assembly and heater ducting mounted on the upper portion of the outer tub. However, although this configuration is found in a wide variety of makes and models, there are many variations of component positions possible, as can be seen from the accompanying photographs. A breakdown of the various components of both types of system is as follows.

Heater unit

This unit is of metal construction (usually die-cast aluminium). Housed within it are the heating elements (sheathed type) used to heat the air prior to it entering the inner drum. Often the unit forms the inlet ducting to the drum via the door seal, but variations can be found which have direct access to the drum via the outer tub. Some machines incorporate a flap within the ducting to prevent steam produced during the normal wash cycle condensing within the heater unit. Air flow during the dry cycle pushes the flap valve open. It is possible for the flap to stick in the closed position and

Combined fan motor, housing and heater detached from the large Ariston drying group of components

cause overheating within the duct. If your machine has such a flap/valve, check that it is free to move.

Insulation materials (aluminium foil and fibreglass) are often found covering the heater duct. Ensure that if fitted, it is in good condition and if it has to be disturbed avoid skin contact or inhalation of the insulation material. **Note:** *Make sure that the aluminium foil and the metal tape which is used to secure it are clear of all components and electrical connections.*

Should element failure occur within the unit, some manufacturers will supply individual spares, whereas others will only supply a heater unit complete with elements. There are normally two elements which allow for delicate or high heat settings for the drying cycle. Overheat thermostats, TOCs or thermistors are also mounted upon or within the unit. The removal of fixing screws or bolts will allow most heater units to split into two parts. If the unit is to be dismantled for any reason (element renewal or blockage, etc.), inspect the joint closely as many are sealed with heat and steam resistant sealant which once disturbed, must be renewed. With the condenser machines (sealed systems), it is possible under certain circumstances for fluff to build up within the unit at various points. As with the dry-only machines, it is advisable to check for such build-ups regularly in order to avoid problems developing.

Fan, motor and housing unit

The fan, motor and housing may be either an integral part of the heater unit casing or condenser unit, or a separate motor and fan housing fixed to the heater unit. In the case of condenser machines, the unit may form the link between the condenser unit and the heater unit. The fan housing may be made of cast aluminium or injection moulded plastic depending on the make and model of machine. Fan chambers on condenser machines often have mounting positions for thermostats or thermistors to monitor the temperature of the air being circulated within the sealed system. Like the heater unit on condenser machines, it is possible for fluff and lint to accumulate within the fan housing or at the inlet and exit points. With care most units can be dismantled for cleaning, inspection or repair. However, as with the heater unit, heat and steam resistant sealant may have been used during the assembly of the unit. It is essential that any such sealant is renewed with a suitably resistant replacement once it has been disturbed. The lower portion of the fan housing usually has a small drain hole to allow any condensation forming in the chamber to drain away. Ensure that the whole of the fan chamber is clear of any blockages or fluff build-up.

Within the fan chamber, fixed directly to the fan drive motor shaft will be a tangential (centrifugal or barrel style) fan. Various types of fan to shaft fixings are used, threaded shaft and nut, slide fit and grub screw, and taper and collet. The blades of the fan should be kept clean and if it is removed for any reason, (e.g. removing fluff build up from rear), make sure it is correctly re-positioned on the shaft to avoid jamming or chafing when the fan assembly is rebuilt.

Motors used to rotate the fan can be one of three types, shaded pole induction, asynchronous induction motor (capacitor start) and series wound brush motor. Some of the more common problems that may occur with all of these motors are as follows:

Shaded pole induction. Failure of one or both motor bearing(s) allows the rotor to foul the stator. Fluff on or behind the circulation fan, or the fan out of position on the motor shaft may cause the motor to stall and overheat or burn out if not fitted with a TOC.

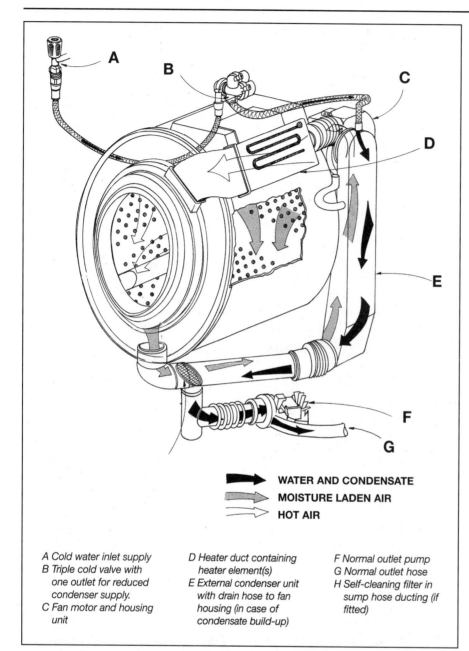

WATER AND CONDENSATE
MOISTURE LADEN AIR
HOT AIR

A Cold water inlet supply
B Triple cold valve with
   one outlet for reduced
   condenser supply.
C Fan motor and housing
   unit

D Heater duct containing
   heater element(s)
E External condenser unit
   with drain hose to fan
   housing (in case of
   condensate build-up)

F Normal outlet pump
G Normal outlet hose
H Self-cleaning filter in
   sump hose ducting (if
   fitted)

This illustration shows one of a number of variations of condenser systems that are to
be found. This system utilises the existing sump hose in place of an extra tub access
point. Also included is a self-cleaning filter – see text for detail

Ensure that the condenser unit is free
from blockages and fluff build-up

The translucent plastic used in this
Zanussi condenser washerdrier system
makes it easier to check for blockages
and fluff build-up. With the rear of the
outer shell removed, dismantling of the
condenser components is relatively easy
as most of the unit is of simple push-fit
construction

Asynchronous induction. This has a low starting torque and as with the shaded pole motor even small blockages can cause a problem. Failure of the capacitor results in overheating of the motor windings, otherwise it is a reliable and quiet drive system.

Series wound brush motor. Jamming is less common on this more powerful motor even when fluff build-up occurs. They are prone to brush wear, sticking brushes and commutator problems. Even when working correctly they are much noisier than the previous two versions.

Condenser unit

The removal of moisture from the air flow within the condenser of combined washerdrier machines is by the creation of a cold area within the sealed system upon which the moisture held in the warm air flow can condense. The area used for this purpose can either be internal, i.e. within the gap between the outer tub and drum (popular with Philco machines) or external, i.e. being an independent unit, usually of semi-transparent

plastic material, fixed to the outer of the tub unit or inner of the shell of the machine, but being so connected as to form part of the sealed air flow system. The latter is the more common version of the two. For condensing purposes both systems are kept cold by the introduction of a controlled flow of cold water. To be effective in removing the large amount of moisture from the air flow, the water introduced to the system must cool a large area. Therefore, the water entering the system may pass through either a trickle bar, or the entry point may be so designed as to create a capillary action or spray. Each system creates

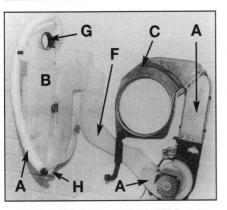

Shown is the large condenser drier unit from an Ariston combined machine. The whole unit fits into the space around the outer tub unit. A double door seal is used in this instance with the large circular metal inlet duct (C) sandwiched between

A Restricted cold supply to condenser unit.
B Large condenser moulding.
C Inlet duct.
D Heater duct.
E Fan housing and motor.
F Air return duct from condenser unit to fan.
G Condenser inlet from outer tub. (Warm moist air)
H Water/condensate outlet to sump hose/pump

a broad but thin film of cold water within the condenser unit or tub of the machine. The design and construction of each system allows both the cold water supplied to the unit and the condensate (steam now condensed into liquid) to collect in either the sump of the outer tub or separate sump of the condenser unit. Periodical operation of the normal outlet pump is then all that is required to discharge the water via the normal outlet hose. The now much cooler air, having had the moisture removed from it, is once again recirculated via the fan over the heaters. The time taken to dry the recommended load sizes depends on the efficiency of this sealed system, correct loading and setting of the drying time.

Unlike the vented machines, sealed condenser systems do not have user accessible fluff/lint filters within the air flow. Some rely on the normal sump/filter to do the job, whereas other machines have efficient outlet pumps to discharge any fluff produced during drying down the normal drain/outlet. Some machines have a means of flushing the condenser unit during the water intake of the normal wash cycles. This is normally done by diverting the cold inlet so that both soap dispenser and condenser unit receive unrestricted water supply from the cold inlet valve during filling for wash and rinse cycles. The aim is to flush any fluff/lint that has built up within the unit down into the filter or sump

ready to be removed or discharged during normal operation of the machine. In reality, only a portion of the condenser unit is capable of being flushed in this way, so build-ups and blockages can still occur. Some machines (mainly in the early Servis/Hitachi range) have a filter housed within the sump hose ducting which is designed to be self-cleaning by the water passing back and forth

This vented combined washerdrier has an unusual but functional drying arrangement. The heating elements are housed within the all metal door. The fan and motor are located on the front underside of the machine (see air intake vents at front left-hand side). Air is drawn in via the front vents by the fan unit and ducted into the door cavity at an entry point below the door seal. The heated air then enters the drum from the centre of the door protrusion, passes through the wash load and exits via two rear vent hoses. The two rear vent hoses are connected to the outer tub unit and outer shell of the machine where two large filters are located. Inlet filters are also included to eliminate particles entering the heater duct and a flap valve is located on the exit of the heater ducting to eliminate water/steam ingression during normal wash and spin actions of the machine

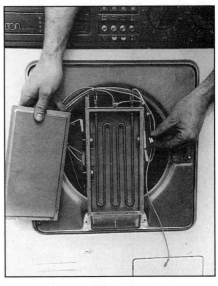

within the hose during the wash action rotations. However, blockages can occur if used to dry several loads without wash cycles in between. If these machines are to be used for continuous dry-only cycles, it would perhaps be wise to intersperse the dry cycles with a short wash cycle (with or without load) in order to keep the fixed filter clear. See your instruction booklet for details.

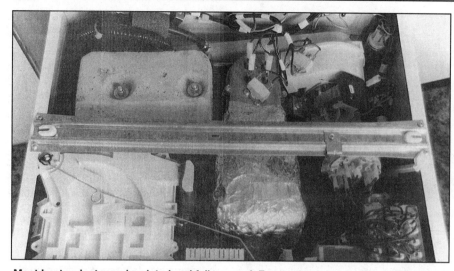

Most heater ducts are insulated and foil covered. Ensure that it is in good condition and sealed correctly

The motor bearings were thoroughly checked for wear or excessive play and for free rotation. The whole unit was cleaned and correctly sealed prior to refitting to the machine

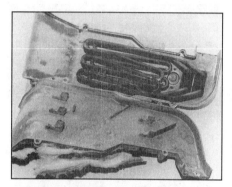

With fixings and insulation removed the casing could then be spilt into its two halves. This revealed that the lower element had failed and that damage had occurred to the aluminium ducting. A complete unit was therefore required along with thorough inspection of all other components

The unit was easily stripped down for cleaning/inspection. The fan in this instance was secured to the motor shaft by a brass collet. Once the nut (left-hand thread) had been slackened a sharp tap freed it from the shaft

This Zanussi combined condenser washerdrier does not have any external drying components other than a timer. There is no fan, fan housing or fan motor. Heating for the dry cycle is by the three sheathed heaters mounted in the top left quarter of the tub (above the normal water level). The hose on the right of the outer tub supplies water to a trickle bar mounted within the outer tub. The load is rotated near the heat source, i.e. the three heaters, whilst the opposite side of the tub is kept cool by the cold water trickle. The process does work but drying times can be very lengthy

With the fan unit removed from the machine positioning marks were made prior to stripdown (to ensure correct assembly)

As with all components forming the condenser system, sealant may have been used at certain points to prevent leaks (both water and air). It is essential that any such sealant is renewed during assembly with a sealant identical to the original.

Poor drying performance sequence (combined condenser machines)

1 Check that the machine is not overloaded, most can only dry half of what they wash. Read the handbook.
2 Ensure the cold water supply is turned on. Condenser machines require a cold water supply during the dry cycle.
3 Check that the fan and heaters are OK Functional testing should prove this. If in doubt, check the continuity of heater and free movement of the circulation fan.
4 Check that a trickle of water is passing through the condenser unit, NOT DRIPS! Note: *A water flow of less than 0.35 litres per minute (1 pint in 100 seconds) will cause ineffective drying in most machines. This will usually occur only with tank-fed cold supplies. Remember the installation requirements of minimum head of water. Also blockages or restrictions to the valve filter, reducer or spray/trickle bar may cause the flow to be too slow.*

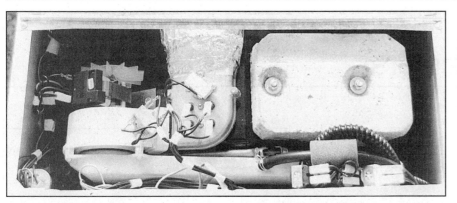

This is a close-up of a rear mounted condenser unit. The ribbed hose on the right is the restricted cold supply and the hose to the centre Is used to flush the condenser unit during normal fill sequences of wash and rinse

Ensure that wiring to the heater ducting is correctly positioned

The Hotpoint condenser washerdrier uses a universal brush motor to drive the air circulation fan. Brush wear and sticking is not uncommon. Brushes are available as spares but other faults require a complete motor unit as shown

If the first four checks prove to be OK then follow the next steps in the order in which they are set out.

1 Check removable pump filter (if fitted) or sump hose catch pot or self-cleaning filter for restrictions. Clean as necessary.

2 Check that the pump operates correctly and discharges a full load of water well within the allotted time, i.e. 1 minute – if in doubt check pump and hoses for blockages. Remember, pumps with TOCs may trip part way through the dry cycle owing to overheating on the long combined cycle. See *Pumps* chapter.

3 Check that the flow rate through the condenser is not too fast. If too much water is entering the chamber it may be picked up by the air flow and deposited on the wash load.

4 Check the water flow through the condenser unit is evenly spread (by capillary action) giving as large a cool surface area as possible. **Note:** *Such observations are not possible on all machines, only those with transparent condenser units. If observation is required it must be done at a safe distance via an RCD protected supply, and with only the minimum of panels removed. Isolate for all*

other checks, before refitting panels or continuing with further testing. Please note, this is the only test throughout the book that may require observation whilst the machine is in operation.

5 If possible try to observe if water droplets are being blown through the inlet duct, e.g. spots on glass or entry point.

6 If droplets are seen to be deposited and the water flow appears correct through the condenser unit, a fluff blockage may be the cause. Strip down the unit and clean it thoroughly. Some machines have an extra hose to the unit to flush any fluff away. Problems can also arise from long hair, animal hair and wool. Check all connections and hoses, etc. Ensure that parts fitted originally with sealant are resealed with the correct sealant. If this is not done, a vapour leak could occur and result in failure of other items or low insulation

7 If all the above tests prove to be correct, the fault may lie in a small weep from one of the inlet valves, i.e. failing to close correctly. This may wet the wash load via the dispenser as the drying cycle works normally. Check for weeping valves by process of elimination. With the machine electrically isolated, remove each hose in turn from its corresponding valve and observe the valve outlet. A little water will be spilt during the removal of the hose and care must be taken to mop it up immediately. Observe the outlet closely (perhaps for some minutes). After the initial spillage, there should be no more water. When a constant drip is observed you have found the offending valve. Although the machine is electrically isolated, the water supply to the valves will need to be on for this type of test.

If condensation Is found at any time under the top cover of the machine (which may be accompanied by white scale deposits in hard water areas), the cause could be a warm air leak (vapour leak) from the fan housing, heater ducting, inlet point at the door seal or thermostats. Ensure all are correctly

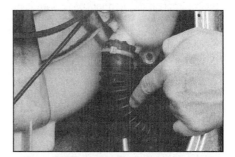

Due to constant movement the hose at the bottom of this type of condenser unit is prone to leaking at the joint and splitting within the convolution of the hose. Check it thoroughly and renew as required

positioned and sealed. **Note:** *Leaks on seals or gaskets may be due to imperfections in mouldings or rags left during manufacture. Carefully remove and smooth any such defects and ensure a good seal is obtained. Some manufacturers use a sealant compound at these points; ensure that only the correct heat resistant sealant is used and do not refit seals without compound if it had been used on the original seal.*

Safety points

1 Always ensure the mains electrical supply is isolated switched off and plug out – when checking. If observing a water flow test, do so with the use of an RCD protected circuit and test its operation before use.

2 Fully isolate the machine before commencing further investigations, stripdown or repair.

3 Ensure moving parts like the blower motor and fan have stopped before continuing with fault finding.

4 Ensure the drier heating elements have cooled prior to checking or stripdown. Also check that the door glass and ducting have cooled sufficiently before you touch them.

Chapter 23
Timers (programmers)

The programmer or timer, as it is more commonly known, is the unit located at the top of the machine, directly behind the selector knob on mechanically controlled machines, whereas machines that are controlled electronically may have the programmers split into two or more circuit boards, modules as they are usually known.

When a programme is selected, the timer (mechanical or electronic) follows a predetermined sequence switching components in and out (i.e. heater, pump, valves), for various lengths of time. Owing to the apparent complexity of this component, it wrongly tends to be regarded as a NO GO area.

The intention of this manual has been to show that the automatic washing machine is not so mysterious, and when broken down into its constituent parts, its simplicity of operation is revealed. To describe the working of the timer in your particular machine would require the make, model number, date of manufacture and the timer number itself. These are needed to ascertain which variation of timer and associated variation of programmes that your particular machine has. In their most infinite wisdom, the manufacturers have seen fit to change their timers, numbers and wiring colours, etc., with regularity.

You cannot normally repair a timer yourself (however see *Alternative to buying a new timer* later in this chapter). Complete unit changes are needed for internal timer faults. However, on some timers, drive motor coils can be renewed if a simple open circuit has occurred, see *Using a meter* chapter.

Without detailed information of the switching sequences of the faulty timer, internal faults are difficult to trace.

ETN style timer with two internally mounted motors, one on each side

Two timers are normally used on combined washerdrier machines – one for programme selection (knob on the right) and one for selecting the length of the drying cycle (knob on the left)

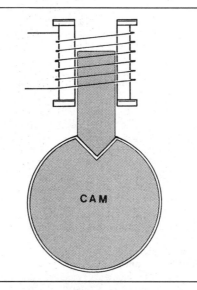

Thermostop coil in de-energised mode preventing timer cam advancing until temperature required closes thermostat and supplies the coil with power

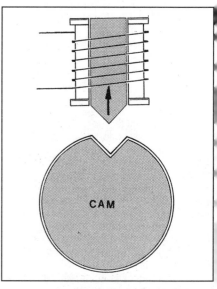

Thermostop coil in energised mode allowing the advancement of main cam barrel, i.e. thermostat closed and supplying power to coil

Note: *The diagrams depict a thermostop system operating with normally open stats (NO). Versions with normally closed stats (NC) will work in a reverse manner to that shown, i.e. when energised main cam advance prevented and when de-energised, main cam advance allowed. Both variations can be found – be aware of the way your particular system functions*

Internal view of thermostop type timer. Main cam barrel right, narrower timing and motor reversal cam centre and thermostop coil and mechanism on the left

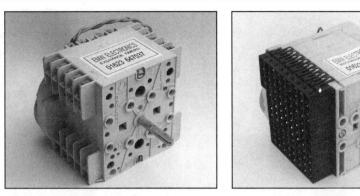

Early and late Crouzet type timers. The timer on the left has individual push on connectors whereas the timer on the right has round pin block connectors to one side only and is therefore much easier to fit

Block connectors like the one shown are becoming more popular. Five individual connectors are used on this timer and must be fitted correctly. Ensure that connections within the block do not push out when fitted

This timer from a Hotpoint machine has both edge connectors and individual amp tag connections to the front switches

Units can often be difficult to fit, unless a logical approach is used!

The main benefits of mechanical timers:

a) Modern mechanical timers are reliable.

b) New units can be relatively low in cost, although this differs from make to make of appliance. Having said that, the price variations for similar parts (e.g. only the cam barrel on some makes is different) between some brands can be extremely wide.

It must be remembered that when a fault is suspected, it is not always the most complicated component that can cause the most trouble. If a process of elimination is used and all other parts of the machine are found to be working correctly, it is only then that the timer should be suspected. (Unless of course in the case of obvious failure, such as a burn out or damage to the timer.) **Note:** *Ensure that the power is turned off and that the plug is removed from its socket at all times. Do not remove the timer from the machine at this point.*

The removal and subsequent exchange of the timer can be a long and tedious task on some machines, and should not be undertaken lightly. However, several of the more modern machines have improved the way in which the wiring harness is fitted to the timer. Multi-block connectors are now used on many machines making timer renewal much easier. Do not fall into the trap of replacing the timer because of the ease of the job. Correct diagnosis of the fault and a methodical approach to both fault finding and perhaps subsequent replacement of the timer is essential.

Do not remove any wiring as yet, but thoroughly check for any overheating of the connections to and from the timer spades (connections), i.e. if a fault is suspected in the heater switch, trace the wire from the heater to the timer. This gives the location of the heater switch and should be examined for any signs of burning or being loose. This would at least confirm your suspicions.

Having decided that the timer is at fault, a note should be taken of all of the numbers

1 In some instances it is possible to renew the timer motor coil if it is found to be open circuit. Do not mix the motors as they normally rotate in different directions. Insert a small flat-bladed screwdriver under the retaining spring clip and lift it slightly

(photograph sequence continued overleaf)

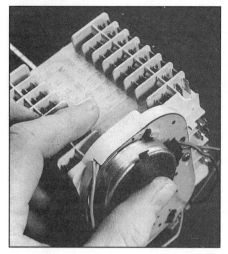

2 Mark the correct motor position and lift the motor free

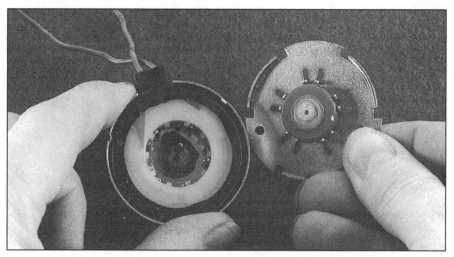

5 The two halves of the casing will part to expose the coil and permanent magnet rotor

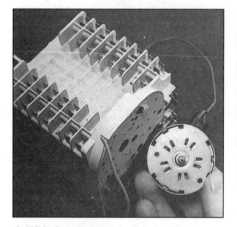

3 With the clip eased, slide it sideways to free it from its position

6 The coil can now be removed from its position. Ensure that the small plastic anti-reverse mechanism is in its correct position in the base of the casing

8 Reassemble both halves and press firmly together to ensure that they locate correctly. Check that the motor rotates correctly (in only one direction) as original. The motor can now be refitted to the timer – a reversal of the removal procedure. Note: This sequence can be carried out with the timer *in situ*, it was removed in this instance for photographic purposes only.

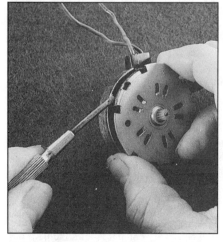

4 Insert the small flat-bladed screwdriver between the two halves of the motor casing and ease them apart

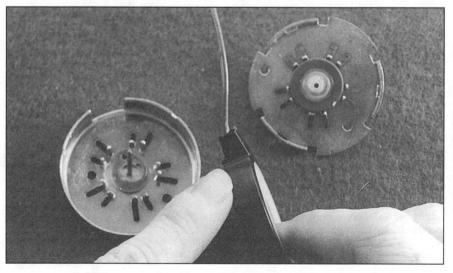

7 Fit the new coil making sure that it is the right way around

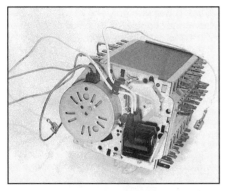

Typical timer with thermostop coil and plate to lower right-hand side. The single timer motor and thermostop mechanism is clearly visible with the rear cover removed. Timer coil renewal is also possible on this type of timer.

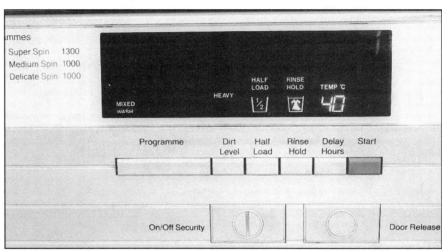

This computer controlled machine has a detailed graphic display panel.

This AKO timer has an exposed thermostop coil and slide operating a plastic arm.

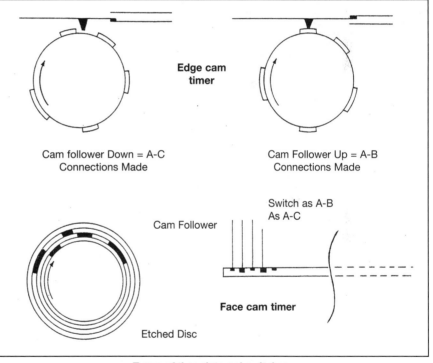

Edge cam timer

Cam follower Down = A-C
Connections Made

Cam Follower Up = A-B
Connections Made

Cam Follower

Switch as A-B
As A-C

Face cam timer

Etched Disc

Types of timer internal switches

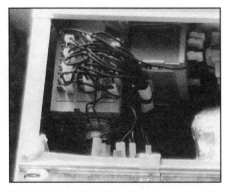

Temperature plus time programmer *in situ* in this condenser washerdrier machine.

that are on the timer, together with the make, model, serial number and age of your machine.

Armed with this information, you can obtain an EXACT replacement. When the replacement has been obtained, visually check that they are identical, as timers will not generally be exchanged by any company, once they have been fitted. You

have been warned! Having confirmed that it is the correct replacement, and any accompanying documents have been read thoroughly, you can proceed to swap the wiring. The only way that this can be done is by placing the new timer in the same plane as the original, swapping the wires or block connectors on a one-to-one basis. (Although very time consuming, this is by far the safest method.) Alternatively tag each wire with its corresponding timer connection number, i.e. 2H, 3B, etc., prior to removal. A mistake at this point would be almost impossible to rectify without a wiring and timer diagram, therefore it is advisable

to ask someone to supervise operations. When all connections have been successfully exchanged, the timer can be fitted into position, ensuring that any parts that are connected to door interlocks, etc., are positioned correctly, then double check the work carried out and earth continuity. Once fitted into position and the covers have been refitted, the power can be turned on, and a functional test programme can be implemented. **Note:** *Some timers have small metal clips that join/link terminals together. These generally do not come with the new timer. Ensure they are swapped from the original.*

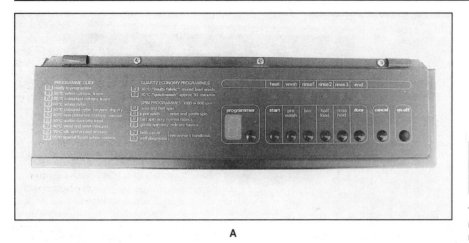

A

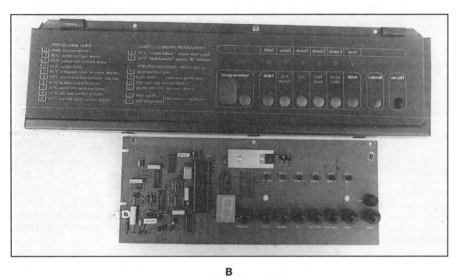

B

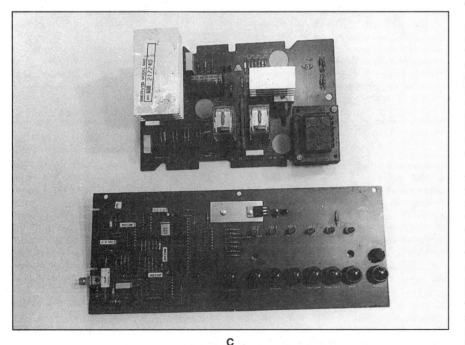

C

The top two photographs depict a typical computer controlled machine facia with selector buttons and LED display. Photograph B is the same facia panel removed to expose the main programme circuit board housed behind it. Photograph C shows both programme board and matching power module from the same machine

Computer controlled machines (electronic timers)

The functional parts of these machines, i.e. motor, drum, pump, etc., differ little from machines with conventional selector knobs and mechanical timers. Micro-processor controlled machines are easily recognisable by their digital displays used to indicate the programme selection. Most have the ability to display an error code when faults occur which relate to a table in the hand book. Faults within micro-processor timer circuitry can be difficult to locate as the complex circuit board components cannot be easily checked. It is best to eliminate all other possible causes of faults before suspecting either the power module or programme unit. If all the other checks prove satisfactory, then check all connections to and from the control boards, micro-processor machines generally have two * – one low voltage board for the micro-processor, selector panel and display, and one power board with transformer, relays and thyristors to operate the mains voltage switching which the processor cannot do directly.

*Note: *Washerdrier computer controlled machines may have three boards. The third board being used for auto sensing of the dry cycle.*

The connections to printed circuit boards are prone to oxidisation giving poor electrical contact especially on the low voltages used by the programme boards. Check closely for poor connections. If the fault remains after all other components have been checked and found to be OK, the only option left is to change one or other (or in some instances, both) of the circuit boards. Owing to the way in which the power board functions (see following paragraph), it is most likely to be a failure in this circuitry or its components at fault.

The power board is generally much bulkier than the programme board and houses a large transformer to drop the voltage to the processor. Electronic circuit faults occur more often with power boards as the mains switching operating the pump, heater, etc., is switched mechanically by relays or electronically by thyristors operated by the lower voltage supplied from the programme board, i.e. processors themselves cannot directly switch mains power and use mechanical relays or thyristors. Try to isolate if a mechanical fault is suspected (e.g. heater not receiving power, maybe a sticking/faulty relay, etc.). Items that short circuit and blow fuses may also damage

This internal view of a computer-controlled machine (wash only model) shows the programme module in place behind the front facia of the machine. The printed circuit board is clearly seen as are the PCB edge connectors. Note in this machine the wiring leading to the power module is ordinary cable not ribbon cable

Ribbon cable like that shown is often used to connect programme board with the power board

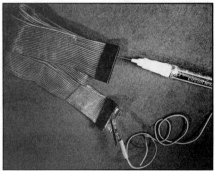

Test ribbon cable continuity by inserting a metal plate in one connection and testing individual wire at the other. A low voltage test meter is essential for this type of test. Move the whole length of the cable on each test to check for intermittent open circuit

The power module in this instance is located in the bottom right-hand side of the machine. Wiring to and from the unit is clearly visible

Power module removed from machine showing complex circuitry of this unit. This particular unit was severely damaged by a simple short circuit of the pump wiring. The fault damaged several circuit board components and the circuitry of the board itself. The simple fault resulted in a complete new unit being required

their control relay or thyristor. For instance, a simple fault such as the live supply to the outlet pump breaking loose during a spin cycle and touching the earthed metal shell of the machine would result in a direct short circuit. Such a fault on a machine with a mechanical timer would blow the appliance fuse in the socket and rectification would be straightforward. However, the same fault on a microprocessor controlled machine is likely to damage the components of the circuit board used to switch the pump supply, resulting in a much more expensive repair.

The programme board may also be referred to as the display board or module. It differs from the power module in that it is much slimmer (but often much wider) than the power board and lacks the larger components such as relays, transformers, heat sinks, etc.

It is usually mounted behind the front facia of the machine although variation in positioning will be found between manufacturers and models within each range.

Obtaining individual components from the machine manufacturers is not possible as only complete boards/modules are supplied as spares.

Faults within the components or circuitry of the board are extremely difficult to trace and as with the power board, only complete units

are supplied by the manufacturer. Before contemplating a board fault, ensure all other components within the machine are OK and that all connections to and from the printed circuit boards are in good condition and are firmly pushed into place. Check thoroughly all connections, wiring and all protective covers. With the machine isolated, look closely at all connections that carry mains voltage when in use, as loose connections can cause overheating and interference which can affect the processor chips. Include all earth path connections in the wiring checks and renew any that are loose, have cracked covers or show signs of damage (e.g. overheated, etc.). Do not forget to include the plug connections.

With persistent or unusual faults, i.e. intermittent operation, random displays, works for short periods and then blanks memory, etc., check the condition of the supply socket. If a poor connection exists between any pin of the plug and its supply connection, again interference will be present which may corrupt the processor, see *Basics – electrical*. Renew if suspect.

A faulty suppression unit may also be the cause of such random and difficult to trace faults. Ensure the unit is securely earthed, see *Suppressors* chapter.

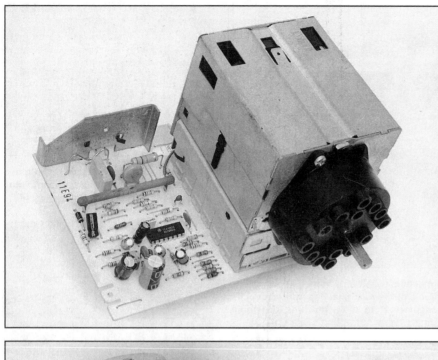

These two timers combine both mechanical programme and electronic speed control in one unit. Combined units such as these are often referred to as 'Hybrid' timers

new unit is needed, it would be wise to inspect the printed circuit board's soldered connections to verify that they are sound, e.g. loose or poor connections, called dry joints, can often be easily rectified. If all these checks prove negative, a new unit will be necessary. Take care to fit the unit correctly on all its mounts and ensure all covers and connections are sound. Take particular care to avoid direct contact with the components of the unit.

Do not touch the processor board's components at all as they are sensitive to static electricity and are easily damaged by careless handling. The power boards are more robust but care must still be exercised when handling them.

Note: *All checks must be carried out with the machine isolated in the usual manner with the taps off and the plug out! Under no circumstances should you try to test the processor board even with a low 9V or similar tester because the micro-processor chip can easily be damaged. Use of the 1.5V tester is recommended for continuity testing of the wiring between the module units. Try to leave the block connectors in place and using the probes of the tester, check for continuity between exposed printed circuit points close to the connector blocks. This will test both the wiring between the modules (usually ribbon cable) and the connection to the printed circuit board.*

On most computer controlled machines faults that develop may be indicated by a code which is displayed on the front of the machine. Codes differ from machine to machine so refer to your handbook to ascertain the meaning of each code.

Hybrid electro-mechanical timers

Many modern machines have timer units that are a combination of electronic and mechanical programme control. Such units are often referred to as 'Hybrid' timers. Depending on the manufacturer the timer and the appliance the combination may be one of two variations:
a) A simple combination of electronic speed control circuitry and mechanical timer (this may be one complete unit or made up of two separate units with block connections.
b) A combination of micro-processor and mechanical control in one unit.

Many of the major manufacturers such as Hoover, Hotpoint and Whirlpool to name only three, currently use this type of programme control. The hybrid is a middle option between the purely mechanical selection of programmes and fully computer controlled selection. When fault finding

With the need to prevent interference from particular components within the machine items, such as the main wash motor, may have small suppression units called chokes, see *Suppressors* chapter, which prevent any interference being transmitted along the wiring of the machine. Ensure that any chokes fitted within the machine are secure and in good condition (e.g. check continuity). If all the aforementioned checks prove satisfactory, then it is most likely that the processor chip is corrupted or the board has

a fault within its circuitry. Such faults will require a replacement unit. Carefully note all connections to and from the unit and keeping in mind the later paragraph regarding handling of the unit, remove it from the machine. Inspect it closely for dirt or debris which may be affecting the circuit or its components. If any dirt is present, it should be blown free (do not use metal items such as screwdrivers). Check the board for cracks or possible moisture damage due to faulty covers, etc. Before finally accepting that a reference to both types of programme control mentioned previously will be required. A point to note is that fault finding on machines with these types of control can be extremely easy. With both the speed control module and timer/programmer combined into one unit fault finding is a simple process of elimination. For instance if the drum fails to rotate and the belt is intact, motor continuity checks are all OK and the wiring to the motor from the Hybrid timer checks out, then it's the timer at fault and needs replacing. Fault finding in other instances can be reduced to simple checking of components and wiring.

Fuzzy logic

With the availability of micro-processor control systems an extremely wide range of logic control options became available. However in recent times another new option has emerged, that of Fuzzy Logic. An introduction to this relatively new form of processing is given in the following chapter *Fuzzy Logic*.

Tumbledry only machines

Both mechanical and electronic (micro-processor) controls are now used for controlling drying programmes and their operation is similar to that mentioned in previous sections. The mechanical timers are much simpler as fewer combinations of switches are required. Computer controlled machines, although very similar in basic construction, usually contain some means of sensing the dryness of the load and match this to a pre-selected setting set by the user, e.g. iron dry, fully dry, etc. Termination of the programme occurs when the selected setting is attained thus preventing over-drying by warming the load unnecessarily.

Mechanical timers

Mechanical timers are by far the most popular type of timer used in the lower and mid price range of tumbledry only machines. They are smaller than the similar timers used in washing machines, but the cam action of switching is almost the same.

Failure of both the clockwork drive and pitting of switches are the most common faults but there are no individual spare parts available. Repair consists of obtaining a replacement unit. As there are several shaft sizes, hole fixings and timers available make sure that the correct replacement is obtained and fitted on a one for one basis.

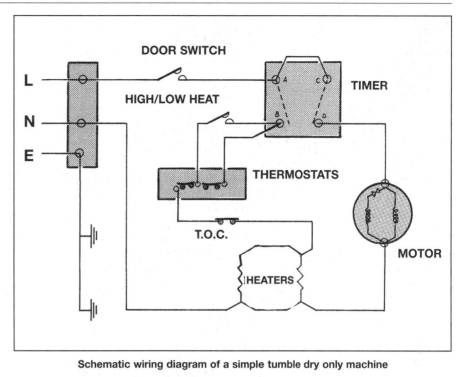

Schematic wiring diagram of a simple tumble dry only machine

On more recent machines, the clockwork-driven timer has been replaced by an electrically-powered motor to drive the timer. As with the previous type no individual parts are available for these timers, therefore with any fault they must be replaced with a complete new unit. In common with all timers, although they all may look the same externally, there are many different combinations possible; fixing points, terminal positions, shaft sizes and length of selectable time, all of which differ with each make and model of machine. It is therefore essential that an exact replacement is obtained.

The clockwork version of timer is restricted to tumbledry only machines whereas the motor driven timer can be used for controlling drying times in tumbledry only machines, washerdrier (vented type) and condenser washerdriers. In both types of washerdriers, motor reversal for the main wash motor will be controlled by the main wash timer.

Shown are three versions of mechanical timers. The top timer is clockwork driven and is restricted to tumbledry only machines. The lower two are electrically driven and can be found in both combined machines (vented and condenser types), and tumbledry only machines. Many variations exist but basic function remains the same

Auto-sensing drying systems (combined machines and dry-only)

Many modern machines, both dry-only and combined types, have the option of drying on either a timed basis or by auto-sensing, i.e. to end the dry cycle when the clothes are dry or when they have reached a pre-selected level of dryness. Auto-sensing is a most useful option, which leads to more economical use. Several different systems are used in auto-sensing machines and what follows is a general description of three of the more common ones in use today. The first can be found in both combined vented machines and some dry-only machines, whereas the second and third versions are at present confined to the more expensive computer controlled models.

1 This simple system monitors the temperature of the air within the outlet duct by means of a bi-metal thermostat. A double thermostat is often used to allow for two levels of dryness to be achieved, i.e. total dry or iron dry (slightly damp to aid ironing). There are also the normal thermostats on the inlet ducting which control the temperature of the air used to dry the clothes and to prevent overheating. A theoretical operation of a combined vented washerdrier would be as follows. The machine, having been set for a dry cycle, starts to blow the heated air through the wash load whilst rotating the drum. The length of the dry cycle, main drum motor control and supply to the drying group are all controlled by the one main timer unit. The main timer is of the thermostop variety and is prevented from advancing the main cam barrel by the intermittent action of the thermostop facility. Supply for the thermostop coil is via either of the exhaust thermostats, which are normally closed. Which stat is in circuit depends on the level of dryness required and is set by user switch selection, i.e. total dry or iron dry button.

Air passing into the drum from the heater unit is controlled, in this instance by a 100°C thermostat, and as it passes through the wet clothing creating the drying effect, its temperature drops. The temperature of the air leaving the drum via the exhaust duct will be appreciably lower but will increase as the clothing dries. The exhaust thermostats monitoring the temperature will have lower settings than the inlet thermostat, in this instance 50°C for iron dry and 55°C for totally dry. Assuming the iron dry thermostat has been selected to control the thermostop supply, once 50°C has been detected in the exhaust duct the thermostat would go open circuit and sever the thermostop supply. With the thermostop now disengaged, the timer is free to move on to the next cam position, which would remove power to the drier heaters. A cool tumble would then take place for a predetermined time prior to the machine automatically switching off. This system is simple yet effective and does not require a separate drying time to be set by the user, only the level of dryness required needs to be selected. For this system to work on machines without a thermostop facility, i.e. timers with two motors, one for timing/motor rotation and the other for cam advance. Normally open thermostats would be used at the exhaust duct. These thermostats would close at the pre-selected temperature and supply power to the cam advance motor to move the main cam barrel on to the next position where the end sequence would then be similar to that described.

2 With this system a micro-processor is used to monitor both inlet and exhaust temperature. Measurement is by means of thermistors mounted at both inlet and outlet points. The resistances of both thermistors are monitored by the processor, which calculates the temperature differential between them. When the drying cycle commences, both thermistors have relatively the same resistance. However, the inlet temperature will quickly rise to its constant working temperature/resistance, whereas the exhaust temperature/resistance will rise slowly in proportion to the dryness of the load until a pre-selected temperature/resistance differential value is attained.

The programme of the processor has resistance variations built into it corresponding to the required levels of dryness of the load depending on which level has been selected by the user. When the corresponding resistance is achieved, the processor will proceed to complete the next step in the sequence, i.e. heater off, cool tumble for set time. Both this system and the following one can have a greater range of dryness settings available which are either user selectable or in the case of combined machines, matched to the wash selected, e.g. delicate, cottons, etc.

3 The third system is again part of a micro-processor or module controlled circuit similar to No.2. Sensing however is somewhat different in that the detection of the required level of dryness is not governed by temperature. This system monitors the moisture content of the load as it rotates in the warm air flow. The electrical resistance of the load is proportional to how wet/damp it is, i.e. when wet, low resistance as water is a good conductor of electricity, and when dry, high resistance (little water to allow electrical flow). The sensing system may sound complex but in fact is quite simple. A metal probe, usually a simple domed bolt, is mounted on the drum surface at a point where it will make contact with the load as the drum rotates. The probe (bolt) is insulated from the metal drum by plastic washers and is electrically connected to the module or micro-processor timer. Owing to the need for the drum to rotate, a moving contact system is employed at some point in the circuit which usually consists of a bus bar and phosphor bronze bush. Within the circuit is a bleed resistor, the function of which is to dissipate any static build up in order to prevent it from being transmitted to the electronic control circuitry where it could cause damage.

The monitoring probe is part of the electronic circuitry and as such, only operates at 5V. The resulting variations in resistance are used in a similar way as that previously described in 2. **Note:** *When testing systems that contain micro-processor controls, ensure that all continuity testing is carried out with a low voltage tester. Do not exceed 9V when continuity testing.*

Before suspecting a fault in the control module, read through the previous section on computer controlled machines. Then check the following:
1 The filter is clean and free from lint/fluff.
2 The vent/hose is not blocked or obstructed.
3 Inlet is not blocked/obstructed.
4 TOCs and fixed thermostats, connections and wiring.
5 Continuity of elements,
6 Firm contact on movable connection on probe circuit.
7 That insulation on probe head is intact, i.e. no cracks, etc.
8 All control board edge connectors.
9 If pressure system (see dry-only machines section), ensure all seals and panels are fitted correctly to prevent air leaks,

10 Ensure that the circulation fan is not jammed. The fan on some machines may be driven by a belt. Make sure that it is intact and not slack (some belts are elasticated and tend to stretch). Renew if suspect. Some machines may have the circulation fan fitted to the motor shaft. Ensure that it has not worked loose from the shaft.

On computer controlled machines, many of the faults shown may be indicated by a code, which is displayed on the front of the machine. Codes differ from machine to machine so refer to your handbook to ascertain the meaning of each code.

The alternative to buying a new timer

The cost of a new programme control (timer) unit can often be extremely high and this in turn often leads to the appliance being considered not worth repair. The other aspect of renewing the whole unit, no matter what the fault, is a sheer waste of materials when the old unit is simply thrown away. However, there is now an alternative to this expensive and wasteful practice, that of reconditioning. This is an interesting and welcome development not only in the significant reduction in the cost when compared with the cost of the new item but also in the 'green' aspect of recycling components and materials. If you choose the right company there are also other important benefits such as:
● Access to technical staff to help decide if it is a timer fault.
● The facility to return the unit if it turns out that it was not the problem. **Note:** *This can even apply to timers that have been fitted and used for a short period as long as they are not damaged (a handling charge will normally be made for this service).*
● The ability to send your old unit for testing.
● All items supplied are thoroughly tested and guaranteed.
● A wide range of programmers/timers, all of which are available by mail order.

To avoid the problems that can so easily occur in removing the old faulty unit and waiting for the replacement to arrive, exchange reconditioned parts are supplied to you in advance. This allows you to do two very important things.
1 Ensure that you have obtained the correct part by comparing it with the original.
2 Fit the reconditioned unit to your machine on a one for one basis and return the old faulty unit back to the supplier when the job is successfully completed.

In addition to programmers/timers a wide range of reconditioned speed control modules can also be obtained on an exchange basis. For further details see chapters *Motors* (speed control) and *Buying spare parts*.

Chapter 24
Fuzzy Logic

Although at present only a few manufacturers are currently using this technique of programme control it is envisaged that it will gain in popularity and become commonplace. This brief overview of Fuzzy Logic has been included to provide the reader with an insight into this latest technical innovation. It is not an in-depth study of this new science, rather an interesting insight at what the future holds. Reading this chapter should help complete your knowledge and understanding of machines past, present and future.

Most of today's front loading washing machines, mechanically or computer controlled, are based on simple logic. For instance, take the action of a fixed thermostat – it is either open or closed. The timer simply waits for the signal to proceed to the next step in the predetermined wash programme. As humans we know that the water being heated is not simply the right or wrong temperature (cold or hot) but warm, fairly warm, etc. When we wash clothes by hand we do not simply take only the temperature of the water into consideration, we access a wide range of both precise and imprecise information such as – what type of material it is, the degree of soiling, what type of soiling it is (mud, grease, etc.). All of these factors and more, ultimately affect the way the garment is eventually cleaned, how warm and how much water, how much detergent will be required for the level and type of soiling and how much rinsing, etc. Unfortunately a thermostat cannot detect this range of imprecise approximations and the control unit can only respond to precise logical inputs.

However, with a combination of microprocessor control, additional sensors and a new way of programming the purely logical approach may not be with us for much longer. This new way of looking at the washing process is called Fuzzy Logic and some makes and models already have varying degrees of this type of control system. The essence of Fuzzy Logic is to produce a machine that can react and adapt the wash process as a human would. To look at a wide range of variables and to make informed decisions based on all of the available information both precise and imprecise. To do this additional sensors are required to supply the processor with the information for the decision process. The wash programme is therefore not just a series of predetermined sequences it has the ability to respond and react to information it receives, in essence Fuzzy Logic thinks the problem through and arrives at a solution based upon the whole range of both precise and imprecise

information. In other words it has the ability to mimic the way we would react.

Some of the additional information the processor requires can be gained from existing controls such as water level switches and motor tacho generators. However, other sensors not normally associated with washing machines, will be required to assist in the decision making process. The most common of these sensors is the optical sensor. This type of sensor is used to detect the turbidity (cloudiness) of the water passing through the sensor.

Opposed mode optical sensing is the most popular system used for this purpose and is often referred to as direct scanning. In simple terms this means that a light source and light sensitive receiver are positioned opposite each other and the wash water is allowed to pass between them. The intensity of light reaching the receiver is dependent on how much soiling is in suspension in the water passing between the two points. The information from this type of sensor can be used to provide information on the level and type of soiling. The way this can be done is as follows. The level of soiling on the wash load can be determined by how transparent (or not) the known volume of water within the tub becomes (a numerical value can be applied to this). What type of soiling is on the wash load can be ascertained by how long it takes to reach the transparency saturation value. Mud and other water-soluble soiling will reach its maximum saturation level fairly quickly whereas grease and other non-soluble soiling will take longer. In this way a relatively simple optical sensor can tell the programme two important factors.

The type of material of the washload can be gained by the use of more sensitive water level detection systems. For instance cotton absorbs water and synthetic materials do not. When a machine fills and the level switch operates, a load of cottons will proceed to soak up some of the water and the level switch will reset to compensate for this loss (this happens

on normal machines as well). However, the second actuation of the level sensing device in this instance also informs the Fuzzy Logic system that the load is absorbent and is therefore cotton. The weight of the load can be determined by spinning the loaded drum prior to commencing the wash. The energy taken to rotate the drum relates to the weight of the load it contains and again this information can be used by the Fuzzy Logic programme. Quite simply a heavy load takes more energy to rotate it and the speed control module pulses the control circuit faster to compensate. **Note:** *An important point to remember is that these sensor inputs are not one-off events, they are continuously monitored and if circumstances/sensor output changes then so will the programme.*

If the machine has the ability to dispense its own detergent then the exact amount required for that specific load can be dispensed.

The number of rinses can also be altered (increased or decreased) by optically sensing the rinse water.

Even the spin cycle can be Fuzzy controlled and a maximum spin speed to match the load (or imbalance) applied at the end of the wash cycle. **Note:** *The spin speed would be applied (or omitted) directly. With Fuzzy Logic the spin would be the result of several efforts to spin as described in out of balance protection in the Suspension chapter.*

The application of this type of technology can give rise to both financial and ecological savings. The time when you can simply put your clothes in the machine and let it decide exactly how to wash, rinse, spin and dry them is not too far away. **Note:** *Fuzzy Logic is not restricted to washing machines, in fact it has been around in industry for several years and applications range from industrial processes to anti-lock braking systems. Only recently has it emerged on the domestic appliance front and can now be found in microwave ovens, domestic vacuum cleaners, cameras and many other mass market items. This trend is set to continue.*

Size of load →	**FUZZY LOGIC CONTROL PROGRAMME**	Detergent, wash time, agitation levels, drum speed, number of rinses etc. →
Type of material →		
Type of soiling →		
Level of soiling →		

Chapter 25
Suspension

During the normal washing and spin drying operations of front loading machines of all types, a great deal of vibration is produced. The level of vibration increases during the spin sequences, especially if the wash load is out of balance or the drum severely under loaded. If the outer tub unit were fixed rigidly to the shell/outer casing of the machine, damage would be caused to both internal components and to the immediate location of the machine through excessive movement of the free-standing machine.

To avoid the transference of vibration produced during wash and spin cycles, the inner tub unit of front-loading washing machines and washerdriers is supported within the shell/outer casing of the machine by vibration absorbing supports, i.e. suspension. Due to the confines of the shell/outer casing of the modern machine, a limited amount of movement is allowed, but any excessive

vibration and movement of the tub unit is removed (damped) by the action of the suspension system supporting the unit.

Note: *To prevent damage to components within the machine during transportation/delivery, some means of packing will be fixed to the machine to stop any movement of the tub unit, i.e. rocking suspension. It is essential that any such packing or transit fixings, as they are commonly known, are removed. There are as many different types of transit packing as there are machines, so read your instruction booklet for a description of how to remove the packing from your new machine. It is advisable to retain these instructions and packing should it become necessary to transport your washing machine again, e.g. moving house. If you do need to refit the transit packing, a good idea is to put a sticker on the door reminding you that the machine must not be used until the packaging has been removed.*

Remember that the suspension is the system that controls all of the movement of the outer tub unit when the appliance is in use. Without the suspension or when it is damaged, the whole outer tub unit will move violently when in use. See also *Out of balance protection* later in this chapter.

What different types of suspension are there?

1 Slide and spring damper – supporting the tub from beneath with only small springs or straps at the top for holding the outer tub unit in the mid fore and aft position.
2 The friction damper – consists of two arms gripping a metal plate tightly, therefore slowing down the movement of the tub.
3 The damper and spring suspension – not unlike the system used on motor cars.
4 The spring only suspension – simply large strong support springs (used only on early slow spin machines).

It must be stressed that any combination of these systems may be found. A damper system may complement a spring system, or a spring system may complement a friction damper system. Please read all sections thoroughly before starting any repair on the suspension system.

The purpose of suspension in the automatic washing machine, whether wash-only or combined washerdrier, is to damp the oscillations of the spring mounted outer tub and drum unit. Counterweights of concrete or in some instances cast iron, are used to help in

Large concrete or metal counter-weights are used to improve balance during spin. The position of such weights vary greatly between makes. Ensure they are securely anchored and cannot work loose. Loose weights give rise to noises similar to bearing failure. If left unattended, serious outer tub damage will result. Pictured is a Candy outer tub unit which has both top and lower front weights

View of slide and spring suspension. This is prone to softening of the rubber mount at the top of the suspension leg. The result is a common condition known as twisted tub

1 To renew the top rubber, the whole unit will have to be withdrawn. Grip the shaft through the spring at the top only, using adjustable pliers inserted through spring

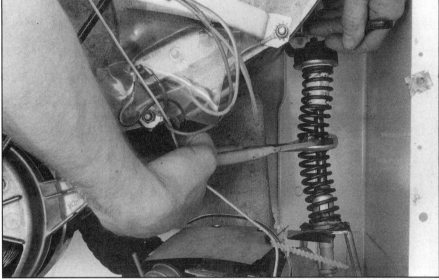

2 Whilst gripping the metal shaft tightly, the securing nut can be removed. (Right hand thread.) Note the correct assembly of parts and pull spring downwards to remove top bush. Do not be tempted to renew one side only – you must renew both sides!

the overall balance of the unit and to add weight to the appliance to further help in eliminating movement during use (especially spin). The suspension system works the hardest during the distribute (pre-spin) and spin cycles. Under normal load conditions the simple suspension and counterweight system works well and reduces tub oscillation as long as all components and connections are secure and in good order. However, if a severe out of balance condition occurs because of a mechanical fault, for example worn suspension, under-loading, e.g. one bath mat, one pair of jeans, etc., over-loading, e.g. large duvet, or by washing unsuitable items, such as trainer shoes, excessive vibration and damage may result. Both the outer cabinet and internal parts may be damaged due to the suspension being unable to cope with adverse oscillations of the tub unit within the confines of the shell/cabinet.

All but the earliest of front loading automatic machines have a pre-spin speed or 'distribute' as it is often called, the action of which is to balance out the wash load by rotating it at a pre-set drum speed. The centrifugal force created by the pre-set speed (usually around 83 rpm on the drum) arranges the wash load evenly over the inner surface of the drum prior to acceleration into the spin. However, this process can fail if:

1 A balled load occurs, i.e. the knotting together of items in a normal wash load usually as a result of poor loading by bundling all items into the machine together instead of separately. Stopping the machine, removing and replacing the items individually is usually all that is required for this problem. **Note:** *It is wise to reset the machine to a rinse position before the spin to allow correct distribution to take place.*
2 Underloading occurs when insufficient

clothes are in the drum to distribute evenly around the entire surface, i.e. half drum surface covered but other half not; thus giving a flywheel effect when rotated. **Note:** *This is a common fault on some machines and aggravated by the user removing items in the hope of improving the matter when in fact extra items are required.*
3 Overloading resulting in little or no free movement of the wash load therefore no distribute action is possible. This will also result in a poor wash.
4 An unsuitable wash load of, for instance, trainers, sleeping bags, etc., will create severe out of balance situations and subsequently damage to the machine and/or its surroundings. Try to load the machine correctly.

What follows are descriptions of each type of system however a combination of systems may be used on some machines.

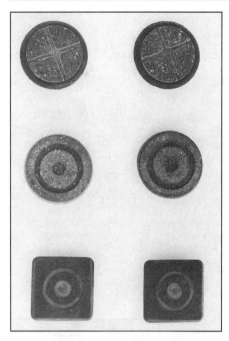

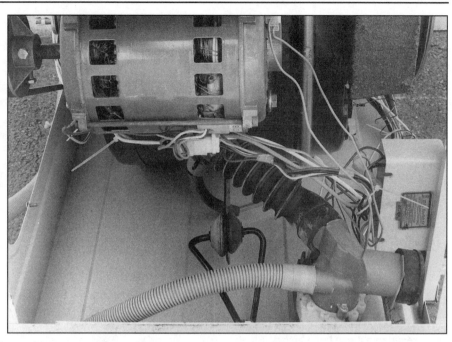

Friction pads from various machines. Top section is pad and mount for Zanussi, middle section pad for Indesit, and lower is square pad for Candy

A typical friction damper system viewed *in situ*. Do not lubricate this type of suspension

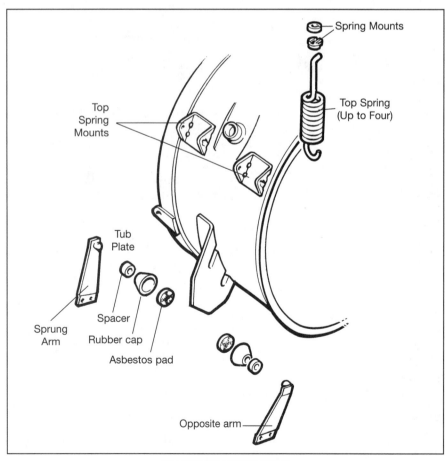

FRICTION DAMPER TYPE

(Labels within diagram: Spring Mounts; Top Spring (Up to Four); Top Spring Mounts; Tub Plate; Spacer; Rubber cap; Asbestos pad; Sprung Arm; Opposite arm)

Slide and spring damper types

The main faults to check for are those of guide wear, allowing the shaft to jump out of position, and also the top rubbers to soften or wear. This results in a phenomenon called 'twisted tub'. The reason for this is the suspension on one side of the tub is not correctly positioned, therefore allowing one side of the tub to bang on the side of the shell and cause damage. A noise fault can also become apparent at the top of the suspension due to soapy water seeping into the suspension via the dispenser or dispenser hose. This is best removed by a spray of lubricant/moisture repellent and an application of Molycote to the top bush and slides. The top and the guides of the suspension are the only parts that should be lubricated in this way.

When fitting top rubbers, the machine should be laid on its face, and the suspension should be held tightly with grips at the top end only. The top nut can then be undone. Do not hold the bottom of the shaft, as any marks will quickly wear the plastic guides. When refitting, thoroughly clean the metal shaft and apply a smear of Molycote lubricant paste to the shaft and upper shaped washers. The plastic slides should also have the same paste applied prior to refitting.

The friction damper system

The friction damper system is not unlike the disc braking system on a motor car. Two support rubbers with asbestos (or similar material) pads are mounted in two spring steel arms. These rest either side of the flat plate attached to the outer tub. When the outer tub moves, the action is slowed down (damped) by the friction of the pads against the plate. This is a very cheap and very effective form of suspension.

When this type of damper is worn, the tub will move excessively and possibly emit a squeaking noise. The noise will be caused by the rubber pad mounts coming into contact with the moving plate, due to the friction material being worn. This is easily overcome by the renewal of the pads themselves. After isolating the machine it should be laid on its back or side to enable the steel spring arms to be opened. When opened, the pads can be prised from their ball and socket joint.

Note: *If the pads on this system become glazed and/or shiny on their contact faces, a chattering sound will be noticed. It may be possible to avoid renewal by slightly roughening the faces with sandpaper to remove the glazing and then refit. If unsuccessful, the pads will have to be renewed. Do not under any circumstances put oil or grease on friction damper systems.*

Warning: *Do not inhale the dust from the friction pads, as this can be harmful to the lungs. Moisten with water during removal and cleaning to avoid airborne dust particles. Do not blow them clean. Dispose of old pads safely and wash hands after contact.*

The damper and spring system

The damper type system is similar to the shock absorbers on your car, and they do the same job. If the smaller version of the system is used, the tub will not actually rest on the damper, but will be hung from springs at the top of the tub, using the dampers at the bottom for shock absorption only. In the larger systems however, the tub is held only by much larger dampers at the bottom of the tub, with retaining straps/springs at the top to limit movement fore and aft.

Faults found with this type of solid damper will have the same symptoms as the friction damper system. The only remedy in this case is the complete renewal of the faulty damper. This can be done by laying the machine on to its face, taking the usual care and isolation procedures. Access to the dampers can be gained by removing the back panel, and unbolting the damper from the shell and tub mounts.

The spring only system

The spring type suspension, which is simply large strong support springs, is used only on early slow spin machines. The spring or the mounts can be changed separately if required or replaced as a complete unit. **Note:** *The left and right springs of all systems are usually of different ratings. Be sure to specify the required side when obtaining a replacement. Also, where two*

small springs are used for fore and aft support during repair, it is possible that they may become dislodged. It is essential that they are refitted correctly. Examine the correct positions and make notes of all springs, etc., before you start.

Out of balance protection

Reference to Fuzzy Logic OOB detection and implementation can be found in the chapter Fuzzy Logic.

The best way to avoid out of balance problems is to load and use the machine correctly; although even having done this, an out of balance situation may still develop. Many modern machines, especially most computer-controlled models and many ordinary machines with microchip based speed control modules now incorporate means of detecting out of balance situations. When problems are detected, steps can implemented by re-balancing the load by extending the distribute phase or by terminating the acceleration up to full spin speed, thus limiting or avoiding further vibration or damage.

Many computer controlled machines and the more sophisticated speed control modules will have 'out of balance' spin limitation systems similar to this.

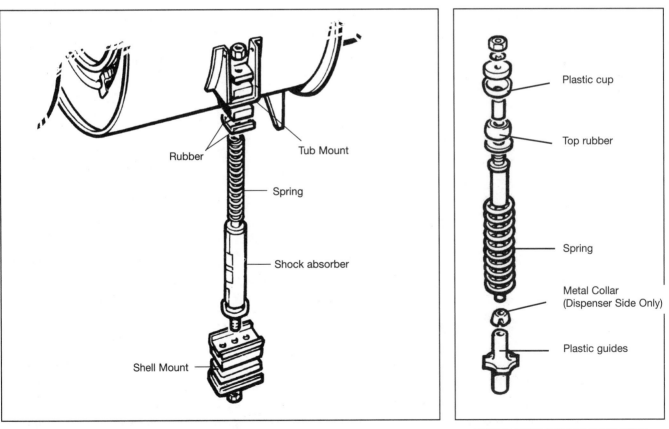

LARGE DAMPER AND SPRING TYPE

SPRING ONLY UNIT HOOVER TYPE

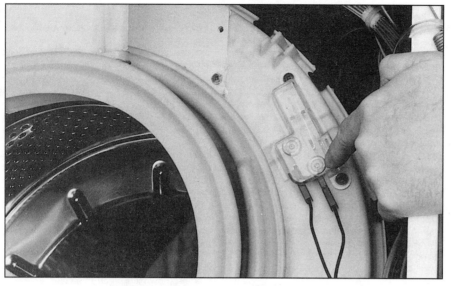

Mechanical out of balance (OOB) switch.

How does out of balance detection work?

OOB detection as it is known can be detected in two ways:

a) Electro-mechanically. This method uses light action microswitches strategically mounted on the edges of the outer tub or on the suspension legs. They may be actuated by a weight on the arm of the micro-switch or by a contact bar, either of which will be adjustable for calibration of OOB movement. The microswitch is linked into the motor speed module control circuitry, see *Motors* chapter (speed control). Excessive movement or inertia resulting from an out of balance situation will actuate the microswitch at a predetermined level. The impulse caused by the microswitch's operation terminates the build-up to the spin speed selected and normally allows only the distribute speed to operate. After a period of time governed by the circuitry of the module, a spin sequence will be reinstated in the expectation that a second distribute has cleared the OOB problem. If this

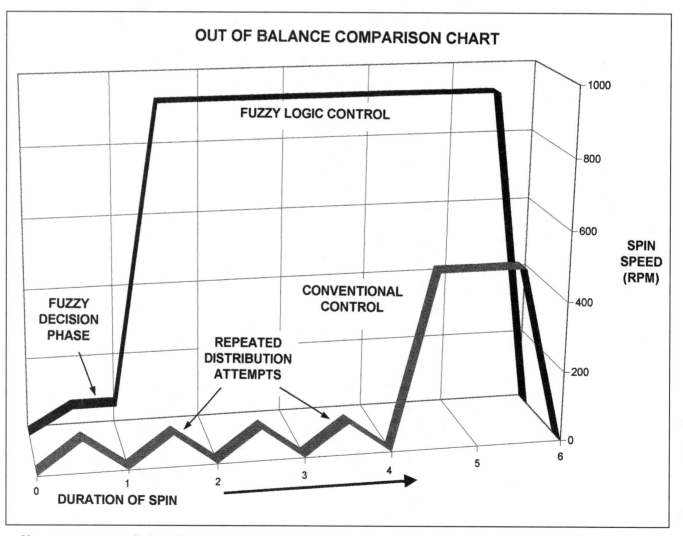

Many computer controlled machines and the more sophisticated speed control modules will have 'out of balance' spin limitation systems similar to this

is not so, the process is repeated. With mechanical programme timers, this process may continue, dependent on the make and model of the machine, until the time allotted for spin has elapsed. Computer controlled machines are often programmed — see *Timer (programmers)* chapter — to accept only three OOB impulses before terminating the spin or remainder of the programme completely. The setting of the mechanical OOB detection microswitches differ greatly between the different makes and also between the different models from the same manufacturer, hence no specific adjustment details can be given within this text. **Note:** *Ensure actuation of microswitches are free and all connections to and from them are in good order.*

b) Electronic only. The electronic OOB detection system is found on computer controlled models and many machines with microchip-based speed control modules. It is only the detection process which differs from that already described in section a. Detection in this instance is by monitoring the motor speed reference voltage from the tacho coil, see *Motors* (speed control) chapter. During an out of balance situation the motor speed will vary, i.e. rise and fall on each revolution of the drum proportional to the degree of the imbalance. If this reference exceeds the pre-programmed tolerances for that particular programme setting or spin, a fault sequence similar to that described in section a) is implemented and distribution occurs. As before, this may be limited to three or more such cycles before termination of the set programme and in the case of computer-controlled machines, the display of a corresponding fault code.

Reference to OOB detection and implementation can also be found in the chapter *Fuzzy Logic.*

Conventional electronic out of balance control

Many computer controlled machines and the more sophisticated speed control modules (especially combined Hybrid timer systems) will have 'out of balance' spin limitation systems similar to the one described here. Prior to spinning the wash load a distribution sequence is implemented to balance the load. The distribute sequence will have a predetermined (by the manufacturer of the appliance) optimum drum speed, in this instance 90 rpm. During the intermediate and final spin phases the optimum distribute speed will be monitored by the micro-processor from information provided by the tacho. Loads that fail to balance correctly will adversely affect the optimum distribute speed and therefore the tacho output. If a load fails to attain the required distribute speed; further attempts at distributing the load will automatically take place. The ramp up to full spin speed will therefore not occur until a satisfactory distribute speed has been detected. **Note:** *The figure of 90 rpm is used only as an example, reference to individual manufacturers will be required for specific makes and models.* **Note:** *Only a predetermined number of re-balancing attempts will be allowed. Should a correct distribute speed not be attained, the drum speed will be limited to the distribute speed for the duration of the spin phase.*

Chapter 26

Low insulation

What is low insulation?

Low insulation is best described as a slight leak to earth of electricity from the wiring of one or more of the components or wiring in an earthed appliance. If very slight, this will not harm the appliance but is an indication of faults to come and should be corrected immediately for safety reasons. A gradual breakdown of the insulating properties of a normally electrically leak proof system which will eventually result in a short circuit to earth if the root cause is left unattended.

How is it caused?

This can be caused by normal wear and tear over a long period, resulting in a breakdown of the insulating coating on wiring, motor windings, heater elements, etc. Such a breakdown of insulation may not result in a failure of the part at this point and the appliance may still function as normal. However, this is no excuse to ignore low insulation as failure to trace and rectify low insulation is both foolhardy and in the long run can be costly in both money terms, and above all, safety. Faults such as leaking/weeping shaft seals can give rise to water penetrating the motor windings and resulting in low insulation. If not corrected, this could lead to a complete failure of the motor, or worse. A simple renewal of the shaft seal and careful cleaning and drying of the TOC and windings may be all that is needed to save money and improve safety for all concerned. It is important not to compromise on safety by ignoring such symptoms.

How can it be detected?

When an engineer tests for low insulation, he will use an instrument called a Megger/low insulation tester. The law requires repair engineers to test for low insulation, and there is a low minimum allowable level. The law requires that the following tests are made by commercial repair engineers.

Earth continuity

Between the earth pin and the plug and all earth connection points within the appliance, the maximum resistance should be 1 ohm, i.e. very low resistance, a perfect connection.

Insulation test

With the appliance turned on, but unplugged, test between the live pin on the plug and the earth pin on the plug. The minimum resistance should be 2 megohm (2 million ohms). Ideally the reading should be much higher than this minimum figure, i.e. very high resistance, no discernible connection at all. Repeat this test between the neutral and the earth pin of the plug, repeating both tests at various programme settings.

In practice one test lead on the meter should be connected to both the live and neutral and the other to the earth pin. This avoids the possibility of inadvertently passing the high test voltage through the normal live-neutral circuit and simultaneously tests both supply conductors. **Note:** *For best practice connect the red lead to the earth pin and use the black lead to bond (join) the live and neutral pins.*

Testing of individual components can be carried out easily by removing connections to the suspect item and connecting one lead to one of the free terminals and one to the earth terminal and testing, minimum resistance should be 2 megohm, then repeat the test using the other connection. **Note:** *Items controlled by double pole relays will also need to be tested in this way.*

These tests are carried out using a meter designed to test insulation by applying a high voltage (500V DC) at a very low amperage for safety to test the insulation quality of the part to which it is connected. It is an unfortunate fact that some engineers do not possess such an instrument, and therefore do not check for low insulation. This does not mean that you should not!

A professional meter to test for low insulation would cost upwards of two hundred pounds and is therefore out of the reach of most DIY people. However, low priced insulation test meters may be found in mail order outlets such as Maplin. An alternative (rather than no test at all) is to utilise an in line circuit breaker (see *Flowchart*). The appliance is plugged into the circuit breaker, which is then plugged into the socket, unless an RCD already protects the circuit or socket. As mentioned in *Basics – electrical*, the purpose of the device is to detect low insulation or leakage to earth and turn off the power to the appliance. Although this is not the ideal way of testing for low insulation, it will help in locating more severe cases of it (well below the 2 megohm level) and provide additional safety for the appliance and its user.

It is wise to test RCD systems on a regular basis to ensure they function correctly and are fully operational when needed. Follow the instructions shown on the unit or on the leaflet accompanying the adapter. If a fault with the unit is suspected it will need to be tested and possibly re-calibrated for maximum performance by a skilled electrician using a special RCD test meter. If a fault is suspected in an RCD unit, have it checked as they are there for your safety.

The use of an RCD in this way is to aid those who do not possess a low insulation test meter. It must be remembered that the units have a wide range of uses and cannot only be used in this manner. RCDs are designed to ensure safety when using appliances or equipment such as lawn mowers (where there is a danger of cutting through the cable), irons, washing machines, etc. (where water and electricity are in close proximity).

If any appliance trips an RCD (or similar) system, do not use the appliance until the fault has been rectified. If tripping occurs with no appliances or load on the system, then a

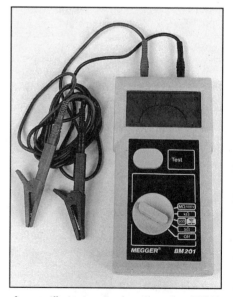

A versatile test meter incorporating 500 V DC insulation test facility

Modern consumer unit with RCD main switch and MCBs on all circuits

Double socket RCCB for use in home or workshop

fault on the house wiring is indicated and the trip switch should not be reset until the fault is found and corrected.

Have your RCD tested regularly by an approved electrician or electricity board to ensure that it functions correctly and safely at the correct speed of no more than 0.4 of a second. Such tests require an RCD test meter that calculates the trip time of the unit. On simple tests the unit may trip but take too long for it to be classified as safe.

Points to remember about low insulation

Ensure that any disconnection or removal of wires is safe and not earthing via another wire or the metal case of the appliance, etc.

Whilst disconnecting any wires during the testing for low insulation, it should be remembered that the machine must be isolated from the mains supply at all times and the panels or covers must be replaced before the appliance is re-tested, i.e. **Do not** test with exposed wiring.

LOW INSULATION FLOWCHART

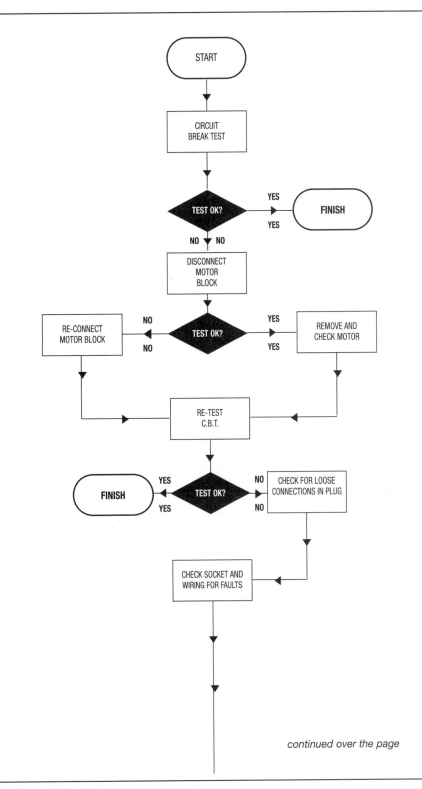

continued over the page

Before testing for low insulation using a circuit breaker, all earth paths of the appliance should be tested. This is done by connecting a meter between the earth pin of the plug, and all other metal parts of the appliance in turn. Maximum resistance should be 1 ohm. See *Using a meter* chapter.

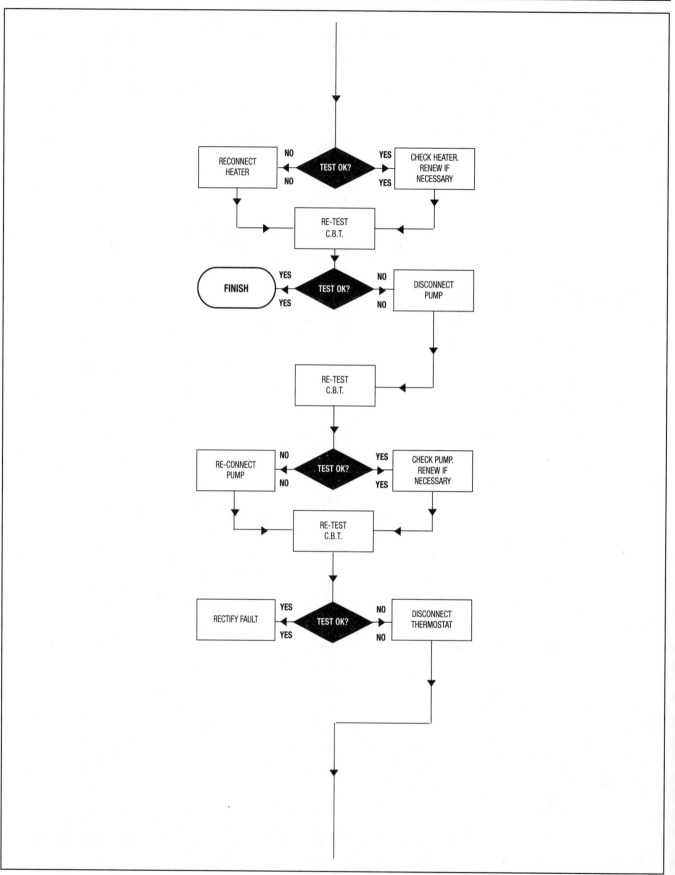

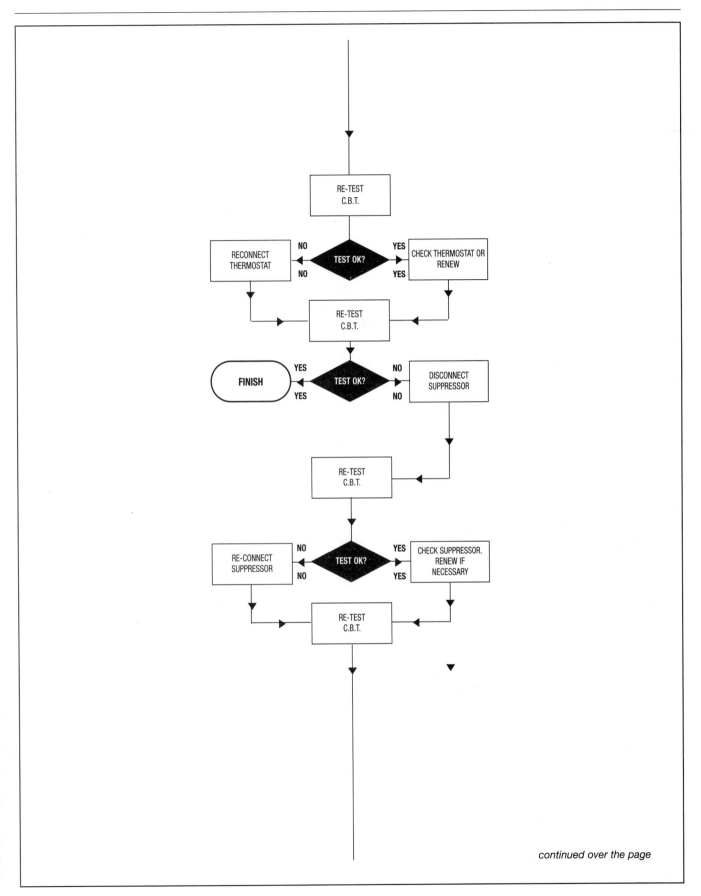

continued over the page

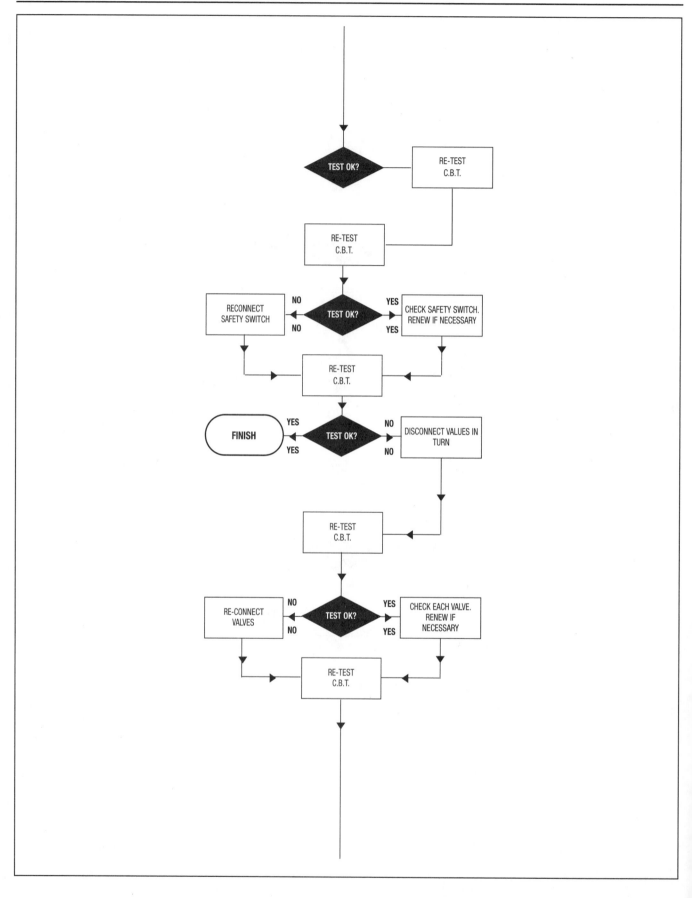

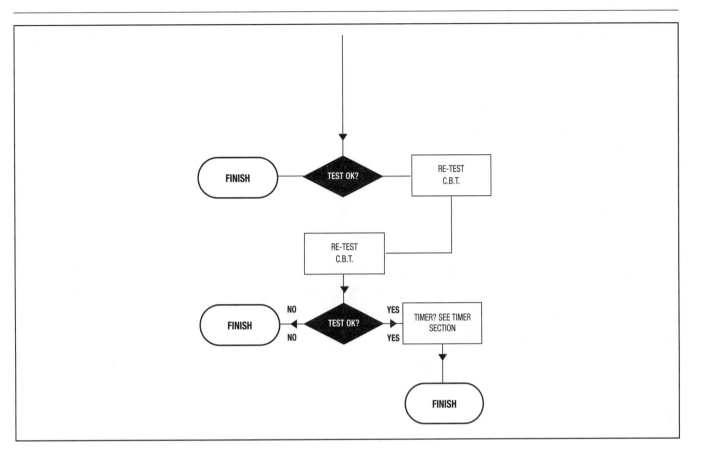

Chapter 27
Motors

There are three types of main wash motor used in today's machines; the universal AC brush motor, permanent magnet (PM) motor and induction motor. **Note:** *This chapter covers the range of motors found in combined washerdriers and tumbledry only machines.*

Where is the main motor located?

On washing machines and combined washerdriers the motor will usually be bolted to the underside of the outer tub. The exception to this is the Hotpoint front loader where the motor can be found bolted to the top left-hand side of the outer tub (viewed from the rear). Tumbledry only machines normally have the main motor mounted on the base of the machine but some top mounted versions can be found.

Brush motors

These normally consist of two sets of electromagnets. An outer fixed set called the field coil and an inner set which are free to rotate called the armature. The armature is made up of many separate windings and is configured in such a way that power is only supplied to one set of windings at a time via moving contacts called a commutator. Rotation of the armature is produced due to the energised field and armature windings being slightly out of line to one another. The corresponding movement induced in the armature continuously brings a new set of windings into circuit, whilst the previous winding circuit is broken. The windings are continuously out of synchronisation, therefore inducing continuous rotation of the armature

This type of unit normally requires renewal if faulty, although some brushes and patterned armatures are available separately

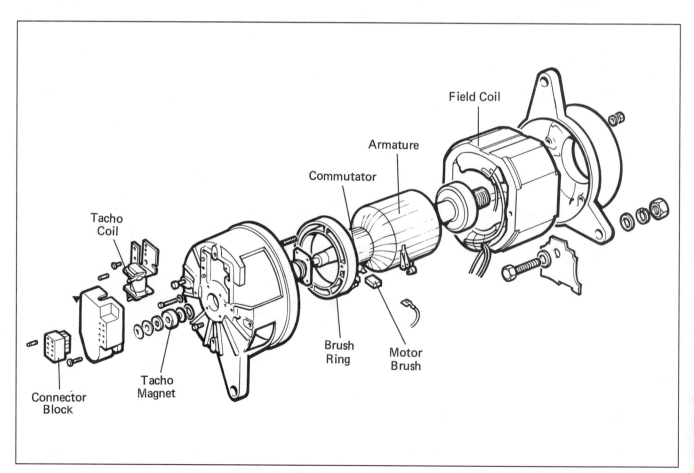

whenever power is supplied. Reversal of the motor is normally achieved by reversing the power flow through the armature windings via a set of reversing switches in the timer. This type of motor can be used with alternating current (AC) from the mains, or with direct current (DC) from a battery, and is often used for the main drive motor in washing machines, especially on machines with drum spin speeds above 1000 rpm.

Induction motors (capacitor/relay start)

This type of induction motor has a capacitor/relay to 'kick' the rotor into action by putting a delay into the motor's start windings. The resulting imbalance (called phase displacement) creates rotation in the direction of the run winding current flow. A reversal of power in the run winding reverses the motor. Basic speed variations are governed by the amount of windings supplied with power. Further speed control may be available via a speed control module. Induction motors of this type are found in both combined and tumble-dry only machines.

As all of the work is done by a complicated set of windings in the stator, this motor is generally not repairable and must be changed for a new unit. Capacitor failure often results in the motor failing to run. This can result in burn out as the rest of the motor windings are receiving power but no rotation is possible. Overheat is inevitable, even when TOC (thermal overload cut-out) protected. **Warning:** *When checking for faults, the machine must always be isolated from the mains. Turn off at the wall socket and remove the plug. The capacitor(s) will still contain a charge although the mains has been isolated. This must be discharged by using an electrically isolated screwdriver. Do this by 'shorting' the terminals of the capacitor with the shaft of the screwdriver ensuring that you are only in contact with the insulated handle. It is not safe to proceed further until this has been done.*

If the stator windings of an induction motor are faulty, it may continue to run although appearing sluggish and getting extremely hot even when used for a short time. Therefore, if you have been running the machine to determine the fault, proceed with care as the motor will remain hot for some time. If the motor appears to be very hot, the motor winding may be faulty and the unit should be replaced.

What does a capacitor look like?

Capacitors used for motor starting can have either metal or plastic outer casings with an insulated top with two terminals.

Shown is a Fagor motor, typical of the new style induction motors, that are capable of variable speed build up via a module. Note the tacho connector at the rear of the motor

How does a capacitor work?

What follows is a simplified version of what happens within a capacitor in an AC circuit.

The two terminals of the capacitor are in fact completely insulated from one another. Internally they are connected to two sheets of metal foil and between this foil is an insulator. This package of large surface area is rolled into a tube formation, which fits into the shell of the capacitor. If the two terminals and their connected sheets of foil are insulated from one another, you may ask how do they pass a current when in use? The answer is that as the voltage supplied to one terminal is in fact alternating, (i.e. at 50 times per second – 50 Hz) so does the polarity of its connected foil. An opposite movement of electrons is produced in the other foil even though they are insulated electrically. This effect causes a delay in the electrical path at this point, and this, in the case of an asynchronous induction motor gives the out of phase feed to the start winding.

The storage capacity of a capacitor is measured in microfarads (µF) and is displayed on the shell. Any replacement must be of the same µF rating.

If the motor fails to run on wash, but runs on spin and there are two capacitors fitted, it is possible that one of them is faulty. Change the capacitor with the lowest µF rating and re-test. If only one capacitor is fitted then the motor should be thoroughly checked.

If the motor runs on wash but fails on spin and there are two capacitors fitted, there are two possible faults. Change the capacitor with the highest µF rating and re-test, remembering the previous warning about an isolated capacitor retaining an electrical charge. If the door interlock is connected directly to the motor spin circuit, and the door is not closed properly, then the spin will be prevented from operating. A fault within the interlock would also prevent the spin, refer to the *Door switches (interlocks)* chapter.

Typical capacitor for use with induction motors. Do not confuse capacitors with suppression units. They may look similar, but their functions differ.

What is a relay?

A relay is an electro-mechanical device used in this particular instance for induction motor starting in place of a capacitor.

What does a relay look like?

The most common relay consists of a plastic moulding with three terminal tags, two at the top and one at its base. On the centre section is a wire wound coil.

How does a relay work?

The main aim of the relay in the context of asynchronous induction motors is to cause a delay in the start winding supply, similar to the capacitor. The main difference is that the relay achieves this operation mechanically. The wound coil is connected in series with the run winding. When power is supplied to the motor, the current to the run winding passes through the coil and on to the motor run winding. This current induces a magnetic force in the coil, which in turn attracts the metal core of the relay. The metal core is

A relay may be placed in circuit to cause the phase displacement necessary to start the induction motor. This is a mechanical delay as described and it is essential that the relay is upright when energised

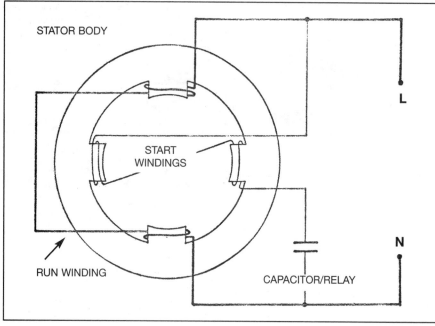

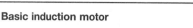

Basic induction motor

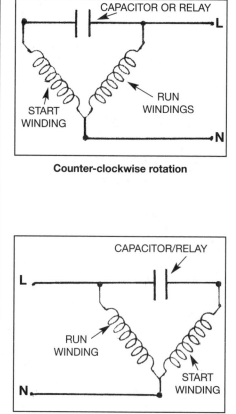

Counter-clockwise rotation

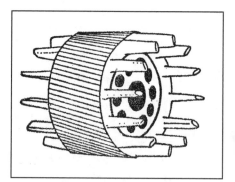

Clockwise rotation

linked to an internal contact switch and when 'made', allows current to pass to the start winding (see diagram below). This operation gives the required delay to induce starting of the induction motor.

When power is switched off, gravity resets the relay core. It is, therefore, essential that the relay is in its correct position and the machine upright for this item to function correctly.

The relay may also be matched to the run winding of the motor, i.e. as initial power draw of the stationary motor is high, the magnetic attraction of the relay coil is great enough to attract the core. When the motor is running, the initial high power draw drops and weakens the magnetic pull of the coil, the core drops and open circuits the start winding allowing the motor to continue running more efficiently. Always make sure that the correct replacement is obtained by quoting model numbers and manufacturer when ordering.

Faults to watch for are, open circuit of the coil, metal core sticking (in either position),

and contact points failing. Renew any suspect relay immediately as the failure of this item, like the capacitor, can lead to motor failure.

If you have to renew a damaged stator coil or complete motor and it is relay started, it is wise to change the relay at the same time as it may:

a) have caused the original motor fault or

b) have been subsequently damaged by the motor failure.

Induction motors (centrifugal start)

A third system for induction motor starting may also be utilised although it is restricted to tumbledry only machines. It is used on some makes of machine both old and current. The stator, as before, is split into start and run windings. The start windings are connected in series with a microswitch, the switching arm

Induction motor rotor

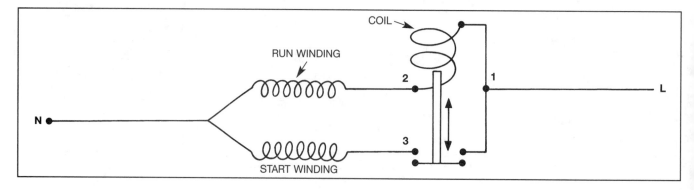

of which rests on a movable circular collar forming part of a spring and weight system fixed to the rotor shaft. When power is supplied to both windings of the motor, rotation is induced by the phase displacement of the two windings. **Note:** *This may be increased further by the addition of a capacitor within the start winding supply.*

As the rotor increases in speed, centrifugal force lifts the weights and the movement produced is used to pull the collar away from the microswitch arm and in doing so, switches off the start windings. The motor continues to run with only the run windings in circuit.

Switching out the start windings in this way (centrifugal or relay start) greatly improves the efficiency of the motor and reduces any heat caused if the start winding imbalance were to be left in. Remember the imbalance is only there to induce initial rotation. Once rotation is achieved they are, in effect, no longer required for the motor to continue running.

In addition to the normal motor faults relating to capacitor (if fitted), worn bearings, faulty windings, etc., there are three further possible mechanical faults:

1 The microswitch may fail in either the closed or open position. If permanently open circuit, the motor would overheat when first turned on as only the run windings would receive power (but rotation would not occur).

Should the microswitch fail in the closed position, the motor would start. The collar and weights would move but the run windings would remain in circuit. This permanent imbalance would result in a slower speed than normal and overheating of the motor.

2 Failure of the centrifugal system to reset when the motor stops leaves the start windings open circuit and the fault will arise when the machine is next used. See No. 1 for fault symptoms.

3 The failure of the centrifugal system to move the collar from its rest position results in the start windings being left in circuit. See No. 1 for symptoms.

Faults 2 and 3 may be attributable to infrequent cleaning of the interior of the tumbledry only machine, which would lead to fluff jamming the centrifugal mechanism.

Machines that use a centrifugal switch system can be identified by the distinct noise that the motor makes shortly after initial start up and just before stopping rotation when the motor is switched off. The noise (a faint whirr and click) is caused by the movement of the weights, collar and switch, both on initial run up to speed, i.e. switching out the start winding, and run down when the motor is turned off, i.e. resetting of weights, collar and switch.

Ensure all moving parts are securely fitted, clean and free to move. Do not over-lubricate

as this can itself cause a fluff build up. Apply a very small amount of light machine oil only to the moving parts of the mechanism.

Induction motors (shaded pole)

This type of motor is associated with pumps and low power air circulation fans, etc., as it has low starting torque, i.e. this style of motor is easily impeded from starting, as the initial rotation is only from copper segments bound into the stator. When power is applied to the stator coil, the copper segments create a permanent imbalance in the magnetic field produced. This induces rotational movement of the rotor.

The shaded pole motor is one of the most simple of all induction motors and is similar in basic format of rotor and stator. However, only one stator coil is used to create the magnetic field. Obviously this alone would not induce rotation of the rotor, only a constant magnetic field. To start rotation, an imbalance in the magnetic field is required and is created quite simply by copper band inserts at the pole ends of the stator laminations. The copper bands within the mild steel stator laminations (dissimilar metals) distort the magnetic field in a given direction, therefore inducing rotation in

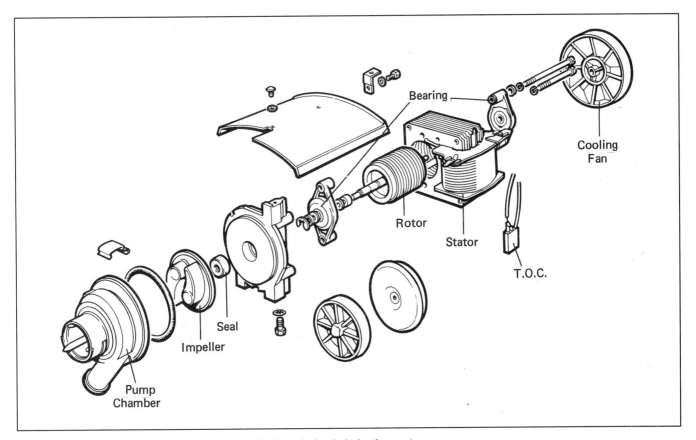

Typical shaded pole induction motor pump.

the stator. Reversing the supply to such motors does not effect any change in motor direction as this is governed by the direction of the fixed shaded poles. These motors do not have a high starting torque and because of the magnetic imbalance being fixed, heating of the stator occurs which, under normal conditions creates no problems, but most stator coils are protected by TOCs for safety.

Induction motors (permanent magnet rotor)

This extremely simple style of motor is used to drive all versions of mechanical timers, both for timing and cam advance. Consisting only of a wound circular coil fixed around a permanent magnet rotor and supported at both ends by simple sleeve bearings, this motor can be made extremely small and at a low cost. As with all induction motors, its simplicity of construction limits it for use to AC supply only. A larger version of this principle is now being used to power outlet pumps in many modern machines. The PM

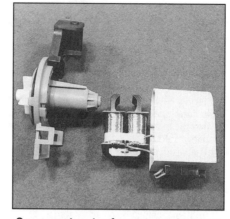

Component parts of a permanent magnet rotor pump. Only complete pumps are available if they fail in any way. It is shown here dismantled to illustrate its simplicity

rotor is housed within a sealed plastic chamber, but is still free to rotate by the alternating current (AC) supplied to two externally mounted stator poles. The rotor drives the impeller of the pump in the normal way, only the motor of the pump differs.

Small permanent magnet rotor type motors have been used for many years to drive mechanical timers

This type of motor has been used for many years to power the timing and advance mechanism of washing machine programmers. Some versions are now used to drive the outlet pump of some machines. It is the most simple of electric motors, quiet to run and cheap to produce. It also avoids some of the more common pump problems.

A circular multi-pole permanent magnet forms the rotor of the motor and its construction is similar to that described in the speed control section relating to the tacho. Within the casing of timer motors a finely wound coil encased in plastic surrounds the permanent magnet rotor. Permanent magnet pumps have two coils wound on to a laminated steel stator. In both instances, supplying AC power to the coil(s) induces rotation of the magnetic rotor. However, rotation could start in either direction and this, in the case of timer motors, would be most unwelcome. To ensure that rotation occurs in the required direction, i.e. clockwise or counter-clockwise, a small plastic cam is positioned within the casing (seen as a small plastic pip on the rear of the motor casing), which allows rotation in one direction only. Should the motor try to start in the wrong direction, it hits the plastic cam, which flicks it back, thus inducing correct rotation.

The ability to run in both directions is utilised to its full extent when this style of motor is used to drive an outlet pump impeller. Should the impeller of the pump come into contact with an item such as a button (this would normally jam/stall a normal shaded pole motor), the motor may be nudged into revolving in the opposite direction and clear the blockage or continue to pump whilst running in the opposite direction.

The construction of the sealed PM pump rotor chamber helps alleviate the problem of shaft seal leaks and bearing failure which are common to shaded pole versions.

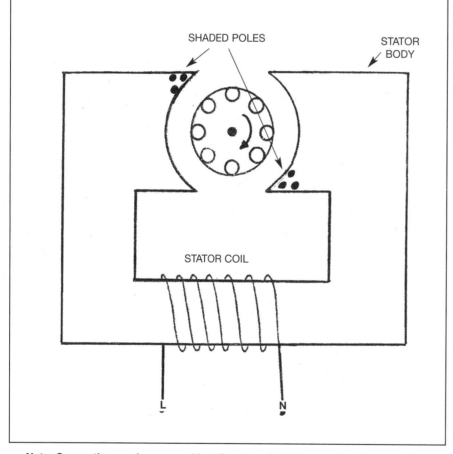

SHADED POLES

STATOR BODY

STATOR COIL

L   N

Note: Connection can be reversed but direction of rotation remains the same. It is governed by the shaded poles only

1 Isolate the machine and remove the rear panel

Armature change – Hoover type model

The main aim of this photographic sequence is to show the removal of a motor from a machine and the detailed removal and refitting of a new armature and brush ring. This was possible in this instance as the individual motor parts were available.

The motor shown is of a universal type, which is found in many early wash-only and vented washerdrier machines in the Hoover range. Later machines and condenser washerdrier types are more likely to have motors where only the motor brushes are available as replacement items. This practice is now common to a large proportion of machines from all manufacturers such as Creda, Ariston, Zanussi, Servis, Indesit, etc.

It must be remembered that any connections that are to be removed should first be noted to ensure correct refitting at the end of the repair.

2 In this case a low insulation test disclosed the motor fault. Remove the motor bolts and withdraw from the machine

4 The four end rivets can be drilled out or removed with a sharp chisel, as in this instance

6 When the end bolts are removed, use a hide mallet (or similar) to free and remove the front end frame

3 After noting the motor block colours, positions and connections, remove the plastic cover to reveal the tacho coil. The tacho coil and magnet can be removed carefully. (The clip on the shaft can be lifted with a small screwdriver)

5 Mark the position of the end frames, by marking with a pencil. When marked, remove the four securing bolts

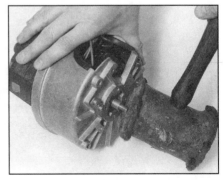

7 Knock the armature tacho end shaft free. Remove armature and inspect for faults

8 Check copper segments on armature for damage, i.e. burnt looking or loose/raised segments, and for carbon build-up. (This one is badly damaged)

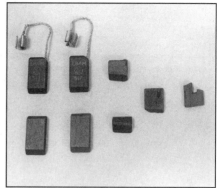

12 Shown are new and old brushes. The left lines show tagged and non-tagged type of brushes. The right lines show split and worn brushes

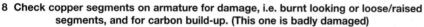

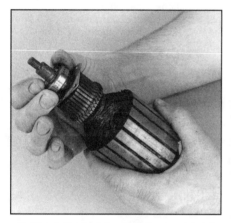

9 Check the bearings for free and quiet running by spinning them on the shaft. Also check for tight fit to shaft. (This one had damaged the shaft)

11 Old brush ring inspected for damage. Carefully check for smooth brush slides. Also check that no carbon deposits have caused low insulation. Change if in any doubt. (This one has burnt slides)

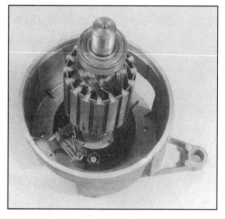

13 New armature and brush ring fitted to rear end frame

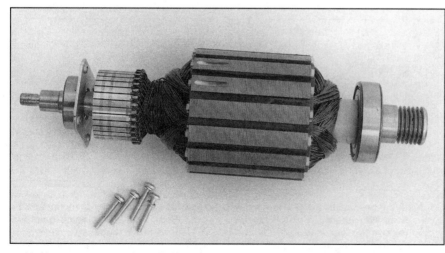

10 New armature ready to fit. Note screw plates and screws instead of rivets to aid fitting. Fit replacement unit if in any doubt as to condition of old unit

14 Refit tacho magnet and clip. Ensure that when fitted the magnet will not turn on the shaft, i.e., it should be locked to the armature

Brush replacement – GEC type motor

15 Adjust tacho setting (if necessary). Screw centre up to the magnet and turn back 1½ turns only

1 GEC type motor. Early type can now have similar armature change as Hoover type, but generally only brushes fitted

3 Slide out brush holder complete with brush. Note length of new brush and check for good movement of brush in slide. This brush has worn very short

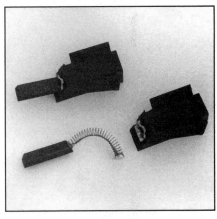

16 Refit front end frame and reassemble motor, lining up the marks made in step 6

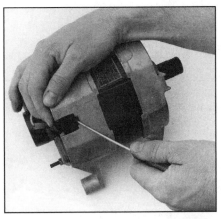

2 Removal of brush and holder from GEC type motor. Insert screwdriver and lift tongue of plastic at base of holder

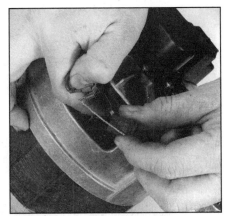

17 Fitting of new brushes. Ensure free movement of brush in slide. Make sure all connections are tight and do not foul metal body of motor.
Ensure insulation strip is fitted to brush opening. It will fit easily if warmed first. The motor is now ready to fit to the machine for function testing when all panels have been refitted

4 View of new brush and holder complete. Early screw-on type brush holders have separate brushes as above

Shown also is the brush replacement for the GEC type motor, variations of which can be found in Hotpoint, Indesit and Creda machines. **Note:** *Any other fault with this type of motor requires a complete change of unit.*

Speed control for series wound brush motors

It must be remembered that all motor speed faults are not directly attributable to the motor. The fault could be caused by a piece of electronics called a module which is connected between the timer and the motor and controls the speed of the motor. There is no standard location for the module but it is easily identified by its distinct printed circuit board (PCB) and large heatsink. Computer controlled machines normally integrate the speed control into the power module, see *Timers (programmers)* chapter.

On the rear end of the motor's armature is a circular magnet that revolves in unison with it. Close to this magnet is a coil of wire (this may be encased in plastic), which is called a tacho generator. If a magnet is rotated next to or inside a coil of wire a voltage/frequency is produced which is proportional to the rotational speed of the magnet. Therefore, the faster the motor is running the more current is produced or the higher the frequency. This voltage/frequency is fed to the module as a reference voltage/frequency and is used to monitor the performance of the motor by comparing the relative speed of the motor with a known voltage/frequency via a comparator circuit. If the reference voltage/frequency is found to be lower than the comparator, the module will increase the pulse rate, therefore increasing the speed of the motor. If the voltage/frequency is found to be high, the pulses are slowed, therefore

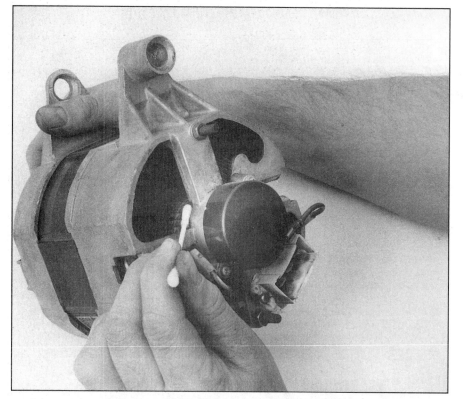

5 Ensure that any carbon dust deposits inside motor casing and armature are removed. (Brush out dust and clean with pipe cleaner or similar). Take care, do not inhale the dust

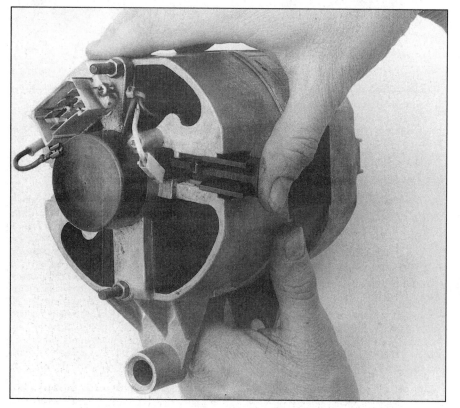

6 Refitting of GEC type brush holder and complete brush assembly. Slide back into position carefully ensuring that tongue of holder engages into position

decreasing the motor's speed. This happens many times a second, and is undetectable.

The rotating magnet of the tacho unit produces an alternating voltage and frequency both of which are proportional to the speed of rotation. The speed control module can be designed to respond to either the voltage or the frequency produced. Early modules operated predominantly on the voltage output whilst most modern modules and computer controlled machines operate on the frequency. Visually they can look very much the same, however it is essential that the correct replacement is obtained.

Checks on the tacho magnet and tacho coil

a) If the magnet is loose or broken, this would result in incorrect speeds at lower motor speeds.
b) Severe damage or complete loss of the magnet would cause the motor to spin on all positions.
c) A break in the coil on voltage module systems would result in a spin on all positions. This is because a 'good' coil is usually about 200 to 1600 ohms resistance. In open circuit situations the tacho generator is not returning any voltage, therefore the module speeds the motor up. The increased speed is not detected, so the process is repeated *ad infinitum*. Modules that operate on the frequency output of the tacho have an in-built test-circuit and will not operate if the tacho circuit is open. This results in no motor action.
d) Breaks and/or poor connections of the wires leading to and from the tacho can have the same effect. This is especially true at the connection block with the motor, and the connection at the module.

It should be remembered that any loose connection will be aggravated by the movement of the outer tub on the suspension and this should be taken into account when testing for such faults. The following chart can be used to help locate the module faults and assist in establishing the correct course of action. Do not attempt to adjust the tachometer other than as shown in the armature change section.

How to check if the module is at fault

Warning: *The machine must be isolated from the mains. Turn off at the wall socket and remove the plug. If any of the internal components of the module have burned out, i.e. charred or burnt looking, the motor should be checked for any shorting, loose wires or low resistance, as these may be the probable cause.*

The modules shown are a small selection of modules that are fitted to today's machines. Their appearance and function differ very little from one another, but are

Shown is the module from a Hotpoint Automatic. Note the discoloration that has occurred on the centre of the PCB. This is a sure sign that the module is at fault or will fault soon

strictly non-interchangeable. Always ensure that the correct replacement unit is obtained by quoting the make, model and serial number of your machine when ordering spare parts.

If the fault persists the module is probably at fault. This should be replaced with a new unit, ensuring that the correct type is purchased. To fit, make a note of the connections, remove them and replace them on the new unit. It is important that the 'Duotine' (edge) connector fits tightly on the module (the connections can be closed slightly by inserting a small screwdriver between the back of the tag and the plastic Duotine. Care should be taken not to close it too far as this may result in the tag not making contact by being pushed back into the connector).

The machine must be isolated from the mains supply. Turn off at the wall socket and remove the plug. **Warning:** *The large metal back of the module is used as a heatsink. This means that it is live when in use, and therefore should be fitted correctly and securely to its plastic mounts. Even when testing, any contact with the earthed shell of the machine will render the unit useless.*

Module control induction motors

Many modern machines that use induction motors now use electronics to help control the selected pole speed more precisely and help smooth the transition from one speed to another. They differ little from their predecessors and still require a complex set of windings within the stator to give a series of fixed speeds. However, they do have the addition of further speed control via a speed control module and tacho coil and magnet arrangement which is similar to the system used to control brush motors.

The module works by ramping (slowly increasing) the voltage to the pre-selected (by the timer) stator windings. This achieves a smooth operation of the main motor. The tacho magnet and coil produce a small voltage/frequency proportional to the rotational speed of the motor which is used as a reference to the electronic module. This simply means that speeds can be increased gradually, for instance, allowing a slow build-up to spin from distribute. This minimises the jump in speeds as the windings are simply switched in and out causing the excessive vibration normally associated with early induction motors.

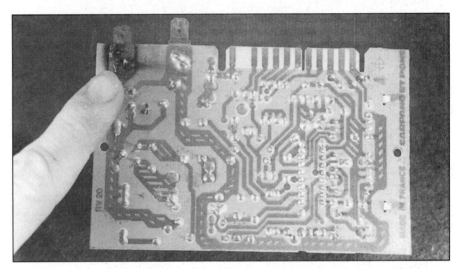

The burnt connection on this Ariston washerdrier motor module was caused by a loose connection creating arcing and localised overheating

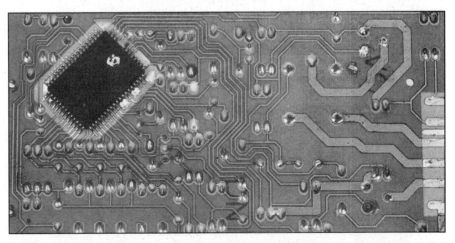

This small motor control module has an extremely wide variety of motor speeds and complex OOB control. It also carries out motor reversal and timing functions normally carried out by the timer. The ability to carry out this wide range of tasks come from the use of a surface mounted microchip (clearly seen on the left of the photograph)

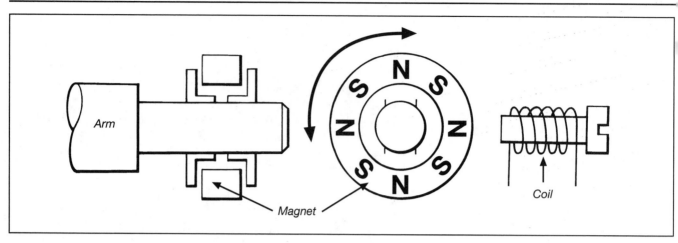

Tacho generator

Check Operation		Interlock	Motor	Tacho	Module		Tacho	Timer
		Check Interlock and Latch	Check Complete Motor Circuits	Check Circuit Late M/C's	Fit New One	Replace Original	Fit New One or Adjust	Check Timer moves on at all
Spin	None	●	●	●	●			
	Slow		●		●			
	Cont		●	●	●			●
Distribute	Cont	●	●		●			●
	None		●	●	●			
	Fast		●	●	●	●	●	
	Slow					●	●	
Tumble	None	●	●		●			
	Fast		●	●	●			
	Slow			●	●	●	●	
	Cont		●		●	●	●	●

Incorrect Drum Action

The reverse side of the PCB with the heat sink removed to show the components of the module clearly. The faulty components can be seen directly behind the area of discoloration. The component (a resistor in this case) has been overheating and subsequently failed. Repairs to modules are not merely a simple replacement of obvious components, as micro-chips within the circuit may have been damaged. We therefore advise that the module be removed and replaced with a complete new unit

	WOOL WASH	DELICATE WASH	NORMAL WASH	VIGOROUS DELICATE WASH	VIGOROUS NORMAL WASH	DISTRIBUTE & O.O.B	SLOW SPIN	FAST SPIN
DRUM SPEED (rpm) WASH ↓	35	45D	45N	55D	55N	100	500	1000
CODE 1 Switch A	X		X			X		
CODE 2 Switch B				X			X	X
CODE 3 Switch C		X				X		X
CODE 4 Switch D	X			X			X	

This chart shows the wash codes and the 4 timer switches A, B, C and D. A cross in the box indicates what function is selected when that switch is closed and the corresponding drum speed. Refer to the chart above for timing details of how long the rotation is for that particular wash. For instance – a woollens wash has timer switches A and D closed. This results in a drum speed of 35 rpm on this chart and rotational timing of 12 seconds clockwise, a pause of 9 seconds followed by counter-clockwise rotation for 12 seconds

Wash Cycle	Drum Rotations Per Minute.	Timed Rotation Clockwise Seconds	Timed Pause Seconds	Timed Rotation Anti-Clockwise
Woollens	35	12	9	12
Delicates	45	8	7	8
Delicates	55	12	7	12
Normal	45	12	6	12
Normal Wash Rins-	55	15	6	15
Drying Cycle	35	20+20	3	20+20

This chart shows the variable agitation sequences that are applied throughout the various wash and rinse cycles. The motor has a 'soft' start action and ramps slowly up to the selected speed during the timed sequence. Refer to the chart above for drum speed variations

Ramping in this way allow the clothes in the drum to balance out more evenly by centrifugal force, resulting in a much smoother spin and less vibration of the machine. Another benefit of the electronic speed control is that a small potentiometer linked to the module and fitted to the facia panel of the machine enables the user to vary the spin speed to their own desired level (usually between 500-1000 rpm, with a switch facility on the potentiometer for no spin at all).

Speed and combined programme control

When combined with mechanical timers the electronics of some modern speed control modules may also include other functions such as temperature and basic programme control. As can be seen in the *Timers (Programmers)* chapter, the trend towards electronically controlled machines is increasing and this combination is a further step in the process. The inclusion of a microchip within the speed control circuitry open up a wide range of control options. What follows is an overview of a system currently in use and one, which many manufacturers will surely follow in the future. Transferring control of functions such as motor reversal and rotation times, etc., greatly reduces the complexity of the main programme unit. The motor control is by simple basic switch commands called wash codes supplied by the timer (e.g. wash at code 1). These basic switch commands actuate a series of complex predetermined sequences stored within the integrated

circuit (IC) within the module circuitry. With the predetermined sequence selected the module then controls and monitors all functions such as motor speed, direction of rotation, wash action, i.e. length of time for rotation and pause, normal, delicate, wool, distribution speed and both spin speeds. A tacho generator like the ones described previously is used as a reference for the module control unit. Simply by varying the combination of 3 or 4 timer switches a whole range of wash variations can be achieved. The two charts on page 123 show the way in which a typical system of this type works and the range of variation possible. It would be very difficult and complex to achieve this level of control and variation with a purely mechanical timer. The system also has OOB capabilities; details of which can be found in the chapter on *Suspension*. When used on combined condenser washerdriers the module may also be used to control the intermittent timing sequence of the drain pump during the drying cycle.

The alternative to buying a new speed control unit

The alternative to buying a new speed control unit is to purchase a fully reconditioned replacement on an exchange basis. This is a welcome development in the field of repair work not only in the significant reduction in the cost when compared with a new item but also in the 'green' aspect of recycling components and materials. In addition to speed control modules a wide

range of reconditioned programme/timer units can also be obtained on an exchange basis.

For further details see chapters *Timers (programmers)* and *Buying spare parts*.

Centrifugal pulleys

The centrifugal or variomatic pulley is the large pulley that can be seen on some induction motors on the Candy, early Ariston, Indesit and Philips washerdriers. **Note:** *Some early Candy machines also utilise a centrifugal drum pulley.*

What does it do?

It is fitted to help increase the drum speed when the machine spins.

Why have complex pulleys?

The reason for having adjustable pulley drives relates mainly to the need for faster spinning at the end of the wash cycle. Adding a large pulley to the motor to create an increase in drive ratio to the drum pulley for the spin, causes problems for induction motors. The low speed wash action would require extra windings to slow the rotation whilst high spin speeds would be affected by lack of torque as the number of poles are reduced to increase the motor speed. In the past when spin speeds were much slower (500-800 rpm) the induction motor was the ideal choice. However, the need for ever faster spin speeds has outstripped the capabilities of the normal induction motor. To compensate for this

OPERATION OF A CENTRIFUGAL PULLEY SYSTEM

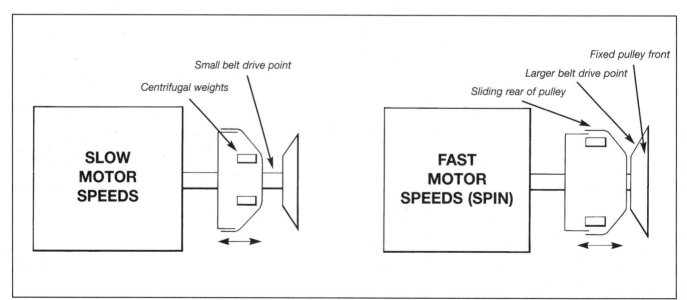

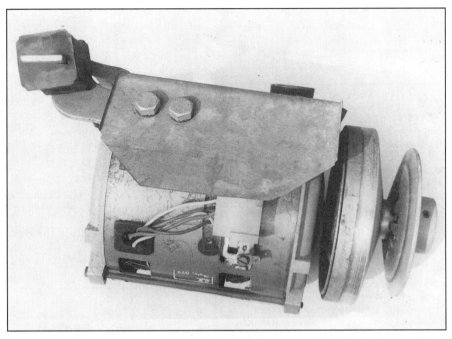

This large induction motor with centrifugal pulley is supported only by the large rubber mounts to the rear of the motor. This allows the weight of the motor to self tension the drivebelt and to rise and fall as the pulley increases and decreases in diameter with speed. Increased belt wear is common with this system

over-tighten the drivebelt on machines with a centrifugal pulley. **Note:** *Some are self-tensioning by the weight of the motor, i.e. motor only supported by rubber mounts on the rear end frame, allowing the weight of the motor to tension the belt and the motor to rise as the pulley size and drive increases during the spin.*

The addition of a mechanical pulley system to an otherwise simple and reliable motor increases the risk of faults. In addition to the normal induction motor faults, problems occur with the mechanical action of both centrifugal motor pulleys and drum pulleys (if fitted). Due to the belt being constantly squeezed along its edges, belt wear is accelerated and regular checks are advised. Renew if suspect as spin efficiency will decrease and/or excessive noise will occur.

Pulleys are made either of plastic or cast aluminium and as such, wear ridges form on the belt contact faces. This may lead to restricted movement of the belt resulting in poor drive (poor wash, spin or both), noise, excessive belt wear or jamming and finally, possible motor failure.

The Zanussi geared systems are similar, with noise and internal gear wear being the most common problems. There are no individual spare parts available for these types of drive pulleys, therefore if faults do occur, complete pulleys will be required. However, it is not uncommon for some manufacturers to supply the pulley and motor only as one unit, no matter what the fault.

inability to comfortably reach higher drive speeds, further mechanical additions have been made to the drive pulley and in some instances (Candy) to both drive and drum pulley. Some Zanussi machines use a gear and clutch arrangement to help in increasing the drive speed of their induction motor. Both of these systems are still limited to a drive ratio that produces a maximum spin speed of 1000 rpm (of the drum). However with modern electronics some Italian produced machines now have induction motor spin speeds of 1200 rpm.

Universal brush motors are normally used for machines with spin speeds that exceed 1000 rpm (many modern machines now attain spin speeds in excess of 1500 rpm).

How does it work?

Weights within the pulley are pushed outwards by centrifugal force when a fast motor speed is selected. As the pulley is constructed in two halves, the outward movement narrows the gap between the front and back plate of the pulley, therefore increasing its diameter.

This increase in diameter increases the drive ratio between the drum pulley and the motor pulley. When the motor speed slows, the reverse occurs, i. e. the back plate moves away from the front plate, and the belt rides on the smaller diameter of the pulley.

Similar clutches can be found on Ariston and Philips machines. Candy machines also have a similar centrifugal pulley on the drum,

although this opens at the higher speeds, thus giving a smaller drive ratio. This produces an increase in speed with a constant belt tension, without having to resort to expensive motor windings. Do not

Geared clutch drive as used on some Zanussi induction motors

Chapter 28
Belts

The main drive belts used in automatic washing machines, combined washerdrier and dry-only machines are of two distinctly different types. Both kinds are found in a multitude of size variations, but each machine must be correctly fitted with the exact size and type and no other. The two types of belt are the Vee, so called because of its location on Vee shaped pulleys, and Multi Vee belts which are much flatter and have a series of Vee formations on the drive face. The use of a Multi Vee formation gives a greater contact surface area in relation to the belt width. This is necessary as the belt is designed to be driven by a much smaller and therefore faster rotating drive pulley than the larger single Vee drive pulleys.

In general Vee belts are to be found on washing machines with induction motors and Multi Vee belts are found on washing machines with brush gear motors of all types. Tumble-dry only machines in the main use Multi Vee belts (of a smaller width and fewer Vs) to rotate the main drum via an induction motor. However, a combination of Multi Vee and Vee belts can be found on some early tumbledriers such as Burco and Hotpoint. It is also possible to encounter an elasticated round section belt on some tumbledry only machines which is used to drive the independent fan unit. Machines such as Candy, Hoover and Burco appliances can be found with this configuration, see *Dry-only machines* chapter. Some modern tumbledriers now use elasticated main drum drivebelts. These are very similar in appearance to the normal Multi Vee types but are NOT interchangeable.

What are drivebelts made of?

Both types of belt consist of woven nylon cords upon which a synthetic rubber is moulded. The single Vee belt has sides of approximately 40 degrees and terminating in a flat base. The Multi Vee belt is a series of peaks and troughs, the number of which varies with the work load requirements of the belt. Always ensure that a replacement belt is the correct size and width. Most belts have sizes or size codes printed on the outer face. However, such marks are often illegible on old belts due to wear. Take a note of the make, model and serial number of your machine along with any legible belt code when obtaining a replacement belt.

Removal and renewal

The single Vee belt drive system requires both drive pulley (the one on the motor) and drum pulley (the larger one on the drum shaft), to have a recessed groove the same dimensions as the belt. Multi Vee systems can have two variations:

1 Both drive pulley and drum pulley are grooved to accept the Multi Vee configuration of the belt.
2 Only the drive pulley is grooved (to aid grip on its much smaller surface area) and the drum pulley is smooth and slightly convex in

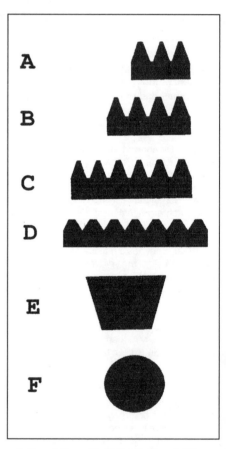

A, B and C are Multi Vee belt variations. A is predominantly used in tumbledry only machines whereas B and C are found in both wash only and combined machines. D is a wide low profile (thin) 'H' section belt used solely in tumbledry only machines. E depicts the profile of a Vee belt and can be found in wash only, combined and tumbledry only machines. F is a cross section of an elasticated or solid belt restricted to use in certain tumbledry only machines

Typical simple Vee belt drive. Belt tension is by motor adjustment

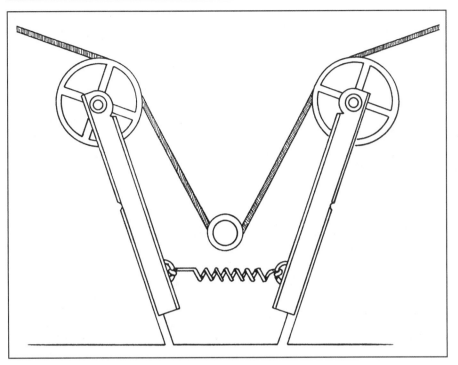

Double jockey pulley system required for reversing tumble dry only machines

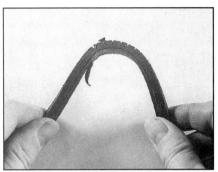

Turn belts inside out to check for problems. Do this over the whole length of the belt This belt has detached outer cover and cracked inner wedge. A fault such as this requires renewal of the belt

Note: *It is advisable to use protective gloves as the pulleys on machines can have very sharp edges.*

Belt care

Ensure pulleys are in good condition, i.e. not chipped or buckled, etc., and are aligned correctly. Misalignment will shorten the working life of both types of belt. Poorly aligned belts will shed the rubber compound coating from the cords leaving tell tale dust or flakes in the base and surrounding area of the machine. This may block the V section of Multi Vee belts and cause the belt to fly off usually on a spin cycle. Single Vee belts may twist within the V section when misaligned. Close inspection of belts is essential and reversing the belt and bending it is the best way to inspect them. Check the whole length in this way. If any defects are found, renew the belt.

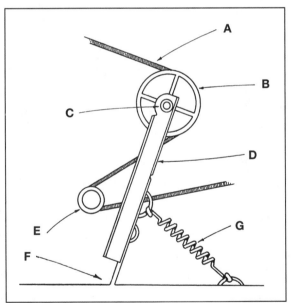

Typical jockey pulley components and configuration. Note: Most but not all belts will be tensioned as depicted in the two diagrams. Before removing the old belt make a note of the correct position of your machine as some of the alternative methods of tensioning are not so obvious

A **Main drum drive belt Multi Vee.**
B **Jockey pulley.**
C **Pulley shaft.**
D **Tensioning arm.**
E **Multi Vee drive pulley on motor shaft.**
F **Pivot point.**
G **Tension spring.**

Belt tension

It is natural for some degree of stretching and wear to occur during use which will result in the need for re-tensioning. Some machines may be self-tensioning, i.e. the weight of the motor keeps the belt under tension (this system was popular with some early washerdriers). On most tumbledry only machines, a spring tension jockey pulley (so called as it rides on the belt) is used to keep the belt under tension. **Note:** *Two may be found on reversing tumbledriers. However the majority of washing machines and washerdriers rely on motor adjustment, i.e. two fixed belts and one slotted, to tension the belt.*

Setting the correct tension is essential. Too tight will quickly wear the belt and worse still, it will damage the drive pulley and cause premature motor bearing failure. Too slack

shape. Grip is created on the drum pulley purely by it having a greater contact area to the belt when in use even though this is only on the peaks of the belt. The convex shape keeps the belt in place on the grooveless pulley and reduces wear if misalignment occurs. A similar system is used in tumbledry only machines where the belt runs directly on the outer of the drum, the size of which gives a much greater surface area and, due to its width allows the belt position to line up with both drive pulley and tension wheel.

When removing a belt for inspection or during repair, care must be exercised to avoid damage to the belt itself. Do not use screwdrivers or similar to prise belts on or off as this can easily damage the belt cords and moulding of the soft aluminium pulleys used on washing machines. Slacken off the motor bolts to reduce tension (on most washing machines) and pull the belt towards you midway between the pulleys whilst carefully rotating the drum pulley slowly clockwise. This will allow the belt to smoothly ride out of position. Reverse this process for refitting.

Machines that have fixed motor positions use special elasticated drive belts. Ensure you obtain the correct type of belt.

Removal and renewal are by winding off and winding on as described below and there is no need to loosen the motor.

The correct tension of an adjustable belt depends on its free distance between pulley contact points. As a rule a 12 mm deflection per 30 cm of free belt is required. Most washing machines have in the region of 30 cm of free belt between pulleys and therefore a 12 to 13 mm deflection is optimum. When fitted and tensioned correctly the belt will have a springy feel. Some stretching will occur to new belts, but modern good quality belts are much less affected. However, the belt will need to be checked at a later date and readjusted if required. Do not over-tension a new belt in the misguided hope that this will overcome any initial stretching that may occur. Over-tensioning can lead to belt damage and motor bearing wear.

Machines that have fixed motor positions use special elasticated drivebelts. Ensure you obtain the correct type of belt.

Elasticated Multi Vee belts

These belts are made with an internal elasticated braid and can be found on many modern front loading automatic washing machines, combined washerdriers and tumbledriers. Using this type of belt on tumbledriers eliminates the need for jockey pulleys. Due to this the drier is much quieter when in operation. No adjustment is required or available on most models with these belts and this may create fitting problems on some models and may require the slackening of the motor support bolts to aid fitting. Re-tightening the motor mounting bolts creates the correct tension.

The use of elasticated Multi Vee belts is now extending into automatic washing machines and several models in the Whirlpool, Hoover and Zanussi ranges (among others) use them. They are expected to last the service life of the machine and therefore no adjustment system is provided. Should it be necessary to renew the belt (for whatever reason) simply pull on the centre of the free section and slowly rotate the drum pulley, this will allow the belt to ride free from the pulley. Refit in a similar manner ensuring that the belt is positioned correctly on both the motor and drum pulley. There should be no need to slacken the motor mounting bolts when renewing or replacing this type of drivebelt.

Points to note

It is not uncommon for belts to be warm after use even when correctly tensioned. This is

and belt slip will occur resulting in poor wash, excessive vibration or heating of the belt which will result in belt damage or failure. On machines with aluminium pulleys, slipping can create ridges on the pulley grooves. If this does happen, the damaged pulley/pulleys will need renewing as any new belt fitted to such a pulley will soon become damaged by the uneven pulley surface.

Note: Some modern machines including some models in the Hoover and Zanussi range use belts with an elastic braid construction that do not require adjustment, in fact some models do not have any provision for adjustment. The intention being the belt should last the lifetime of the machine. However, renewal is sometimes required and it is essential that the correct version of belt is obtained for these machines.

due to the energy absorbed as the belt flexes and is proportional to the load. If the belt is hot or very warm after use, this would indicate incorrect tension or overloading causing belt slip and friction heating. Correct the problem, but check the belt for any cracking caused by overheating. If in doubt, renew the belt.

Noise

This is usually a squealing type of noise most often heard on wash rotation and prior to spin (distribute) when the belt is under most load. This may simply be incorrect belt

tension, slack, or worn pulleys, ridges on the pulleys, misaligned belt or machine overloaded. Again, isolate and correct fault and inspect belt closely for damage. If in doubt, renew it. It may be possible to reposition the drive pulley on some motors. Use a long straight edge to check alignment.

Ensure Multi Vee belts align correctly if both drive and drum pulley are grooved, note position of original belt, i.e. first groove on drive pulley is used then first groove on drum pulley is used. Misalignment of Multi Vee belts is easily done, so ensure that they are correctly fitted to avoid premature belt wear or the belt flying off during spin or wash cycles.

Machines with centrifugal pulley systems, see *Motors* chapter, create quicker belt wear due to the constant squeezing and movement of the belt. Check the drive pulley closely for wear ridges and be prepared to change belts more frequently on this type of drive system to maintain peak performance.

The main drivebelt on tumble dry machines normally leaves a running mark on the drum, use this mark to position the belt when renewing/refitting the drive belt. Failure to align the belt with the jockey pulley system can result in the belt jumping off the driveshaft when the machine is started. Running a machine with a misaligned belt can result in premature belt wear, noise and damage to the jockey pulley and bearing.

Chapter 29
Suppressors

What is a suppressor?

A suppressor is a device designed to eliminate the formation and transmission of spurious radio waves that may be produced by the operation of the motor and switches within the appliance during normal operation. When switching occurs within the appliance and it is not suppressed, small sparks at the contact points or brushes may produce interference on radio and TV channels or audio equipment plugged into the same electrical circuit, i.e. not only through air waves but also down the mains cable.

Why should all appliances have them?

By law, all domestic appliances must be suppressed to conform to the regulations on radio interference, and it is an offence to use an appliance that is not suppressed to these standards.

Where are they located?

Suppressors vary in style, shape, position, size and colour. Sometimes individual parts are suppressed but more often the mains supply is suppressed, at or just after the entry point into the appliance. This is called 'in-line' suppression as both the live and neutral supply goes through the suppressor and on to supply the whole of the appliance with power. Do not confuse the suppressors with capacitors, which may be used in the appliance for induction motor starting. They may look very similar but carry out distinctly different functions. Suppressors may also be called 'mains filters' because of their ability to remove spurious radio transmissions.

An alternative version of suppression unit can be found in addition to those described above. This is an induction coil, fitted in series between the neutral position at the terminal block and the shell of the machine. As an induction coil is of a far heavier gauge, it only passes suppression current, whereas the two earlier versions carry the full voltage load. Some machines have a combination of both in-line and induction coil types of suppressor. All versions require a good earth path on both plug and socket, see *Basics – electrical*.

Faults with suppressors (filters)

The main fault is one of short circuit to earth usually resulting in the unit 'blowing' both the main fuse and itself. This is often accompanied by a pungent burnt smell. Renewal is a straightforward one-for-one replacement.

Open circuit problems can occur and the unit will fail to allow current to pass through as normal. The suppressor can easily be checked

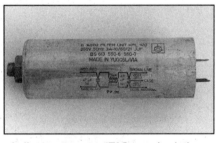

In line suppressor 4TAG type (variations possible)

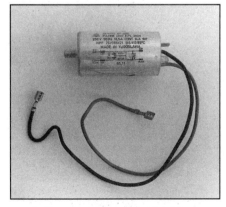

In-line suppressor flying load type (variations possible)

Typical 'choke' suppressors often used on computer controlled models to suppress the main wash motor

New style square suppressor

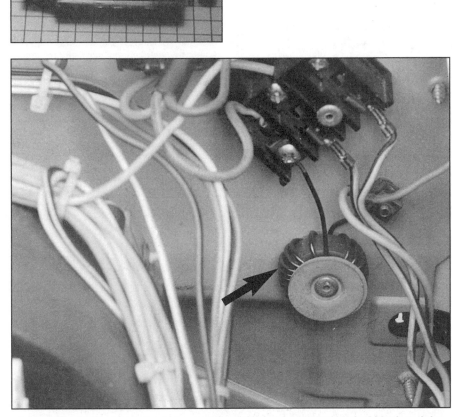

Induction coil fitted in series between the earth position at the terminal block and the shell of the machine

Check suppression units closely for cracks or expansion, etc. If in doubt, renew it. This unit has a small crack across the top but otherwise it looks OK However, internally it is a direct short circuit and potentially dangerous

for continuity using a meter, see *Using a Meter* chapter. When checking, inspect the top insulation closely and if cracked or at all suspect, renew complete unit.

It is common for in-line suppressors to use the earth path as part of their filtering circuit (although very little power passes through it). It is essential for all appliances to have a good earth path. If an appliance with an in-line suppressor/filter has a break in its earth path (due to cable, plug or socket fault) small electric shocks may be experienced when the user touches metal parts of the appliance, especially if they are in touch with a good earth path themselves, e.g. holding metal sink or work top, etc. It is essential that such faults are traced and corrected immediately, see *General safety guide* and *Basics – electrical* chapters.

Although the continuity of a suppressor (lead through type) can be checked easily, its function of suppression cannot be so easily checked. If all other checks, i.e. good earth connection (check for loose/poor connection to shell of machine), no cracks or loose/heated terminals, etc., prove to be OK, and interference to other equipment persists, renew the suppressor.

An additional means of suppression may be found, especially on micro-processor controlled machines. This is a choke type and may be fitted in series between live and neutral positions or individually in-line on both live and neutral supplies to individual components such as a series wound main wash motor. A choke consists of a ferrite core or ring around which the conductor is wound. The aim of the choke is to prevent interference within the brush motor

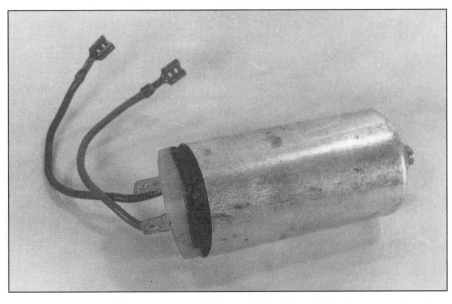

Some suppressors give clear indication of failure

**The motor in this computer controlled machine has additional motor suppression
components attached to the connector block**

(commutator/brush arching, etc.) from being transmitted directly to the microprocessor mounted on the control board. Interference of this nature can corrupt the current programme resulting in random crashing of the programme. This can be an annoying intermittent problem requiring resetting of the programme, which may or may not complete the cycle. In severe cases the microchip may be permanently damaged.

Some appliances use a combination of different types of suppressor. Suppressors of any type should not be by-passed or omitted, as to have an unsuppressed appliance is an offence owing to the interference that it may cause to others. In the case of 'chokes' failure or omission of this device may cause damage to or corrupt electronic circuits within the appliance, see *Timers (programmers)* chapter.

Chapter 30

Bearings

This chapter deals predominantly with the main drum support bearings, although many of the associated problems also relate to other areas such as main motor bearings on both combined machines and tumbledry only machines, and also fan and pump motors on machines which use ball race or roller bearings in these items. For items which contain sleeve bearings, see *Pumps* and *Motors* chapters, and for tumbledrier drum bearing variations, see the chapter which deals specifically with dry-only machines in conjunction with information from this chapter.

Types of bearing

Basically, there are four types of bearing used in washing machines and combined washerdriers:

1 The sleeve bearing. This is simply a phosphor bronze bush in which the motor shaft is free to rotate. It is more commonly used in pump and fan motors and reference to these chapters will give further detail.

2 Ball race bearing. This type of bearing consists of an outer ring in which a small inner ring is supported by circular ball bearings and is free to rotate.

3 Taper roller bearing. The taper roller bearing uses rollers in place of the ball bearing in (2) and as its name implies, the design angles the rollers to give a tapered appearance. The outer ring (shell) is not fixed as with the ball race type, and is fitted into position separately. It is essential that taper bearings are fitted as a matched pair, i.e. inner and outer. If this is not done, then the result will be early failure.

4 Needle bearings. A needle roller bearing is similar in looks and construction to the ball race bearing but use roller (long thin rods) in the inner cage in place of balls.

Top view of this Zanussi washerdrier shows that for drum renewal, it is necessary to remove the outer tub unit from the machine. This is due to only the front section of the outer tub being removable, see clamp bolt arrowed. However, bearing renewal can be carried out without outer tub removal

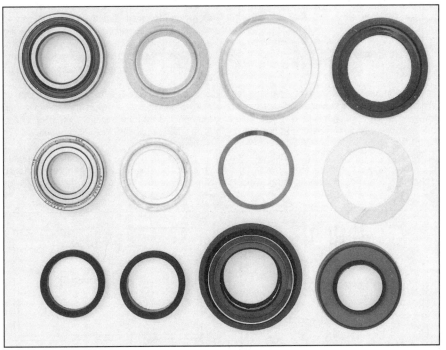

This Creda bearing kit uses the cup seal system. Two shaft seals and a carbon seal set are provided as changes were made during production. Use the seal that matches the one already fitted and discard the other

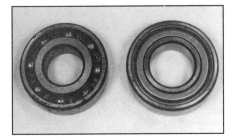

Typical ball race bearings open on the left and shielded on the right

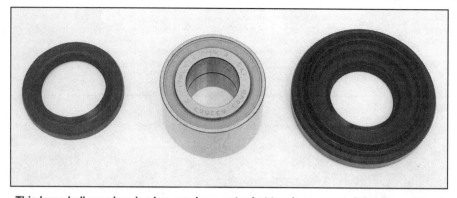

This large ball race bearing has one large outer but two inner races. It is often referred to as a conical bearing and can be found on models in the Zanussi and Ariston ranges

The type of bearings used on the main drum bearing assembly will differ not only between manufacturers, but also between models from one manufacturer, i.e. one range may use ball race bearings when a similar model from the same manufacturer will have taper roller bearings. Although there are only two types of bearing used, the variations in size of both outer and inner are vast, so therefore it is essential to fit identical bearings when replacing old or damaged ones and ensure that all shaft seals and spacers are renewed at the same time. If possible, obtain a bearing kit to make sure that all relevant parts are renewed. Do not cut corners by replacing only one bearing in a set of two or fitting a new taper roller inner to an existing outer shell because the old outer shell is difficult to remove. These short cuts will lead to premature failure and further damage. Be warned!

Why do bearings fail?

There are several reasons why bearings fail, apart from the normal wear and tear over a long period of time. What follows is a list of the most common causes and points to watch out for.

a) The most common failure of both ball and taper bearings is the ingression of water and detergent into the bearing housing. This is usually due to wear or premature failure of the shaft seal. Three basic types of seal are to be found with many individual variations. The first one is a simple shaft seal, which is pressed into the bearing housing on top of the front bearing. When assembled, the lower section of the drum shaft locates within the seal, usually a raised metal shoulder or collar of mild steel or more commonly phosphor bronze, and is fixed to the base of the drum shaft.

The seal has either one or two spring-loaded lips which press firmly around the collar to create a watertight seal. Normal wear, fluff or scale may break this seal down and allow water and detergent into the bearings quickly resulting in failure. Ensure that the collar is secure on the shaft and clean and that both seal and bearings are renewed at the same time. The second type of seal is a carbon face seal. This system relies on two smooth faces of carbon (or ceramic) that are pressed firmly together when assembled. One face is free to rotate, being fixed to the base of the drum shaft, whereas the other, as before, is fixed on top of the front bearing and is spring-loaded. The two smooth surfaces held under the pressure of the spring within the seal creates the movable watertight seal. Again, fluff, scale and normal wear will lead to water ingression.

Ensure that the fixed carbon ring is smooth, not cracked and securely fixed to the base of the shaft. Check the new spring-loaded face seal in a similar way and make sure that it seats correctly into the bearing housing. Application of a little sealant is recommended to make certain of a watertight fit to the housing. Do not allow any sealant or dirt on either of the faces of the seals when assembling them.

The third type of seal is a rubber cup (lip/skirt) seal, which is normally made up of several parts. A specially shaped rubber ring with a cup-shaped recess is positioned at the base of the drum shaft with the cup-shaped recess facing up the shaft. A smooth metal disc is placed within a rubber housing and inserted on top of the front bearing with the smooth surface pointing outwards. A spring clip holds the disc and rubber in place. When the drum shaft is inserted into the bearings the cup-shaped shaft seal will be pressed firmly against the smooth surface of the metal disc creating a rotatable watertight seal. Cleanliness is essential when fitting this type of seal, ensure that both mating surfaces are perfectly clean.

b) Bearings will also fail if incorrectly fitted. Do not hammer in the bearing (or shell, if taper roller type) directly with a hammer as this may crack or chip it. Do not force the bearing or shell into distorted or dirty housings as this will distort the bearing and create overheating resulting in failure. Inspect the drum shaft closely for ridges or rust which again will distort the inner race of the bearing, resulting in overheat or if worn, create a loose fit. Take care to clean all areas and fit only the correct size of bearings carefully.

c) Inspect failed bearings closely, for they will have sizes stamped on them which can be used to ensure the new bearing is of the same dimensions. Failed bearings may also give an indication as to why they failed. Rust would indicate that the seal had failed and prompt closer inspection, cleaning or renewal of the shaft, collar or carbon face. Bearings that are dark blue or black in colour are usually the result of overheating. Check the shape of the housing and shaft and do not overgrease. Flakes of metal from the bearing also indicate some form of distortion or ingress of dirt during assembly.

d) Do not overtighten bearings (especially taper roller types) hoping that it will help seating. The result is usually overheating and premature failure.

Recognising bearing failure

Noise can be a good guide to early recognition of bearing problems. Simply removing the drivebelt should help ascertain if the faulty bearing is in the motor or the drum shaft support bearings. A selection of noise faults are given below along with possible causes.

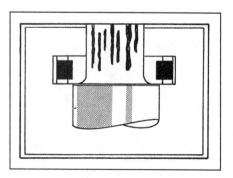

Illustrates scoured shaft

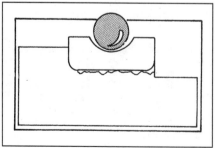

Highlights show the bearing rests on a scoured shaft

Tips on fitting a bearing

To gain maximum life from any bearing, care must be exercised when handling and fitting it. Prior to stripdown and removal of the old bearings, ensure that a note/drawing is made of the position of seals, clips and washers, etc. Inspect both the shaft and housing closely for defects. Ensure the shaft, housing, work area and hands are clean. Remove the new bearing from its protective packaging only when you are ready to fit it.

Ideally, bearings should be pressed into position but in reality, however, this is not always possible and some means of drifting the bearing into place will be required. Great care must be taken if this method is used as damage can easily be done to the bearing at this stage. Endeavour to use a tube when fitting the bearing to enable an equal force to be applied. Only the tight fitting part of the bearing should take the force, i.e. if fitting to a shaft, contact should only be with the inner race and when fitting a bearing into a housing, only the outer race should take the force. Do not apply any force to the part of the bearing that is free to rotate during fitting. To assist in fitting bearings, expansion and contraction with heat can be used although excessive heat must be avoided.

Fitting a bearing or taper roller bearing outer shell into its housing can be assisted by simply putting the bearing or shell into the household freezer for a while and warming the housing with the aid of a light bulb for an hour. This simple technique can help enormously. When fitting a bearing to a shaft, a reversal is required.

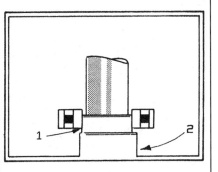

Position 1. Shows a bearing that is incorrectly positioned and is proud of its correct location point. Position 2. Indicates the collar on which the shaft seal will ride. Ensure it is both clean and secure

Cool the shaft and warm the bearing, but be careful not to overheat the bearing (especially sealed bearings) as this may create problems. **Do not** exceed 100 degrees C.

Many ball and needle type bearings are greased during manufacture and sealed on both sides. Such bearings do not require any extra lubrication prior to assembly. Taper roller bearings (and some open cage ball bearings) do require packing with grease. This should be done sparingly as overgreasing results in churning of the grease and heating occurs which results in loss of lubrication. Pack the bearing with grease and rotate both inner and outer with the fingers to allow any excess to be pushed out from the moving parts.

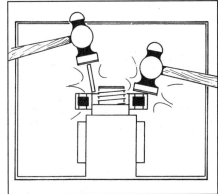

Do not fit a bearing in this manner as damage to the bearing can easily be caused

Typical tapered bearing change

The following sequence of pictures shows the renewal of a set of drum bearings. In this particular machine, the main drum support bearings were found to be worn and water damaged. This has been caused by the carbon seal failing and allowing water and detergent to enter the bearing and housing.

This was suspected because of the noise of the machine especially on spin, and confirmed by removing the drive belt from the motor to the drum pulley, spinning the drum slightly by hand and listening for any grating noise. If this had been quiet, the motor would have been spun in the same way to test its bearings.

To confirm the drum bearing fault, another simpler method is to open the door of the machine and move the bottom of the door seal in order to see the inner drum and outer tub gap clearly, then try to lift the top lip only of the drum. At this point, the gap between the outer tub and inner drum should neither increase or decrease in size and no movement other than that of the outer tub on its suspension should be felt. This applies to all machines irrespective of bearing types. Picture 12 shows that the drum and spider mount was breaking loose from its position on the drum, due to a form of metal fatigue fracturing the drum. The only possible cure for the fracture, was the fitting of a complete new drum assembly. The initial fault was also rectified, being a renewal of the bearings. The owner was unfortunate in needing the drum unit, especially when the support shaft itself was in such good condition.

The removal of the drum and back half assembly on this style of machine is quite straightforward. This style of drum and back half are fitted to many of the leading makes including Hoover, early Hotpoint, Creda and Servis, although in each case the size of

Noises	Possible cause
Loud rumbling especially on spin	Collapsed front drum bearing or seized front bearing. This often results in shaft damage if not attended to quickly
Rattling with intermittent knocking	Ball or roller of bearing defective
Rattling/knocking proportional to speed	Inner or outer of bearing faulty
High pitched metallic noise	Common on worn motor bearings at high speed and on new bearing if it has been forced on to a damaged or oversized shaft
High pitched ringing noise	Indication that bearing has been fitted to a damaged housing or fitted carelessly
Grating and crunching noise	Collapsed bearing cage or dirt between inner and outer race
Squeaking	On old bearing, usually due to lack of lubrication or ingress of water past shaft seal May also occur when new bearings are fitted to machine with carbon face type seals if care was not taken to keep both surfaces clean or if check was not carried out for cracks or scouring on carbon faces

bearing and type of seal differ slightly between machines. As the bearing kits are complete matched sets, no problems should arise.

After isolating the machine and laying it face down on a suitable surface, the removal of the back panel in this instance revealed the back half and outer securing nuts. All of the nuts and bolts securing the back half and tub should be removed. If necessary the top of the machine may be removed to gain access to the top bolts

When this is done, mark all of the connections to the heater and thermostat and disconnect them. The back half assembly can now be manoeuvred from its position and removed from the back of the machine. The back half is made watertight by a rubber seal located on its outer edge. If the back half sticks to the tub, and all of the necessary nuts and bolts have been removed, gently prise the back half from the tub ensuring that no excessive force is used. The drum and back half can now be manoeuvred free of the machine.

The removal of the pulley and bearings can now proceed.

If the bearing set for your machine is of the ordinary ball bearing type, the job is much easier as the old bearing should knock out in one piece. Should this type of bearing 'collapse' or leave its outer shell, the shell can be removed as shown for the taper bearing shell in picture 18. Care must be taken not to go too deep with the drill into the soft aluminium housing.

When greasing the new bearing (this is obviously not necessary on the sealed bearing type) take care not to overgrease them, as this will not help lubricate it and in fact will considerably reduce the bearing life.

The new taper bearing kit will come complete with an odd shaped aluminium washer that fits between the rear bearing spacer and pulley. This is known as a torque washer and is essential for the correct operation of the taper roller bearings. Always fit a new torque washer to this type of bearing system if the pulley is removed for any reason. Do not use the old one. The torque washer is a simple way of putting the taper bearings under a known pressure without the use of a torque wrench.

When fitted together, the torque washer collapses at a given pressure and dispenses with the need for a torque wrench for tightening the pulley bolt.

A full set of instructions for the torque washer should come with the new bearing kit, however a typical taper bearing change sequence is as follows.

If your machine has ball bearings, please disregard the paragraph concerning torque washers, as that type of bearing assembly does not require a torque setting. Renewal of this type of bearing is a simple reversal of the strip-down procedure.

Instructions for bearing change

1 How to dismantle the old pulley and bearings
(i) Remove the bolt (1) and washers (2 & 3) securing the tub pulley and remove the pulley (4).
(ii) When removing the back half gasket, you will notice that it is compressed. It is advisable to replace this item to ensure a true watertight seal between the back half housing and outer tub.

2 Extraction of old bearings
(i) The existing bearing sleeves (9 & 11) will be found inside the tub backplate (10). Extract the bearing sub assemblies and then apply heat to the area containing the sleeves. The sleeves can then be gently tapped out with a small chisel, drift or old screwdriver.

3 Renewal of bearings
(i) Push the new sleeves into place, ensuring that the inner surface of the tub backplate is thoroughly cleaned.
(ii) Insert the first (larger) bearing and washer (12).

(iii) Gently push the seal (13) into place. It is advisable to use a waterproof adhesive around the seal to aid fitting and prevent leaking past the outer edge.
(iv) Clean the new carbon face seal thoroughly to remove all traces of grease, oil, etc.
(v) It is advisable to fit new washers to the front and rear (12 & 7) as it is likely they have been scoured by the faulty bearings. Many bearing kits do not contain items 12 & 7 and these may have to be obtained separately.
(vi) With the drum face down, fit the back half with the new front bearing spacer and carbon seal fitted, to the cleaned and inspected drum and shaft.
(vii) The rear bearing race can now be fitted.

4 Inserting the torque washer
(i) Re-assemble the remaining parts in reverse order to that in which they were removed. Do not use the old torque washer (6) – only use the new spacer supplied with the kit.
(ii) Fit the shim washer from the kit under the torque washer in the position shown (6a).
(iii) Tighten the bolt (1) against the pulley as far as possible without locking the tab washer.

TYPICAL BEARING ASSEMBLY

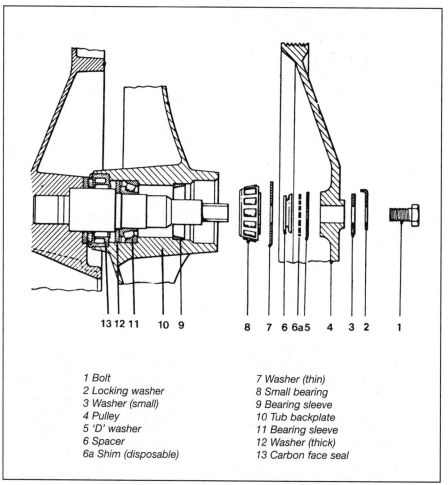

13 12 11   10 9   8 7 6 6a 5   4   3 2   1

1 Bolt
2 Locking washer
3 Washer (small)
4 Pulley
5 'D' washer
6 Spacer
6a Shim (disposable)

7 Washer (thin)
8 Small bearing
9 Bearing sleeve
10 Tub backplate
11 Bearing sleeve
12 Washer (thick)
13 Carbon face seal

(iv) Complete the tightening operation until the 'D' (5) washer fits firmly against the shoulder of the spider unit .

(v) The spacer is now correctly pre-set. It is essential to do this, in order to ensure the correct loading pressure on the bearings.

5 Discard shim and complete reassembly

(i) Remove the bolt (1), washers (2 & 3), pulley (4) and spacer (6). Discard the shim (6a).

(ii) Re-assemble in reverse order again. This time locking the tab washer against the bolt.

(iii) If this procedure on taper roller bearings is not followed correctly, the life of the new bearing set could be considerably shortened.

Below are a few helpful hints on the refitting of the assembly back in the machine.

(a) It is advisable to remove the heater from the back half (if applicable) before refitting the back half and drum into the machine. The subsequent refitting of the heater in this fashion ensures the correct location of the internal heater securing clip, see *Heaters* chapter.

(b) A thermostat pod (if applicable) and the heater grommet can be helped by a smear of sealant to help slide them Into position. If the thermostat grommet looks perished, it should be changed.

(c) Remember to reseal any hoses on the pressure system if they have been disturbed.

(d) Always remember to fit a new tub back half seal.

(e) Check the tension on the main drivebelt and adjust the belt if necessary. This is done by moving the motor up or down to slacken or tighten the belt (like adjusting a fan belt on a motor car). Do not over tighten the belt, see *Belts* chapter.

(f) Many condenser washerdriers will have connections to the back half. There are numerous variations of fixings but correct and secure fixing is common to all. Ensure all connections are tight. Any damaged clips should be renewed along with any sealant used at connection points, etc.

1 Isolate the machine and remove the rear panel. Note all connections to the back plate

2. Protect the face of the machine and gently lay the machine on its front

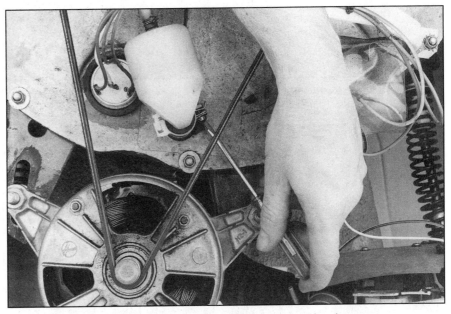

3 Note the position and angle of pressure vessel and remove

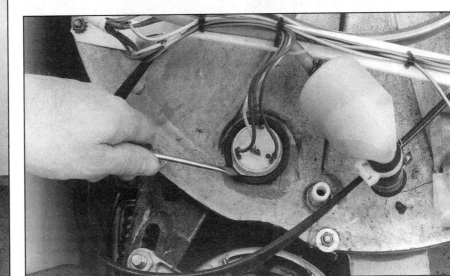

4 Note connections on the thermostat. Remove thermostat with the wires still connected. Use a flat-bladed screwdriver to ease it from the seal

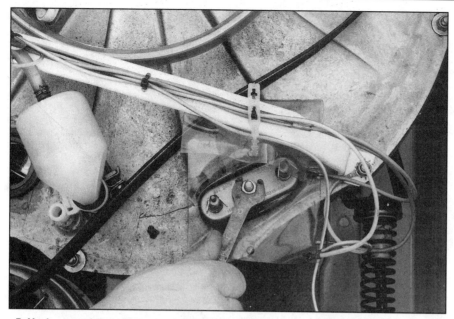

5 Having noted the wiring connections, they can now be removed. Slacken the heater clamp nut and gently prise the heater free

8 With all fixing bolts removed and wires secured out of the way, the drum and back half can be manoeuvred free from the tub

6 Remove the back half bolts from around the perimeter of the tub

9 With drum and bearing unit completely removed from the machine it is much easier to work on

7 The discharge from the drain hole can be seen here, and indicates water penetration of the bearings. The discharge is a mixture of grease, rust and water

10 Unlock the tab on the pulley bolt with the aid of a flat bladed screwdriver

11 Remove the pulley bolt, pulley and spacers, etc., noting their correct order

15 Insert screwdriver and prise out bearing carbon face seal

12 Backplate freed from the drum shaft (The front bearing may seize on the shaft and will have to be drawn off with pullers. If this happens, protect the shaft end by refitting the bolt onto the end of the shaft. This protects the shaft and aids the location of the puller centre)

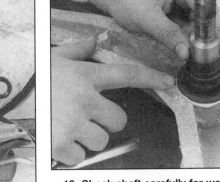

13 Check shaft carefully for wear and ridges at the bearing support points. (Front and rear). Also check carbon face for cracks or loose fit. The example shown is OK

14 (see photo 12) Check the three mounting points for cracks, etc. This drum and shaft are crush bolt fitted, therefore any fault on the drum or shaft requires a complete drum. Not all machines have this system

16 Remove old washer and front bearings. In this case a taper bearing was found. Ball bearings will have to be knocked out with a metal drift

17 With rear bearing removed, knock out rear bearing shell/liner by the inner lip

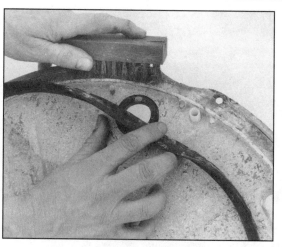

21 Clean all seal and bearing surfaces prior to refitting new parts

18 If there is no visible lip to the front bearing shell, drill two slots opposing each other in the inner of the housing to expose the liner. Do not drill too deeply

22 New set of taper roller bearings, torque washer and carbon seal suitable for this machine

19 Position of drill mark on front inner

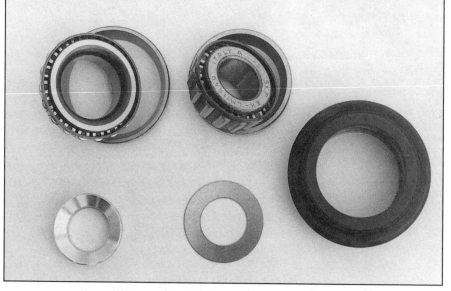

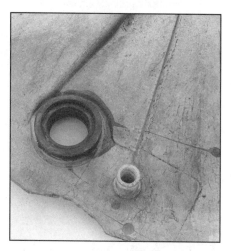

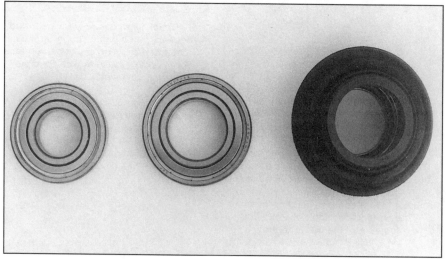

20 Remove the old thermostat seal if it is found to be a poor fit, or perished. Apply sealant to the new seal to ensure a good watertight seal

23 Typical set of ball bearings. Seals and bearing sizes may differ. Not interchangeable with taper bearings, not suitable for this machine

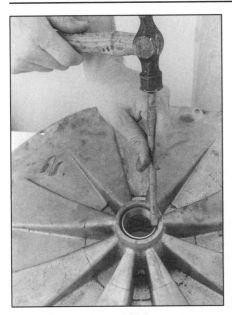

24 Insert rear bearing liner and tap into position firmly, seating to its base using a soft metal drift

26 Grease bearings back and front and reassemble as described in text

25 Now insert front liner and repeat operation as in step 24

27 Back half ready to be fitted to the drum shaft

28 Following the instructions for use of torque washer and shim, the unit is made ready for fitting back into the machine. Make sure that you reset the lock tab on the pulley bolt

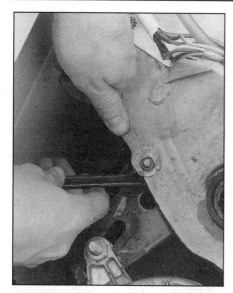

29 Tighten the bolts in sequence slowly using opposing bolts. Do not overtighten

30 Seal and refit all hoses and grommets and secure all connections to the heater, etc. Adjust the belt tension prior to the functional test with all panels in position

HOTPOINT BALL RACE TYPE RENEWAL

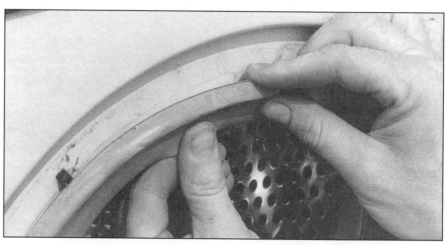

1 With machine isolated, open door and remove the securing screws for the plastic surround for the door seal

3 Free the door seal from the outer shell lip of the machine and allow to rest on inside of the front panel

2 Next, remove the door seal surround carefully. This is in two halves (top and bottom)

4 Remove the screws holding the timer knob in position. On early models, only one plastic screw will be found

5 Pull to remove the soap drawer and remove the exposed screws. This allows the front facia to be removed

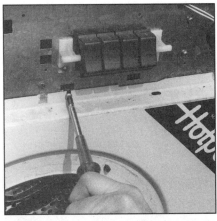

6 Remove the screws securing the top of the front panel

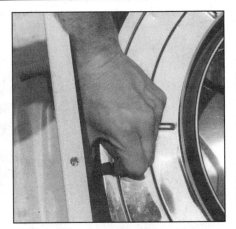

9 Note the position of the clips securing the front of the outer tub and remove carefully

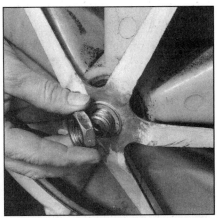

12 Remove the pulley lock nut (right hand thread) and 'chock' the pulley against the tub with wedge of wood

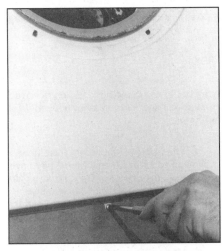

7 Remove the screws securing the bottom of the front panel. Hexagonal headed bolts may be found on early models

10 With the clips removed, the tub front can be removed completely. Take care not to damage heater or connections

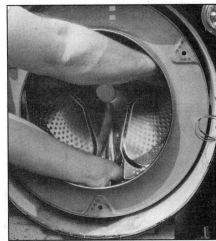

13 With the pulley securely wedged, grasp inner paddles of the drum and turn counter-clockwise. This will unscrew the pulley

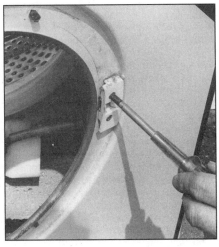

8 With front panel off, remove the door catch and interlock (if fitted)

11 Remove the screws securing the rear panel to expose the drum pulley

14 With pulley removed, tap drum shaft free from the bearings using a soft-headed mallet

15 Withdraw the drum and shaft from the tub. This will allow ample room to 'drift' out the ball bearings and shaft seal. Bearing replacement for this type of drum is quite straightforward. Using a soft drift, knock the new bearing home, taking care not to damage the new seal Reassembly of your machine is a reversal of the previous procedure

17 This style of machine has a 'catch pot' style filter in the sump hose. When removed a large amount of coins, metal screws, curtain hooks and various other household items were found

16 This machine also had severe drum damage as indicated

Bearing changes requiring outer tub removal

Often, the restricted rear access or reverse tub construction will not allow for the renewal of the bearings or drum in the manner previously described. In such instances, for repairs to or renewal of the drum bearings, tub seals or outer or inner drum renewal, it may be necessary for the whole of the outer and inner drum unit to be removed from the shell of the machine before further stripdown can take place. There are two main reasons why this course of action may be required:

1 Access to the rear of the outer tub is restricted because of the very small access panel on the rear of the shell of the machine. However, on machines with external cast iron bearing holders, it is usually possible to manoeuvre the whole unit out through the opening after first laying the machine face down and removing the securing bolts and pulley. Several AEG, Electrolux, Zanussi and Ariston models can have bearings fitted in this way but for inner drum removal/renewal, the whole unit would need to be removed as described, see below.
2 The construction of the outer tub is jointed at the front of the machine and not the rear, and the inner drum can only be removed by first removing the front of the outer tub. Unfortunately, the front shell of many machines are not removable and so the whole unit needs to be removed as described. However, many manufacturers now produce

18 These items should not have been allowed to enter the machine. They have damaged the drum severely. What would have been a relatively inexpensive 'bearing only' repair, has now required the renewal of a costly drum. (The £1.44 that was found did not cover the cost of the new drum!). This could have been avoided with a little care and attention to pockets, etc., when loading the machine

front serviceable machines with removable front panels. Check the model you have to see if it has a detachable front panel. **Note:** *The way in which the panels are secured differs greatly between the manufacturers. Look for tell tale signs such as hidden screws, side joints in the shell of the machine (indicating separate front panel construction). Refer to the Hotpoint bearing renewal sequence earlier in this chapter, which gives an insight into front panel fixing techniques.*

Most models in the Candy range of machines require tub unit removal for both bearing and inner drum problems.

It is not uncommon for manufacturers to buy-in products from another manufacturer and then 'badge' it as their own. This leads to a mix of model designs throughout the range. Until fairly recently, the current production machines were merely updated variations on a basic design, and therefore some continuity and standard format existed. However, this is not always the case nowadays which means that each machine has to be assessed prior to carrying out repairs, e.g. are the bearings mounted in a detachable housing? If access requires removal of the front or outer tub, can the front of the machine be removed to allow the unit to remain *in situ*? (see Hotpoint photo sequence).

If no other option exists, then the outer tub unit complete with drum and bearings will have to be removed to allow for complete stripdown. The removal of this large unit is via the top of the machine shell. The following text describes the removal of the outer tub unit after removing such items as the top/bottom tub weights, pulley, all connections and hoses and electrical connections to the unit. A photo sequence is not used for this as it would tend to mislead rather than help as each machine will have distinct variations depending on the original manufacturer.

It is advisable to remove all knobs from the front of the machine to reveal the fixing screws of the items behind them. This will help when servicing the drum bearings, outer tub and seals on machines that require the removal of the complete outer tub unit from the machine via the top of the machine's cabinet. Various items will need to be unscrewed and the components laid over the front facia or side of the machine. If possible do not disconnect any wiring, but detailed notes of all connections and fixings should be kept in the event of items getting misplaced or dislodged. Release the screws securing the dispenser unit to the cabinet and remove the hose from the dispenser unit. Lay the dispenser unit over the front or side of the machine. Remove the top tub weight (if fitted)

and release the front fitting of the door seal. To help slide the tub unit out of the machine, two pieces of wood (2" x 1" x 4') can be inserted down the left-hand side of the machine between the tub and cabinet to support the tub during its removal. **Note:** *If your machine has the timer on the opposite side to that shown in the diagram, the wood should be inserted down the right-hand side and the machine laid over correspondingly.*

Now lower the machine onto the left-hand side after making sure that the cabinet side and floor are protected, and release the shock absorber or friction damper mountings. Now disconnect the sump hose, pressure hoses, heater connections, thermostat connections and motor block connections. Remove the drivebelt and drum pulley and check that all connections are free from the outer tub unit. At the top of the machine, release the suspension springs by pushing the tub unit towards the top of the machine. It will now be possible to slide the tub assembly out of the cabinet. At this point a little help may be useful as the unit will be quite heavy and needs manoeuvring out of position. At this time ensure that the lower friction plate is being supported by one of the wooden strips. Hold the door open during the tub withdrawal.

Once removed, the unit is then easily accessible and the bearing renewal is similar to that shown in the previous photo sequences. Make a note of all clamp positions, tub front and back positions, etc. It is advisable to re-seal and check all hoses and their fixing points prior to refitting the unit. It is important to do this when the tub is out of the machine as this may be difficult when the unit is replaced.

Refitting is a reversal of the removal procedure. After refitting, ensure that all

This picture shows a machine with the front panel removed, illustrating the excellent access that can be found with this type of machine

electrical and earth connections are replaced correctly and securely and an RCD protected socket is used when the functional test sequence is carried out. **Note:** *Remember, many manufacturers now have machines on the market with detachable front panels. With these types of machine, the drum and bearing assemblies can be removed and changed with the outer tub in situ, thus avoiding the extra work involved in tub removal.*

With the Hotpoint machine, the pulley is threaded to the shaft and is secured by a lock nut. To release the pulley, chock it with wood

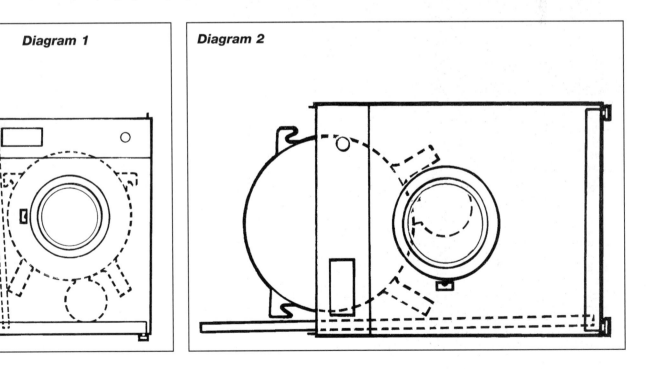

Diagram 1

Diagram 2

and rotate the drum anti-clockwise from the front of the machine. When refitting, apply some locking compound to the shaft thread (this can be obtained from any good DIY or motorists shop).

Alternative pulley fixings

As can be seen from the photographic sequences the way most pulleys are secured to the shaft are relatively simple and with a little thought and reference to this chapter most can be worked out. However, a not so obvious method of securing the drum pulley to the drum shaft is by means of a tapered cone and pulley. Two popular makes that use this type of system on some of their models are Creda and Ariston. In this system a drum pulley with a tapered centre is secured to the drum shaft by means of an opposing tapered cone. When the securing bolt is tightened the pulley and cone are forced together. This reduces the diameter of the cone, which grips the circular drum shaft. When fitted for some length of time the separate parts can become very tight. If after removing the centre securing bolt the pulley remains firmly attached to the shaft and cone, loosely refit the centre bolt and tap the bolt with a hide/plastic hammer to shock it free. If this fails it may be necessary to insert opposing metal wedges between the rear bearing inner race and the thick base of the pulley to apply pressure (it is not recommended to use pullers on the aluminium pulley). When handling the metal pulley, gloved hands are recommended, as the moulding of the pulley can be sharp.

With the pulley and tapered cone removed, refit the securing bolt to protect the threads and use a hide/plastic hammer to free the drum shaft from the bearings.

What you do next will depend on which type of bearing housing your machine has, either cast iron bearing housing, large metal back plate or moulded plastic outer tub.

When removing the bearing housing/drum, note the position and assembly of the sealing system both on the bearing face and the lower end of the drum shaft. Depending on the make and model a cupped/lipped seal or spring loaded carbon seal systems may be found. Ensure that the replacement kit is the same as the one already fitted to your machine. With cup seal systems ensure they are fitted the correct way up so make a note of the old seal before removing it. When removed clean the shaft base thoroughly and use a little sealant to secure the new seal into position. DO NOT contaminate the front skirt of the rubber lip seal. The old bearings and seal can now be knocked out and the new set fitted (ball race types will be pre-

greased, no extra required). Refit the front seal system/contact plate, again sealant can be used around the edge but DO NOT allow contamination of the smooth metal/carbon surfaces. With the rubber cup seal system the contact between the smooth metal plate and the shaft seal skirt is all that creates the watertight seal, cleanliness is therefore essential. It is a good idea to apply a little petroleum jelly (slight smear only) to the new shaft seal skirt and it's metal contact plate on the front of the bearings prior to assembly. Refitting is a simple reversal of the stripdown process, however you may find that the shaft of the drum may not protrude far enough through the new bearings to allow the fitting of the pulley. This is usually due to the new bearings being a little tight on the shaft. To overcome this problem, open the door of the machine and with the flat palm of the hand, hit the rear of the inner drum to seat the shaft firmly into the new bearings (do not use tools for this as they may dent the drum rear). Although the pulley can be fitted, failure to seat the drum shaft correctly will allow water to bypass the new seal.

Cast iron bearing housing

A Zanussi machine has been chosen to illustrate a typical cast iron bearing housing stripdown. Many manufacturers use similar systems and the information given can be adapted to those machines, where possible additional details are given. In this particular range of machines, two types of bearings can be found – a conical bearing (one single outer case with two inner races) or two normal ball race types, the sizes of which will depend on the individual model.

Refitting is a simple reversal process, but remember to make sure that the captive washers on the centre bolts go behind the plate with slots in and NOT between the plate and the spider unit, otherwise leaking will occur. Another tip is to glue the washers to the bolt heads prior to refitting so that they cannot go out of position. When refitting the outer bolts, ensure that the two bottom bolts go in first. This allows all the compression of the new rubber seal to be done when lining up the top bolt. You may find that the shaft of the drum may not protrude far enough through the bearing to allow the fitting of the pulley. This is due to the new bearings being a little tight on the shaft. To overcome this problem, open the door of the machine and with the flat of the hand, hit the rear of the inner drum to seat the shaft firmly into the new bearings, DO NOT use tools for this as they may dent the rear of the drum. **Note:** *Details of machines with 50/50 split shells can be found in the chapter* Useful tips and information.

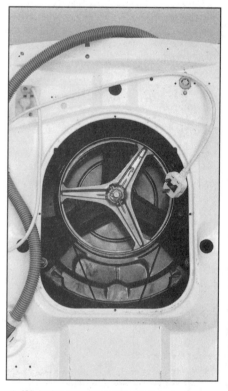

Typical cast iron bearing housing. This type of bearing housing is used on many different makes such as Ariston, Zanussi, Electrolux, and AEG

1 With the machine fully isolated remove the top and back panels

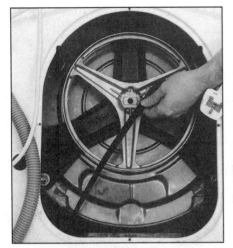

2 Remove the drivebelt, locking tab, bolt and pulley

3 If the pulley is stuck to the shaft, loosely refit the centre bolt and tap the bolt with a hide/plastic hammer to free it off

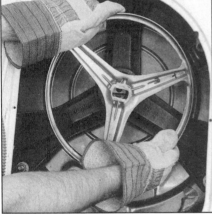

4 When loosened, waggle the pulley free without using too much force, (gloved hands are recommended, as the moulding of the pulley can be sharp)

5 Refit the securing bolt and use a plastic hammer/hide mallet to free the drum shaft from the bearings

6 On some models you may need to remove the concrete top block to gain easy access to the top bolt of the bearing housing, however this is not required in this instance

7 With suitable protection carefully lay the machine on its face for the following sequences

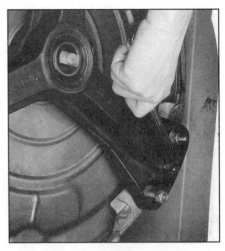

8 Remove the end bolts securing the remaining legs. For models with additional centre bolts, loosen but do not fully remove the three centre nuts

Note: *On Zanussi and similar models these are in captive slots and do not need complete removal. However, this may not be the case with other makes/models. A finger inserted behind the centre lip can usually detect if captive slots are used*

If you cannot get a spanner (13mm) behind to hold the bolt head, a good tip is to hold the exposed thread of the centre bolts with self-locking grips and undo the nut a few turns. As the nut need never be completely removed, thread damage is no problem

Note: *This can only be done on machines with captive slot fixings*

When the outer bolts are out and the inner bolts loosened, the spider is free to be rotated clockwise 2" – 3" allowing the captive bolts to be free of their slots.

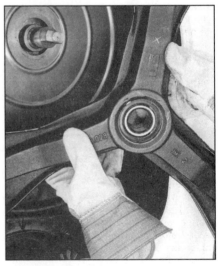

9 Next, pull the spider from the drum shaft and manoeuvre the housing out of the back of the machine

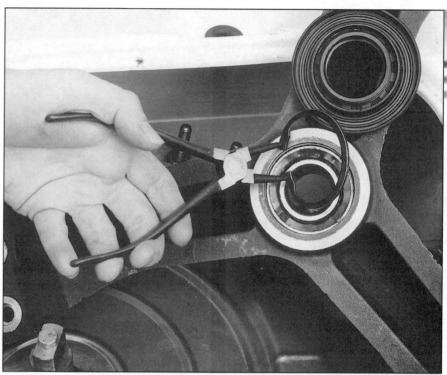

10 Ensure the shaft and the phosphor bronze bush on the drum shaft is clean and free from scale, etc.

11 On this model a large circlip is located behind the shaft seal and you need to lever out the old seal to gain access to remove it with circlip pliers before trying to remove the bearing(s). Bearings without circlip fixings can be simply knocked out and the new set fitted. It is a good idea to apply a little petroleum jelly to the new seal and bush on the shaft to allow them to slip together when refitting

Chapter 31
Using a meter

Throughout this book, references have been made to meters and their use in continuity testing of individual parts of appliances and their connecting wires. All such testing and checking for 'open' (i.e. not allowing for current flow), or 'closed' circuit (i.e. allowing current to flow), must be carried out using a battery powered multimeter or test meter. Under no circumstances should testing be carried out on 'live' items i.e. appliances connected to the mains supply. **Remember:** *completely isolate the appliances from the mains supply before starting any repair work or testing.*

Although some meters and testers have the facility to check mains voltages, I do not agree with their use in repairs to domestic appliances. Faults can be easily traced by simple low voltage (battery power) continuity testing, proving that the simplest of meters or even a home-made one like the one described are perfectly adequate for some faults. Remember that safety is paramount and under no circumstances should it be compromised. Always double check that the appliance is unplugged; a good tip is to keep the plug in view so that no-one else can inadvertently plug it in. The simple home-made continuity tester described later will help trace faults only in the wiring of the appliance. A multimeter similar to the ones shown will be required for individual component testing.

If you decide to buy a test meter, you could find yourself faced with quite a variety to choose from. Do not be tempted to get an over-complicated one as it could end up confusing and misleading you when in use. Before using your new meter, read the manufacturer's instructions thoroughly and make sure that you fully understand them. The Rapitest meter used in some of the photographs is very simple to use when continuity testing and has a scale that reads 'open' circuit or 'closed' circuit. It was purchased from a local DIY store and was very reasonably priced. The meter will also help locate faults with car electrics, but as previously stated, using on live mains circuits should not be entertained.

Some multimeters are able to show the resistance value of the item being tested as well as indicating continuity. This can be extremely useful if the correct value of the item being tested is known, i.e. correct resistance of motor winding, armature and element, etc., although this is by no means essential. Detailed use of the multimeter for this function will be found in its accompanying instruction leaflet.

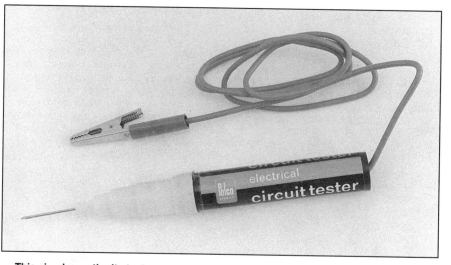

This simple continuity tester was purchased from a local automart for a reasonable price. It is a manufactured version of the home made type described

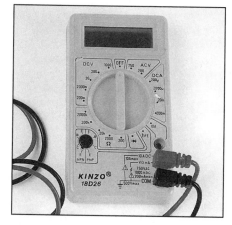

Small digital test meters such as this one are now widely available and readings easier to interpret. They are also available in auto-ranging versions, which automatically display the correct scale

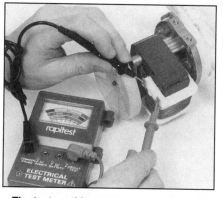

The test on this outlet pump stator coil proved to be OK (i.e. closed circuit/continuity). This meant that the supply or neutral to and from the pump required checking to discover the reason why the pump failed to work at any point in the programme

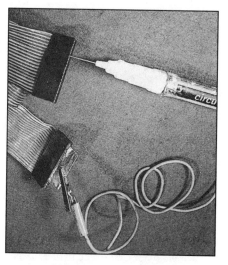

A simple test is all that is required to trace harness faults

Electrical fault finding

A simple continuity tester for wiring

This simple device can be used to trace wiring faults in most appliances and is very easy to make. It uses the lack of continuity to its full advantage. To make this tester, you will need a standard battery, bulb and three wires 1 x 5" (13 cm) and 2 x 10" (25 cm). Connect the short wire to the positive terminal of the battery and the other end of that wire to the centre terminal of a small torch bulb. Attach one of the longer wires to the negative terminal of the battery and leave the other end free. The other wire should be attached to the body of the bulb again, leave the end free.

The two loose ends now act as the test wires. Press the two ends of the wires together, and the bulb will light. If not, check that the battery and the bulb and all connections are OK. When 'open circuit', the light will stay off, and when 'closed circuit', the light will be on. **Note:** *Low voltage bulb type testers of 1.5V or 3V are unsuitable for testing the continuity of components within the machines. A test meter like the ones shown will be required to test high resistance items such as pumps, timer coil, valves, etc. Ensure that the machine is isolated from the main supply before attempting to use a meter.*

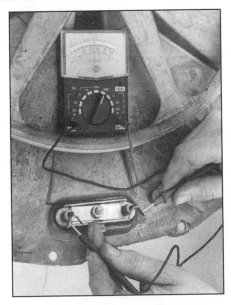

The testing of the heater element to check for a circuit 'through it'. In this instance, the heater does have a circuit as shown by the meter needle. This means that the 'no heat' fault on the machine is not a fault of this component. The next step would be to test the wiring and connections to and from the heater in the same way. Also check the timer and/or the thermostat if in the heater circuit

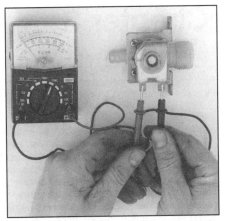

The testing of this water valve proved that the coil was open circuit. This is shown by the meter needle staying at its 'rest' position. This shows that the 'no fill' fault on the machine was in fact due to the water valve failing to energise and allow water into the machine. (On components such as these, it is a good idea to try to move the terminals as a poor internal connection may cause the bad reading). This problem was cured by renewing the valve

How to test for continuity using a test meter

To test for an open circuit, note and remove the original wiring to the component to be tested. (If this is not done, false readings may be given from other items that may be in circuit.) The ends of the two wires of the meter should be attached to the component that is suspected. For example, to test a heater for continuity, place the metal probes on the tags at the end of the heater and watch the meter. The needle should move.

If the heater is open circuit, i.e. no movement, the heater can then be suspected and tested further. If closed circuit, the heater continuity is OK.

Leap-frog testing – using a meter

Often the most effective way to trace a fault is to use a very simple, but logical approach to them. One such approach is called the leap-frog method and can be used to find the failed/open circuit part or parts. In this instance, let us assume that the appliance does not work at all when functionally tested, therefore you cannot deduce where the problem lies purely from the symptoms. A quick check of the supply socket by plugging in another appliance known to be OK will verify (or not) that there is power up TO that point. This confirms that the fault lies somewhere in the appliance, its supply cable or plug. We know that during normal conditions, power flows in through the live pin

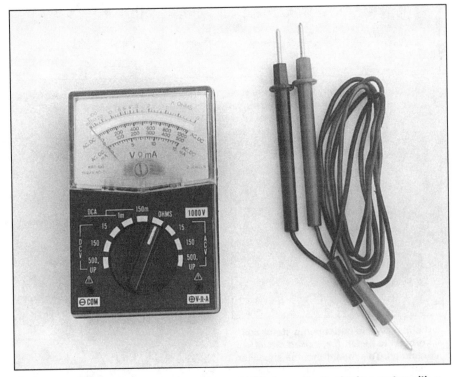

A multimeter of the type to be found in most DIY stores. Try to obtain a meter with a good information booklet. This proved to be useful for many other jobs around the house and car

on the plug, through the appliance (when switched on) and returns via the neutral pin on the plug. The fact that the appliance will not work at all even when plugged in and switched on indicates that an open circuit exists somewhere along this normal live to neutral circuit.

Test that the meter is working correctly, i.e. touch test probes together and the meter should indicate continuity. With the machine unplugged (isolated) connect one probe to the live pin of the appliance's plug and the other on the live conductor connecting point in the plug. Continuity should be found which confirms that the pin, fuse and their connections are alright, but faulty if open circuit occurs. If this check proves to be OK, move the probe from the live conductor point in the plug to the live conductor connection in the terminal block within the appliance. Again, continuity should be found, if not, a fault between plug and terminal block is indicated. **Note:** *On cable continuity testing, it is best to move the cable along its length during the test to ascertain if an intermittent fault may exist.*

If this test is alright, proceed to move the probe to the next convenient point along the live conductor, in this instance, the supply side of the on/off switch, which may be part of the main programme switch on some machines (usually the front terminals).

Again, continuity is required. An open circuit indicates a fault between terminal block and switch connection. The next step is to move the probe to the opposite terminal of

the switch. Operate the switch to verify correct action (i.e. on continuity, off open circuit). If OK proceed to the next point along the wire, in this instance the door interlock connection. Again continuity is required, If OK, move probe to the terminal on the return side of the heater within the interlock (see *Door switches (interlocks)* chapter). This again should indicate continuity through heater of the interlock. At this point we will assume that an open circuit has been indicated, so go back to the last test point and verify continuity up to that point. If found to be alright, then a fault has been traced that lies within the interlock which requires renewal.

This simple, methodical approach is all that is required to find such problems. With more complex circuits it is best to break them down into individual sections, i.e. motor, heater, switch, etc., and test continuity of each section from live through the timer and the individual parts and back to neutral. This may involve moving the live probe that would normally remain on the plug live pin to a more convenient supply point within the appliance to avoid misleading continuity readings from other items within the appliance circuit. With practice, faults can be found even in complex wiring in this way. **Note:** *The action of switching within the interlock of power back to the timer cannot be verified but continuity of the wiring can be checked in a similar leap frog manner. In this instance, due to the heater being 'open circuit' the interlock would fail to operate and the action of power being returned (switched) to the timer for*

distribution to other parts could not take place. A fault with the main switching action of the interlock would have been indicated during the functional test (See Functional testing), i.e. when the machine was switched on, the door locked but nothing else would operate other than the door locking. This is due to most (but not all) machines having the interlock as the first item in circuit when switched on, therefore incorrect latching of the door or failure of the interlock (other than short circuit of the internal switch) will render the appliance inoperable.

DO NOT trace faults by looking for mains voltages. There is no need to consider or use such dangerous techniques. All testing can and should be carried out with the appliance completely isolated (i.e. switch off, plug out), using only a battery-powered meter or tester to indicate continuity or open circuit.

To check for the correct resistance you will need to select the correct scale and reference to the instruction booklet for your particular meter will be required (unless you have an auto-ranging digital meter).

The ohms reading will differ from item to item. Test for open or closed circuits only. Any reference to an ohm (Ω) reading is a guide only as resistances differ from machine to machine. The objective is to test for either continuity or the lack of continuity of the item being tested.

Chapter 32
Wiring and harness faults

What is a wiring harness?

The term harness is used for all of the wires that connect the various components within the appliance. On large appliances they are usually bound or fastened together in bunches to keep the wiring in the appliance neat and safely anchored. Smaller appliances, however, may sacrifice neatness for safety and route the wiring to avoid contact with heat, sharp edges, etc.

What does it do?

At first sight, the harness may look like a jumble of wires thrown together. This is not the case. If you take the time to inspect the harness, you will find that each wire is colour-coded or numbered (either on the wire itself, or on the connector at either end). This allows you to follow the wiring through the appliance easily. With practice, any wiring or coding can be followed.

As most of the wires in the machine either finish or start at the timer unit, it may be helpful to think of the timer as the base of a tree, with the main wiring harness as the trunk. As the trunk is followed, branches appear (wires to the valves, pressure switches, etc.). Continuing upwards, the trunk gets slowly thinner as branching takes place to the motor, pump, module, etc.

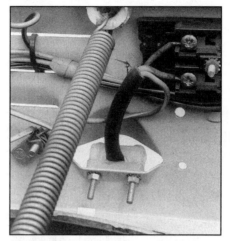

The terminal block is the first distribution point of the power into the machine. Ensure all connections are sound, as heat will be generated if not

Each item is therefore separate but linked to the timer by a central bond of wire. This in turn can be likened to a central command post, communicating with field outposts.

The connecting wires to and/or from a component are vital to that component and possibly others that rely on the correct functioning of that item.

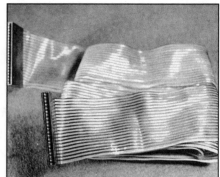

Ribbon cable is often used in computer controlled machines

Luckily, wiring faults are not too common. but when they do occur they sometimes appear to result in big problems, when in reality it is only a small fault that has occurred, i.e. one poor connection can cause a motor not to function at all, and render the appliance unusable.

Do not fall into the trap of always suspecting the worst. Many people, including engineers, blindly fit parts such as a motor or a heater for a similar fault to that mentioned, only to find it did not cure the problem. Often the timer is blamed and subsequently changed. This does not cure the problem and is an expensive mistake. Stop, think and check all wires and connections that relate to your particular fault. Always inspect all connections and ensure that the wire and connector has a tight fit. Loose or poor connections can overheat and cause a lot of trouble, especially on items such as the heater.

Poor connections to items such as the main motor or pump will be aggravated by movement of the machine when in use and may not be so apparent when a static test is carried out.

One of the most easily missed faults is where the metal core (conductor) of the wire has broken and the outer insulation has not. This wire will appear perfect from the outside but will pass no electrical current. To test for this, see the chapter *Using a meter*.

It must be remembered that such faults may be intermittent. That is to say that one reading may be correct and the same test later may prove incorrect. This is due to the movement of the outer insulation of the wire first making, then breaking the electrical connection.

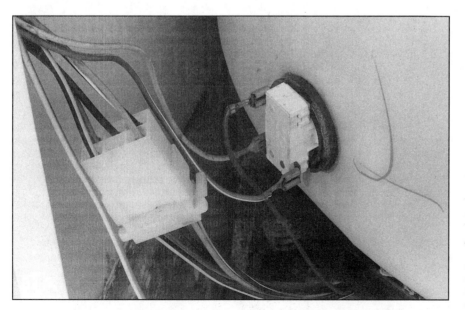

Harness connector block. Again any loose connectors will overheat and cause problems. Ensure a secure fit

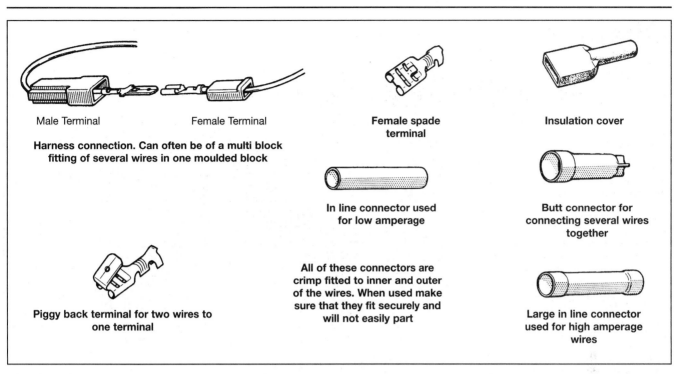

Male Terminal   Female Terminal

Harness connection. Can often be of a multi block fitting of several wires in one moulded block

Female spade terminal

Insulation cover

In line connector used for low amperage

Butt connector for connecting several wires together

Piggy back terminal for two wires to one terminal

All of these connectors are crimp fitted to inner and outer of the wires. When used make sure that they fit securely and will not easily part

Large in line connector used for high amperage wires

When testing for such intermittent faults, pull or stretch each wire tested. An unbroken wire will not stretch whereas a wire that is broken internally will stretch at the break point and rectification is a simple matter of renewing the connection with a suitable connector. Do not make the connection by twisting the wires together and covering them with insulation tape. Use only the correct rating of connector and ensure a secure and insulated joint is made. If a joint is required in a position of cable movement, e.g. wiring from shell to outer tub unit components, it is advisable to renew the whole length of wiring or the joint made in a fixed section of cable. The use of rigid connections in movable wiring must be avoided. Take time to do a few simple checks. It saves time, patience and money. **Note:** *Ensure that the harness is secured adequately to the shell of the machine, at the same time allowing for free movement of the motor, heater, etc.*

Take care that any metal fastening clips are fitted correctly and do not chafe the plastic insulation around the wires. Also make sure that wires are not in contact with sharp metal edges such as self-tapping screws, etc. **Warning:** *Before attempting to remove or repair the wiring harness or any other component in the appliance, isolate the appliance from the main electrical supply by removing the plug from the wall socket.*

Chapter 33
Dry-only machines

Note: *The tumbledriers covered in this book heat the air used in the drying process by electricity, but domestic tumbledriers are now available which heat by gas. Although commercial machines have had this option for many years, it is relatively new to the domestic user. Because of the stringent gas regulations and the obvious need for safety, do not attempt installation, inspection or repair on this type of product. The installation, service and repair of gas appliances must be carried out by those with the relevant knowledge, equipment and gas qualifications.*

The tumbledrier has been with us for many years now. The basic function is to circulate warm air through the damp clothes for a given period of time selected by the user, which is then followed by a cool tumble prior to switching off at the end of the selected time. This is a relatively simple operation requiring a drum to hold the load, a heater to warm the air and a fan to circulate the warm air through the drum. As with combined washerdrier machines, the drum is rotated to allow the whole load to gain maximum benefit from the warm airflow. In most tumbledry only machines the motor that revolves the drum also drives the fan used for air circulation. Being a dedicated machine (drying only) it works much more efficiently than its combined washerdrier counterpart. There are several reasons for this:

a) The drum capacity can be much larger as it is not necessary to have a watertight outer tub, thus allowing for a larger drum taking up nearly all the available space within the cabinet. The larger machines (those with cabinets the same size as a washing machine) can take the same size load, i.e. an 11 lb (5 kg) wash load can be transferred directly into the 11 lb load tumbledrier. The smaller models with a 6 lb (2.7 kg) load capacity, convenient if space is restricted, operates in exactly the same way as the larger models but can only accommodate half a normal wash load. DO NOT overload these smaller machines.

b) The larger drum allows for better movement of the clothing through the airflow, ensuring more even and quicker drying even as the clothing increases in bulk during the drying process. Remember, this increase in the bulk of the load is why the combined washerdrier machines can dry only half its wash load.

c) A larger wattage heater can be used (if necessary) with a greater surface area for warming the air due to more space being available within the cabinet for such components.

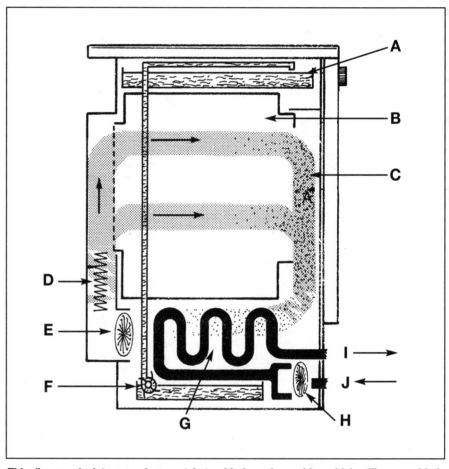

This diagram depicts a condenser style tumbledry only machine which utilises a cold air flow duct to remove the moisture from the sealed warm air flow. Action is as follows: Air within the sealed system is circulated by fan (E) over heater unit (D) and on into the drum (B). Moisture is picked up by the warm air flow (C) and after passing through a fluff filter, is directed over a cool metal ducting or plate (G). The moisture condenses on the much cooler surface and collects in a sump beneath. The condensing plate or duct is kept cool by constant circulation of air created by fan (H). Air is drawn in at (J) and vented at (I). For ease of emptying, the condensate water is transferred by pump (F) to the reservoir tank (A) which requires regular emptying. Alternatively, the machine can be plumbed to a suitable drain/outlet, therefore eliminating the need for manual emptying of the reservoir

d) Again, due to the increase in usable space a larger fan can be used for circulating the air.

Over the years, many additions to the basic principles have been made. Drum rotation on early and current basic machines is in one direction only. Nowadays, the option is to have reverse drum action similar to the wash action (clockwise and counter-clockwise). This obviously requires a more complex motor, which is capable of rotation in both directions, and a more complex timer or motor reversal system. Temperature control, again on early and current basic models is relatively straightforward with selections of high or low heat, but on the more recent and expensive machines, auto-sensing is now a common feature. These systems sense the moisture content of the load being dried and switches off when a pre-selected degree of dryness has been reached. **Note:** *A cool-*

down period will still take place. The advantage of auto-sensing is that it switches off the heater when the load is dry unlike a more basic machine that carries on tumbling and heating for the set time regardless of whether the clothes are dry or not.

Further refinements and extras include computer control (electronic in place of mechanical), intermittent tumble after the drying process is complete which prevents the load compacting at the end of the cycle if left unattended for any length of time prior to removal. Condenser tumbledriers are also available. These operate in a similar manner to the combined washerdrier system by condensing the moisture rather than venting it. Some require water supply and outlet whilst others use cold air instead of water to aid condensing, and a removable container to collect the condensate. The container requires regular emptying (once every two dry cycles on average if not permanently drained in a similar way to the automatic washer, i.e. drain pump and waste outlet connection).

The main benefits of the larger dry-only machines (same sized cabinet as the washing machine), are that they are capable of drying a full wash load. Having two separate machines for the washing and drying process means you can be drying one load whilst another load is being washed, thus saving a lot of time. This can equate to a considerable saving on time when compared with combined machines. **Note:** *Do not use both machines from a single socket via an adapter. See* Basics – electrical. When used correctly the separate drier is also quicker and more efficient than combined washerdriers.

Thermostats are used to monitor the exhaust air temperature, which open circuit the heating element(s) at predetermined temperature(s). This action ensures that an optimum drying temperature is maintained without excessive use of power, i.e. heating an already dry load. Normally, as the warm air passes through the damp clothing during the drying process, its temperature drops as it picks up moisture from the clothing. On basic machines the user judges the length of time for drying the load. However, if the selected time is too long for a particular load, the warm air passing through it once the clothes are dry will not drop in temperature. This will actuate a thermostat mounted in the vent and open circuit the heater. The thermostats used to monitor normal working temperatures are of the self-setting type, therefore cycling of this action will occur until the remainder of the timed heat cycle has ended and the cool tumble begins. Usually, a double temperature thermostat is used in conjunction with high and low heat settings and are designed to maintain a predetermined air temperature throughout the drying cycle whilst at the same time providing an overheat safeguard. Thermostat temperature ratings differ from one make to another and also between models from the same manufacturer, as the temperature ratings are matched to the performances and heater wattage of each machine. Make sure that when required, only the correct replacement thermostat is obtained for your machine. For operation and testing of thermostats see *Temperature control* chapter.

Failure of the normal temperature control mechanisms fall into two categories:
1 Failing to open at the correct temperature. This would cause the thermal overload load (TOC) to operate to prevent overheating. See chapter on *Temperature control* for further details.
2 Failing to reset when cool. This fault would prevent all or a section of a double heating element to remain open circuit. This would result in no heating at all or constant low heat even on high heat settings. **Note:** *The symptoms of this type of fault will depend on the way the two temperatures are obtained. Some models use one heater and select between two thermostats for the different settings. Other models may use a double element configuration i.e. two elements on for high heat, only one for low.*

On computer controlled or auto-sensing machines, a combination of fixed thermostats and thermistors or resistance probes will be encountered. The configuration depends on the make and model of the machine. See chapter on *Temperature control* for further details.

As already described, tumbledriers operate by tumbling the damp clothes in a warm flow of air within the drum. There are two different ways in which this airflow through the clothes can be created – by suction and by pressurisation. Both systems have the same basic components of drive motor, heater, thermostat, tension pulley and timer. The difference lies in the way the airflow is created.

The suction system

With this system the airflow is created by a large extractor fan drawing air through a semi-sealed system. The fan is usually belt driven (elastic or Vee belt) by the same motor, which is used to rotate the drum by means of a second belt (narrow Multi Vee or H section belt). When the drying programme has been selected and switched on, the fan and the drum both rotate. The rotating fan draws air from within the drum and expels it through a vent at the rear of the machine. The cabinet of the machine forms a partially sealed system with an air inlet grille positioned some distance from the fan vent. Air is drawn in through this inlet grille to replace the air extracted from the drum by the fan. The cold air drawn in enters the semi-sealed system and passes over the heating elements (the position of which may vary depending on make of machine) as it makes its way on to the drum. The now warm air enters the drum and passes on through the clothes, picking up moisture as it does so, and exits the system via the extractor fan vent, thus drying the load in the process. At the onset of the cool tumble (10-15 minutes before the end of the selected drying time) the heater is turned off but drum rotation and fan action continues creating a cool airflow for the remainder of the cycle.

Felt seals are used to ensure that air is only drawn though the drum and not from the shell space as this would result in poor drying and reduced airflow over the heating element. A removable filter is positioned within the airflow path to trap any fluff or lint and prevent it being blown from the vent.

The pressurised system

The efficiency of this system relies on the shell of the machine being sealed to prevent air entering or escaping through any other than the correct positions. It is essential that the panels are fitted correctly and that all sealing felt or foam strips fitted on removable parts such as back panel, lid or facia parts are in good order or renewed if damaged. Airflow within this type of system is created by drawing air in via the inlet grille by a centrifugal (tangential) fan normally mounted directly on the main motor shaft. When the motor is running the fan creates a slight pressure build-up within the sealed shell of the appliance.

The drum inner has an exhaust vent usually to the rear of the machine although some models vent to the front via the door, or via a duct to a grille at the top or bottom of the front panel. For the pressurised air to escape through the vent, it must first pass through the heating elements where it is heated, on through the drum and clothing and through a removable fluff/lint trap before escaping through the exhaust vent.

Functional test

Purpose of the test: To test where practical the main functions of the tumbledrier and its installation in the more efficient manner.
1 Ensure that the door of the machine is closed – turn the programme timer to 20 minutes.
2 Check that the drum rotates. If the drier is of the reversing type (drum rotation clockwise and counter-clockwise) check for this action. Length of rotation and pause times differ greatly between makes, so be patient and familiarise yourself with the correct action of your machine.
3 Open the door and confirm that the drum stops. Confirm that warm air is present in the drum. **Note:** *On some machines, closing the door restarts the cycle whereas other machines need to be restarted by pushing the reset button after the door has been closed.*
4 Select the other heat settings (if applicable) and repeat steps 2 and 3 to confirm that heating is taking place.

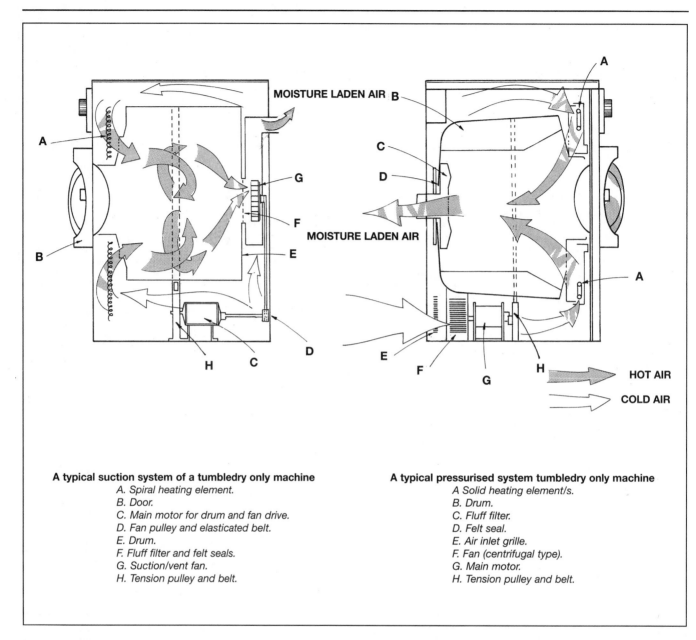

A typical suction system of a tumbledry only machine
A. Spiral heating element.
B. Door.
C. Main motor for drum and fan drive.
D. Fan pulley and elasticated belt.
E. Drum.
F. Fluff filter and felt seals.
G. Suction/vent fan.
H. Tension pulley and belt.

A typical pressurised system tumbledry only machine
A Solid heating element/s.
B. Drum.
C. Fluff filter.
D. Felt seal.
E. Air inlet grille.
F. Fan (centrifugal type).
G. Main motor.
H. Tension pulley and belt.

5 Allow the timer to advance to the anti-crease cycle (cool down 10 to 15 minutes prior to end of programme), and confirm that cold air is now circulating in the drum. Let this action run for 5-10 minutes.
6 Monitor the machine noise during all operations. If excessive, terminate test, isolate the machine prior to inspection.
7 If the drier is permanently vented or a vent hose is normally used, check that it is clear. Check the outlet of the hose or vent during steps 2 and 5, making sure that there is a good flow of air present. **Note:** Some machines may incorporate a second user selectable timer of up to 12 hours time delay. This timer is used to interrupt the main timing control, allowing the timer to be used more economically on reduced rate electrical supply (e.g. Economy 7). To test this timer,

select the shortest time delay possible and ensure that the main timer is also set. Normal action of the machine should commence only after the delay timer has reached the end of the delay selected.

Regular inspection points

Regular inspection of tumbledriers is vital, not only to keep them in good working order but also to ensure that accumulations of lint and fluff do not build up within the machine constituting a possible danger of fire. It is recommended that the following procedure be carried out on a regular basis, the time period of which is dependent on the degree of

usage but should be no longer than twelve months between inspections. The same procedure should also be carried out if a repair is required between the normal routine inspections. A thorough stripdown of the appliance is required to ensure that all components are free from lint/fluff and that all wiring connections are secure and in good condition. Do not relegate this procedure to a quick inspection and a cleaning of only those parts that are easily accessible with only the top or back of the machine removed.

Due to the many variations of machines on the market, a description of how each should be stripped down cannot be given in detail. However, a basic sequence which will suit most if not all machines is as follows and as always should only be carried out with the machine fully isolated.

Popular small front venting tumbledry only machine

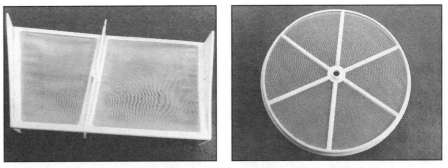

Keep filters clean and renew if damaged, i.e. torn or distorted

Ensure thermostats are fitted correctly and free from fluff build-ups that act as insulation leading to incorrect temperature sensing

Large rear fan housing of a 9 lb load early Hoover machine. The fan is driven by an elasticated belt directly from the motor shaft which also drives the main drum. The motor in this instance is a large shaded pole motor with Multi Vee belt drive at one end and round pulley at the other

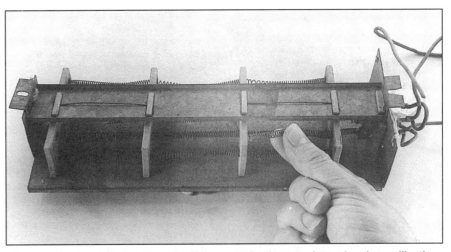

Inspect heating element closely for fluff contamination, sagging or breakages like the one shown. Complete heater units are generally not expensive

1   Check and clean the removable filter. This, of course should not be unduly blocked as cleaning of this item should be part of the normal usage routine.

2   Remove the vent hose (if fitted) and check the outlet duct of the machine for fluff build-up. The full length of the hose or ducting should also be checked along with external grilles on permanently vented systems. Ensure the whole system is free from restrictions.

3   Always, take notes of components, wiring connections and routing within the machine prior to stripdown or removal.

4   Ensure each component is thoroughly cleaned and all traces of lint/fluff removed. This should be done with care using a small dusting brush and/or cylinder vacuum cleaner.

5   Particular attention should be paid to components such as the timer(s), main motor (cooling grilles, etc.), TOCs, thermostats, terminal connections, heating elements and fixing points. Solid elements (sheathed) can be brushed clean but spiral elements must be carefully cleaned to avoid stretching or damage to their ceramic holders. With spiral elements, fluff may build up within the hollow centre. This can best be removed by carefully teasing it free with a needle or similar item.

It is common for the front lip on the drum to be used as the front support bearing. Ensure that it is smooth and undamaged. It will either be supported by a simple felt strip coated in PTFE or by plastic mounts which act as support bearings. All variations are prone to wear

Elasticated belts are prone to stretching and fraying. Renew them regularly to maintain peak performance from your machine

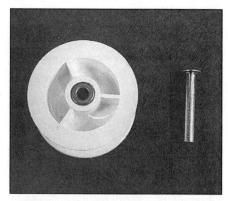

Worn tension pulleys can create a lot of noise or allow the belt to constantly slip or jump out of position. Renew if worn or damaged; also check the supporting shaft for wear. Whenever possible renew both parts as a set as shown

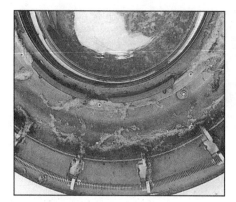

Through lack of regular maintenance, fluff has built-up on and around the heating elements. It can be seen from the photo that the build-up is charred and has smouldered. This is a potential fire risk. Regular de-linting is essential to avoid this problem

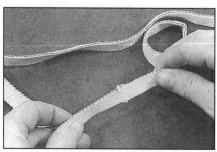

Many Creda machines use a braided webbing as a front bearing. It is glued to the front drum lip and rests on the metal edge of the shell of the machine. When worn, the machine will vibrate badly and become very noisy. Renewing the webbing is straightforward, but it is wise to remove all traces of paint from the worn shell lip and make sure that it is smooth. Lubricate both parts with PTFE prior to reassembly

PTFE lubricant as required by webbing type bearing

When de-linting, check all areas of the machine. In this instance the motor is in need of a thorough cleaning, not only in order to function correctly, but also for safety

6   Renew any suspect or worn components, overheated/poor connections, worn drive belt(s), tension pulley(s). Ensure correct position and lubricate if required, drum support bearings for wear and heater support brackets/cord.

7   Reassemble the machine ensuring that all wiring, protective covers, supports and seals are correctly positioned and fitted.

8   Test for earth continuity as detailed in the *Basics – electrical* and *Using a Meter* chapters.

9   Refer to *Basics - Electrical* chapter and check condition of both plug and socket, i.e. for overheating, damage and correct supply.

10   Functionally test the machine on an RCD protected supply.

Tumbledry only machines are, in essence simple machines, but it is advisable to make oneself aware of capabilities and limitations

of these machines. When cleaning the filter you may be surprised by the quantity of fluff and lint that it has accumulated. However, if used correctly, tumbledriers do not unduly stress the fabrics they dry. It takes around 1000 tumbledry cycles for an 8 oz (227 grammes) item of clothing to lose 1 oz (28 grammes) in this way.

Remember also that the length of time your drier takes is proportional to the efficiency and spin speed of your washing machine. It is a fact that all fabric contains a degree of moisture when they are dry. Unfortunately it is possible to over-dry clothing in a tumbledrier (or combined machine) and so remove the natural balanced moisture content of the fabric which leads to shrinkage, excessive static and wrinkling that will not iron out. Such problems often lead to the machine being blamed when it is often the user that is at fault by selecting a dry setting that is too long, too high a heat setting or both.

1 This 6 lb load machine has a wrap around outer shell with no obvious means of access

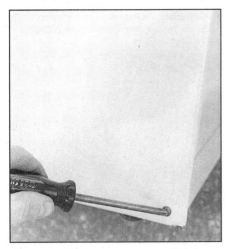

2 First remove the two screws found on the lower edge of each side of the machine

Take into consideration the load content and size when setting the timer, if in doubt, refer to the machine's instruction booklet. This will not only help avoid over-drying problems, but will also save money by reducing the amount of electricity consumed.

Whenever possible, avoid drying woollen items in a tumbledrier as they are particularly prone to the aforementioned problems.

Articles made from or containing foam, sponge, plastic, wax coatings or printed surfaces should not be dried in a tumbledrier as they too can easily be heat damaged and could possibly constitute a fire hazard.

Above all DO NOT use any tumbledrier to dry clothing or materials that have been previously cleaned with flammable spirits or dry cleaning fluids. Ensure any such articles are left in a well-ventilated area to be fully aired and DO NOT subject them to a dry cycle until they have been washed.

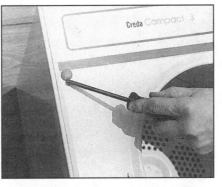

3 Lowering the door exposed a further four screws

4 A note of all screws was made as different sizes were encountered

5 With all eight screws removed, the one piece outer shell of the machine would slide out of position vertically

6 Removing the outer shell exposed the induction motor, drum belt, tension pulley system and door microswitch with actuating arm

7 With the wiring and fixings removed, the front of the machine could be eased forward to expose the front bearing and drum lip

8 Close inspection of the plastic support pads drum lip and sealing felt was made. In this instance they were sound and only required cleaning

12 Although clean and free from lint, the element had a broken ceramic insulator. The TOC also showed signs of contact damage and both parts were duly renewed prior to reassembly

9 Although not as bad as expected, de-linting of the motor, motor relay, microswitch and tension pulley system was required. The drum belt was inspected and found to be OK

13 Reassembly was a simple reversal of the strip down procedure. Ensure that all seals are sound and that all fixing screws are refitted in their original positions. The removable shell locates in slides on both sides and top of the front panel

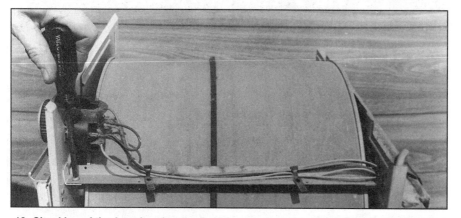

10 Checking of the front bearing required the removal of the bolts from the front of the side stays and the removal of the wiring to the timer (a note of all connections were made prior to removal)

11 The removal of the back panel (held only in position by self tapping screws) allowed access to the fan, heater unit and TOC

Fault finding guide

Most of the fault symptoms listed below will relate to mechanically timed and computer controlled machines both of which are mechanically similar and differ only in the way they are controlled, see *Timers (programmers)* chapter.

Won't work at all

Possible cause	*Action*
Faulty mains lead, plug or socket	See *Plugs and sockets* chapter. Check mains lead for continuity, see *Using a meter.*
Door not closed or latched correctly	Re-close door and ensure it is latched correctly.
Door microswitch failed (open circuit)	Check switch action (audible clicks when door is open/closed) and verify continuity, see *Using a meter*. Inspect closely for overheating and renew if suspect.
Timer fault	Check switching action of manual timers (audible clicks) and continuity. Check for loose selector knob on shaft of timer, i.e. rotating but not setting timer cams or mechanism. On computer controlled machines, check all wiring edge connections to and from the circuit board.

Machine works but no heat

Possible cause	*Action*
Insufficient time set	Remember that the last 15 mins approx. of cycle is a cool tumble on most machines. If a time of less than 15 mins is selected the heater will not be energised, only drum action.
Open circuit auto reset TOC on heater	Check heater TOC for continuity, see *Using a meter*.
Tripped manual reset TOC	Check thoroughly for blockages or restrictions to air intakes, filter and exhaust vents/hoses before resetting TOC.
Broken/open circuit heater element	Check condition of heating element(s) and for continuity. Renew if suspect.
Open circuit exhaust thermostat (if fitted) or thermistors on computer machines	Check for continuity of stat and of wiring.
Faulty timer	On manual timers check action of heater switch and continuity. With computer-controlled machines check all connections to and from the PCB. If OK, possible fault of control board or relay used to switch elements. Eliminate all other possible causes before changing this item.

Heats and trips TOC but no drum action

Possible cause	*Action*
Broken drivebelt	Check belt and renew as required.
Door microswitch open circuit (some models only)	Some machines link the door micro-switch into the motor circuit only. Check door is latched correctly and the switch for continuity and any damage. Renew if suspect.
Belt slipping	Check for overload of clothing and condition of belt, see *Belts* chapter. Check drive pulley of motor, position and tension of jockey pulley(s).
Open circuit motor	Check for free rotation of drum motor, Also, is motor choked with fluff? Clean if required. Check for continuity of TOC and windings. If capacitor start, see *Motors* chapter. If centrifugal start, check action/free movement of this system within the motor. Some early motors had manual reset TOCs. Check motor thoroughly before resetting.
Faulty timer	On manual timers, check action of motor switch and continuity. With computer controlled machines, check all connections to and from the PCB. If OK, possible fault on control board. Eliminate all other possible causes before changing this item.

Works for a while and stops and restarts after 10/15 mins (if manual timer has not timed out)

Possible cause	Action
Motor overheating and tripping its self-setting TOC	Common fault on several machines for various reasons. Check for the following: fluff blockage in and around the motor or air intake grilles. Worn bearings on motor end frames allowing rotor to chafe on stator as motor runs. Loose cooling fan on motor. Motor overheating due to internal wiring fault. Temperamental TOC within motor windings tripping at normal working temperature, often caused by infrequent cleaning of motor. Worn drum bearings slowing both drum and motor causing overheat within the motor. The majority of these problems can be avoided by regular cleaning.

Noisy when in use

Possible cause	Action
Drum bearings worn *Also causes black or other marks being left on clothing dried in the machine.*	Check condition of both front and rear bearings.
Loose fan (pressurised machines) *Also causes poor drying of load.*	Check that large centrifugal fan on main motor is secure on shaft and is not rotating independent of it. Ensure that the fan is not damaged or catching on other items. Renew if suspect.
Fan shaft/bearings worn (suction machines) *Also causes poor drying of load.*	Check for excessive movement of both pulley and shaft. The shaft should be free to rotate without lateral movement. Renew if found to be worn.
Worn or damaged jockey pulley(s)	This type of fault can give rise to a chattering noise if the pulley is damaged or a high pitched squeaking noise if dry. Check for excessive wear on pulley shaft, i.e. lateral movement. Renew if damaged or suspect in any way. If OK, lubricate pulley centre support shaft.
Loose, worn or broken motor mount	Inspect motor mounting closely and renew if suspect.
Loose panels or facia parts	Ensure all covers and panels, etc., are fitted correctly and that all seals (if fitted) are in good order. Make sure all securing screws are fitted and are tight.

Machine works but poor drying performance
Also see second and third causes of *Noisy when in use.*

Possible cause	Action
Too little drying time selected for load	Reset timer for sufficient time to dry the load. See instruction booklet for guide to drying times for your machine.
Incorrect heat setting selected	Check that the low heat setting was not set for fabrics needing extra heat, eg. cottons. See instruction booklet for more information.
Heater self-setting TOC tripping	Check for restrictions in filter and all air vents. If OK, check TOC continuity. If nuisance tripping is suspected (tired TOC), renew with correct replacement.
Open circuit heater	Check condition and continuity of heater.
Vent thermostat fault	Check for continuity.
Recycling of exhaust air	If the machine is not vented correctly, it is possible that the moist air expelled from the exhaust vent could be taken back into the machine via the air intake vent. Check for this action and rectify if found.

Excessively tangled clothing
Tangling of the load is more likely to occur in mono-directional rotating dryers than in reversing models.

Possible cause	Action
Loose or worn drum drivebelt	Check condition of drivebelt, see *Belt* chapter. Ensure correct position of jockey pulley(s) and that the tension spring is OK.
Rotation of drum too slow	Check for overloading and drum bearings for wear or binding which may slow drum rotation.

Computer controlled (electronically controlled) machines are often capable of a degree of self-diagnosis. When a fault or problem occurs, a fault code will be displayed on the LED or LCD display panel. Occasionally the display will describe the fault, but more common is the display of a range of alpha-numerical codes, e.g. F1, E4, etc. The code indicated relates to a particular problem detected by the micro-processor. Reference to the manufacturer's instruction booklet will give the meaning of each code. See *Timers (programmers)* chapter for more detail. The machine will not continue with the remainder of the programme setting until the fault has been rectified. Although the fault display codes may differ from one manufacturer to another, many of the faults they indicate are covered in the Fault finding guide.

Faults, which are uncommon or difficult to isolate, may be caused by poor connections to, or faults within the electronic control boards, or penetration by moisture due to faulty or incorrectly positioned seals. Ensure that all connections, covers and seals are sound and correctly fitted and eliminate all other possible faults before changing a control panel. As stated in the *Timers (programmers)* chapter all circuit testing on micro-processor-controlled machines must be carried out using a low voltage tester, i.e. 1.5V to avoid damage to the electronic components. Do not handle the components of the circuit boards as damage can also be done by static discharged from the fingers.

This type of damage is not always immediately apparent. However, static discharges can corrupt the processor chip's internal programme memory and result in unusual and often intermittent fault symptoms, some time after the initial damage was done. Handle the boards only by the edges if it is absolutely necessary.

Another feature of electronically controlled machines is that a self-diagnostic functional test routing can be initiated. How the sequence is started differs with makes and models and is usually restricted to service personnel. Most machines need to be turned off (at the socket) for at least 45 seconds to clear any previously set programme. Starting the functional test then requires the pressing of two of the selector buttons simultaneously whilst switching the machine on. This particular sequence is used only to highlight the way in which a test sequence may be initiated and does not indicate the way in which any particular machine would operate. Owing to the number of different ways in which this system can be set, it is impossible to give specific details in this text.

Chapter 34

Useful tips and information

An RCD is essential

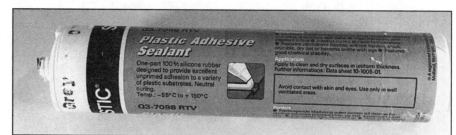

Combined washerdrier machines often require sealant at joints or connection points. Always renew damage or disturbed sealant. Due to the high temperatures and damp conditions, it is essential that only the correct sealant is used

For damage or rust to the shell of your machine, domestic appliance white paint is available. Shown are spray and brush on types

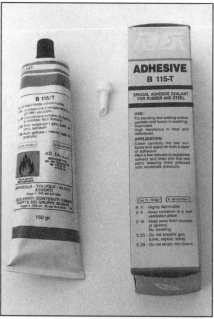

Sealants like the one shown can be used for pressure system hoses and for aiding the fitting and sealing of new hoses, grommets, etc.

Tumble drier bearing faults often require PTFE lubrication. This is available in liquid or spray form

A little washing-up liquid or fabric conditioner can be smeared on grommets or rubber mouldings

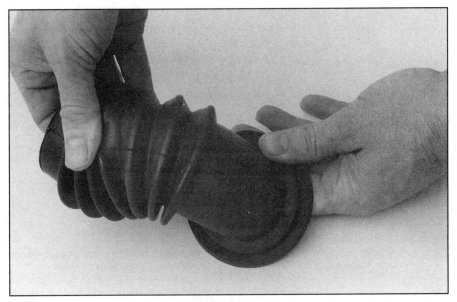

Check all hoses thoroughly for perishing and/or cracking. With corrugated hoses (as shown), stretch the hose to ensure a thorough check. (It is wise to check any new hose before fitting)

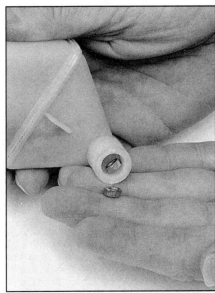

If you have difficulty trying to clean a sealed pressure vessel simply pop in a couple of small nuts, add a little water and shake. Rinse and repeat until the vessel is clean and the water runs clear

Some machines may have a wire surrounding the door seal. This retaining ring can be removed using a flat-bladed screwdriver. The machine shown is a Philips/Whirlpool

When removing the wire door seal securing band it is advisable to wear eye protection. This is also essential when drifting out old bearings. Wear sturdy gloves to protect your hands from the rough casting or other sharp edges when handling cast aluminium pulleys

Access to machines with 50/50 split shells

The photo sequence shows how to remove the rear half of the shell, the front half of the shell can also be removed in a similar manner. The best way to do this is by first removing the rear panel as shown. This allows access to the various internal components that need to be disconnected to allow the front shell to be removed, such as the wiring loom supports and the two screws securing the front shell to the base. The control panel must now be removed from the front of the machine. Start by removing the selector knobs by inserting a small screwdriver in the hole and turning counter-clockwise (this can be a little tricky). Removing the knob front covers exposes the shaft fixings (usually simple nut or plastic locking tab) and carefully remove the control knob components. Now remove any screws/clips holding the front shell to metal cross member (this may include the timer screws/plastic cam clips and remove the soap dispenser drawer. The plastic facia panel can now be removed by disengaging the plastic tabs/clips along the top (holding the facia to the cross member) and similar clips along the bottom edge of the facia. **Note:** *The bottom tabs/clips are accessible through slots along the bottom edge of the facia and disengaged using a flat-bladed screwdriver.*

Next refit the rear shell and its top fixings and carefully lay the machine on its back (with suitable support/protection). Remove the screws securing the top of the front panel and free the door seal from the shell lip after first removing the front clamp band. Next remove the screws securing the door interlock unit and ease the shell upwards and free from the base checking for any other fixing that may need removal/disengaging (due to changes in models etc.).

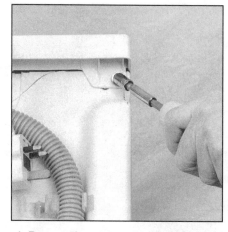

1 Remove the screws securing the work top and slide the top backwards to remove it

2 Locate and unscrew the two plastic caps on each side of the cabinet near the base

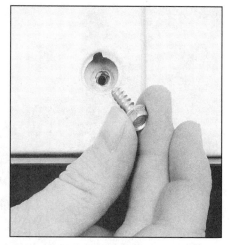

3 Remove the two screws exposed when the caps are removed

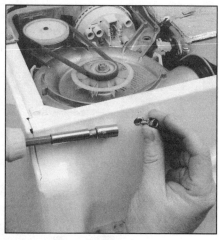

4. Remove the two securing screws at the top rear.
Note: *On combined washerdriers a third screw will need to be removed*

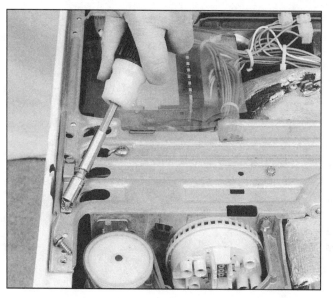

5 At either side of the top of the machine is a metal plate bridging the shell joint. Remove only the rear fixing screws

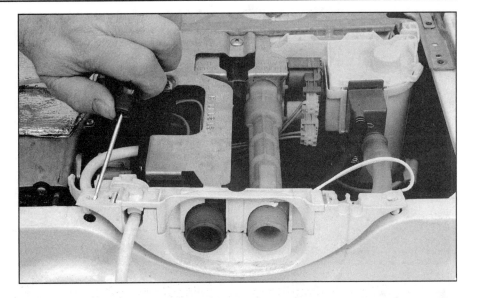

6 Detach the plastic clips holding the cable grip and inlet valve support. Note: *Some models may have screw fixings as well as plastic clips*

7 Carefully ease the rear half of the shell away from the base

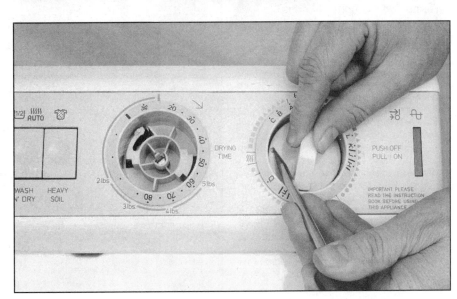

8 A small screwdriver and counter-clockwise twisting action is used to disengage the knob cover on this particular machine

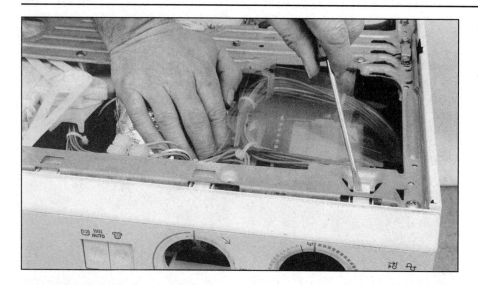

9 The top of this facia is held in place by plastic tabs/clips. Disengage each tab/clip by pressing them and easing the facia forward. Use only enough force to free the fixing, do not over stress the plastic

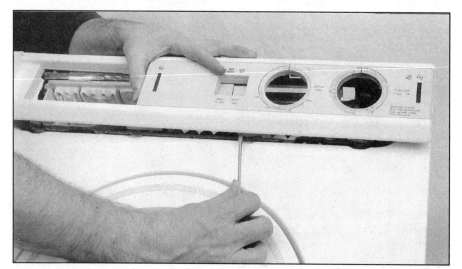

10 The lower facia tabs/clips are accessed through slots along the bottom edge. When all the fixings and the front lip of the door seal have been removed the front shell can be lifted free

Removing the control knobs

One of the most awkward tasks you can come across when repairing your machine is that of removing the control knobs. There are no particular ways in which control knobs are secured and each manufacturer has their own and often individualistic methods. Due to the wide variety of fixing methods used it is not possible to show each and every variation. The range of fixing methods differs from the simplest push-fit versions to rather ingeniously disguised and complex hidden varieties. The following photographs and information is provided to illustrate several of the most common principles and methods of fixing. Use this information along with other instances that are shown throughout this book to access the type of fixing that your particular machine has and to adapt the methods shown for use on machines that vary from these particular types.

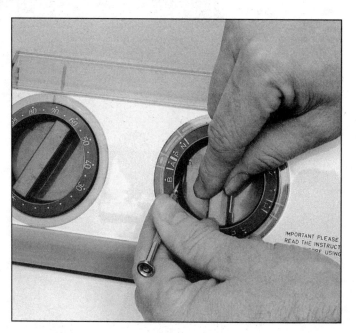

1 With this Zanussi timer knob a small screwdriver is inserted into the hole on the outer edge of the knob inner

2 Press down on the small plastic catch and twist the knob anti-clockwise. Removing the knob/cover exposes the internal fixing securing the indicator barrel to the shaft. In this instance a nut is used but plastic tabs/clips will be found on thermostat and drier timers

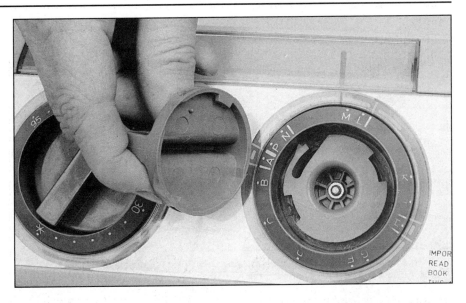

1 Some knobs are a simple push-fit. Often they cannot be pulled off by hand. Remove them using a pair of pliers/grip and a piece of cloth

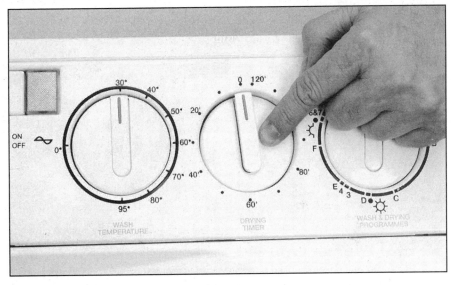

2 Place the cloth between the jaws of the grips and apply firm but not excessive pressure and ease the knob from the shaft

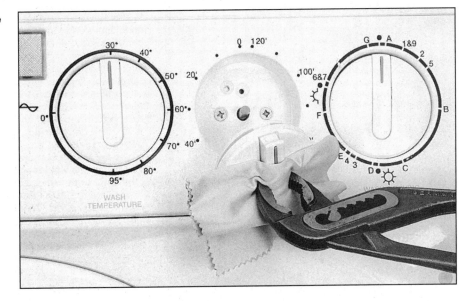

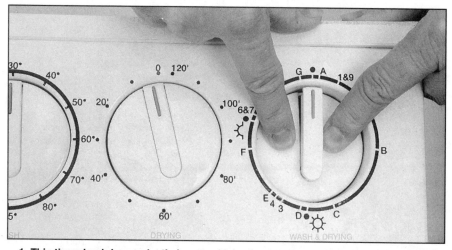

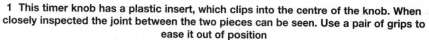

1 This timer knob has a plastic insert, which clips into the centre of the knob. When closely inspected the joint between the two pieces can be seen. Use a pair of grips to ease it out of position

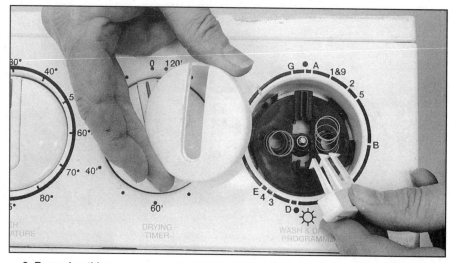

2 Removing this cover exposed a circlip securing the rest of the knob components

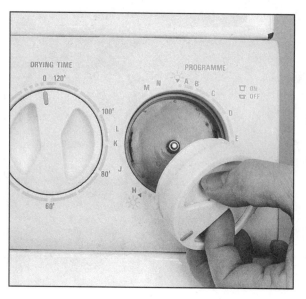

3 This Philips/Whirlpool model has similar looking control knobs. However, both are secured in different ways. The timer control knob is removed by turning the knob backwards, this unlatches the knob from the inner and it can then be removed. However, if you do the same to the thermostat and drier knobs you will break the knob or the shaft. These are only simple push-fit knobs. Note: *This particular style of machine may also be seen under Servis and Electra brand names*

Smells originating from washing machines

Smells in washing machines are commonly caused by leaving the door of the machine closed and/or 'underdosing' (using too little detergent over a period of time). The latter allows the build-up of soiling in the warm, damp atmosphere of the machine, creating an ideal environment for common micro-organisms to multiply and cause a smell.

The micro-organisms responsible are widespread in nature. They can be found in water supplies, but are more likely to originate from the soiled laundry. Normally these organisms would be destroyed in the washing process – either by temperature, or chemically by the bleach components found in some detergents.

Nowadays, many washes are carried out at lower temperatures and many 'Colour' products and liquid detergents do not contain bleach. However, when these products are used according to the manufacturer's instructions, the results are excellent, there is no build-up of soiling in the machine, and there is no likelihood of a smell developing.

If, however, higher temperature washes are never carried out, and a detergent containing a bleach is never used, underdosing will increase the chances of the washing machine developing a smell. This can be prevented by the use of an occasional high temperature wash, or by the occasional use of a detergent which contains a bleaching ingredient.

Where a smell has already developed, carrying out a maintenance wash – high temperature, without a wash load and using a detergent containing a bleaching ingredient can cure this. Alternatively, again without a washload, a final rinse, preferably incorporating a rinse hold, can be carried out, with a domestic hypochlorite bleach such as Domestos being added in place of fabric conditioner.

To help prevent recurrence of the malodour, and also to help to prevent door gaskets becoming sticky, ensure the door gasket of the machine is cleaned at the end of each wash programme and leave the door slightly ajar to allow air circulation to take place for a short while. **Warning:** *It is possible for small children to climb into washing machines and injure themselves ensure measures are taken to avoid this.*

Chapter 35

Buying spare parts

The aim of this manual has been to assist in the DIY repair of both your automatic combined washerdrier or tumbledry only machine. I hope that now, you will not only have a greater knowledge of how these machines work, but also the knowledge to prevent faults.

Above all, I hope that, armed with this information, you will feel confident enough to tackle most (if not all) of the faults that may arise with your machine from time to time.

However, all this knowledge and new found confidence could be wasted if you are unable to locate the spare parts needed to carry out the repair. In the past this would have been a problem, but in recent years the availability of spares have increased for several reasons:

1 The reluctance of people to pay high call out and labour charges for jobs that they feel they can do themselves.

2 The general interest in household DIY coupled with the saving from call out and labour charges, gives a feeling of satisfaction when the job is successfully completed.

3 The growth in size and number of DIY stores in recent years.

4 The improvement in the availability of pre-packed spares.

Many independent domestic appliance companies have been reluctant to supply parts for the DIY market in the past, but the current trend is to expand the amount of pre-packed spares. This has been confirmed by the three biggest independent spares suppliers of genuine and non-genuine (patterned) spares. The range of off the shelf spare parts in both retail outlets and mail order companies is most welcome, and many machine manufacturers who do not have local dealerships will supply parts by post if requested. (Unfortunately this can sometimes be a lengthy process.)

One way of obtaining the parts you require is to find a local spares and repairs dealer through the Yellow Pages or local press. This is best done before your machine develops a fault, as you will then not waste time when a fault arises. In many instances you may possess more knowledge of your machine than the assistant in the shop, so it is essential to take the make, model and serial number of your machine with you to help them locate or order the correct spare part for your requirements.

You may also find it quite helpful to take the faulty part(s) with you if possible, to confirm visually that it is the correct replacement. For instance, most pumps will look the same from memory, although quite substantial differences may be seen if the faulty item is compared with the newly offered item. The casing or mounting plate, etc., may be different. It is most annoying to get home only to find that two extra bolts are required,

Patterned parts

Certain parts that are widely available are marked 'suitable for' or 'to fit'. These are generally called patterned or patent parts. Such terms refer to items or parts that are not supplied by the manufacturer of your machine, but are designed to fit it.

Some are copies of genuine parts and others are supplied by the original parts manufacturer to an independent distributor which are then supplied to the retailer and sold to the customer. This avoids the original manufacturer's mark-up as it is not an official or genuine spare part. This saving is then passed onto the customer.

Many of the appliance manufacturers disliked this procedure in the past, as the parts were of an inferior quality, but this is not the case today as the supply of parts is very big business and quality has improved dramatically. Although great savings can be made, care must be taken not to save money by buying inferior spare parts. Check the quality of the item first wherever possible. A reputable dealer should supply only good quality patterned or genuine parts.

Many of the original machine manufacturers are now discounting their genuine authorised spares to combat the growth in patterned spares. This is very good as it can only benefit you, the customer.

Genuine parts

Parts supplied by the manufacturer of your machine or by their authorised local agent, are classed as 'genuine' and will in many cases, carry the companies trade mark or colours, etc., on the packaging. Many of the parts in today's machines are in fact not produced by the manufacturer of the finished machine, but a sub-contractor who also may supply a distributor of patterned spares with identical items.

Patterned spares producers will only take on items that have volume sales and leave the slow moving items to the original manufacturer of the machine. Generally it is a long procedure to obtain spares direct from the manufacturer as many are unwilling to supply small orders direct to the public. Another system used to deter small orders is to use a *pro-forma* invoicing sheet that will delay the receipt of parts until your cheque has cleared.

With the increase in DIY, manufacturers are slowly changing their view regarding spares supply. This is simply to fend off the patterned spares, by making the original parts more available and competitively priced. Again this will in turn benefit the consumer.

Parts by post

Through the company below you can readily access over 495,000 popular domestic appliance parts and a further half a million by special order. The range of spares covers 90 major manufacturers and brands. Simply write or e-mail your requirements to:

Spares-by-Post
Cranswick
Driffield
East Yorkshire
YO25 9QJ
England
Tel and Fax: 01377 270666
E-mail: sales@spares-by-post.co.uk or dixon@globalnet.co.uk
Website: www.spares-by-post.co.uk

Parts orders and inquiries can be sent by post, fax, telephone or e-mail. All are supplied at competitive prices and payment can be made by cheque or credit/debit card.

Ensure you quote the make, model and serial number of the relevant machine(s).

A range of both DIY and more technical training material (manuals and videos, etc.) is also available. A detailed practical and instructional 55 minute video which complements the information relating to washing machines given in this publication is also available priced at only £14.95 + £3 UK post and packing. For further details and overseas rates please contact/write to the address above.

Exchange reconditioned timers and modules

The company below offers a range of reconditioned timers and speed control units for a wide range of makes and models. For details of the service provided and a catalogue contact:

E.M.W. Electronics
Units 11 & 12 Oaktree Business Park
Mansfield
Nottinghamshire
NG18 3HQ
England
Tel: 01623-647537
Fax: 01623-634200
E-mail: tech@emwelec.co.uk
Website: www.emwelec.co.uk

In conclusion

Finally, the decision between genuine and patterned spares is yours, cost and speed of availability may have to be taken into consideration, but do not forsake quality for a small financial saving

As a guide we have compiled a list of manufacturers' names and telephone numbers where parts may be obtained. It may also be helpful to check your local Yellow Pages.

Further information

Make	Telephone No.
AEG	01753 872 325
Ariston	01895 858277 (or see Yellow Pages under Merloni Domestic Appliances)
Asko (was Asea)	0181 568 4666
Bauknecht	01345 898 989
Bendix	Yellow Pages
Bosch	0990 678 910
Candy	0990 990 011
Colston	see Ariston (above)
Creda	Yellow Pages
Electra	see Electricity Board
Electrolux	01325 300 660
Fagor	01245 329 483
Frigidaire	01977 665 590
Hotpoint	Local Directory
Hoover	Yellow Pages
Indesit	01895 858 277 (or see Yellow Pages under Merloni Domestic Appliances)
Kelvinator	0151 334 2781
Miele	Yellow Pages
Merloni	01895 858 277
Philco	0181 902 9626
Philips (now Whirlpool)	01345 898 989
Servis	0121 526 3199
Whirlpool (was Philips)	01345 898 989
Zanussi	Yellow Pages/Local Directory
Zerowatt	0151 334 2781

NOTE: This information was correct at the time of publication, but may change with the course of time.

Chapter 36
Know your machine

Most of us, you'll agree, would be completely lost without the range of gadgets we've become accustomed to using every day. Learning to take advantage of these time saving appliances, particularly your combined washerdrier or tumbledrier, will give you the freedom to look after yourself and your family in more important ways.

With our special needs in mind, washing machine manufacturers have developed the combined washerdrier and tumbledry only machines to help in both washing and drying our clothes.

Used properly, both types of machines can provide a thorough method of washing and drying. The special wash action of the front loading combined machines with their horizontal rotating drum mechanism creates sufficient agitation to effectively remove all dirt particles and even stubborn stains. However, it is important to use the correct types of washing powders/liquids in these machines. The low suds washing powder recommended by many major machine manufactures is Persil Automatic. The free movement given by the controlled lather level allows the clothes to be washed thoroughly and efficiently to give perfect results across all machine programmes, from a cotton boil wash to a cool programme for silk and woollens. Automatic machines will also ensure that sufficient rinses are made to

remove the dirty wash solution leaving your clothes completely clean, fresh and cared for.

Overloading your machine will greatly reduce cleaning efficiency, as the free movement of the clothes will be restricted. Your machine has a maximum load capacity which should not be exceeded.

This handy table over the page will help you check your dry weight loads and was compiled with the help of Lever Bros.

Rule of thumb

To help in assessing the correct wash load, the drawing illustrates the maximum dry load size per selected programme.

A Woollen and other fine fabrics requiring gentle washing – only a quarter of the drum should be occupied.

B Synthetic and man made fibres requiring delicate washing – only half the drum space should be occupied.

C Cottons and robust fabrics requiring higher temperatures and normal wash action – can occupy a greater proportion of the drum, leaving approximately a hand's width space at the top.

This information is a guide only and the spaces represent the space left when the clothes are loaded normally. Do not compress the load to achieve the recommended amount of vacant space.

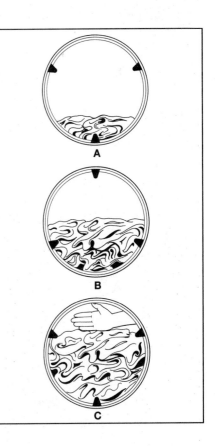

Clothes

Blouse	cotton		150g	(5oz)
	other		100g	(3½oz)
Dress	cotton		500g	(1lb 2oz)
	other		350g	(12oz)
Dressing Gown			700g	(1lb 8oz)
Jeans			700g	(1lb 8oz)
10 Nappies			1000g	(2lb 3oz)
Nightdress			150g	(5oz)
Pyjamas	cotton		350g	(12oz)
Shirt	cotton		300g	(10oz)
	other		200g	(7oz)
Skirt			200g	(7oz)
Suit, bulked polyester			1500g	(3lb 5oz)
Sweater	wool		400g	(14oz)
	other heavy		350g	(12oz)
	lightweight		200g	(7oz)
Tracksuit			1000g	(2lb 3oz)
Teeshirt			125g	(4½oz)
Vest			125g	(4½oz)

Household items

Bedspread	candlewick	(D)	3000g	(6lb 10oz)
		(S)	2000g	(4lb 6oz)
Blanket	wool	(D)	2000g	(4lb 6oz)
		(S)	1500g	(3lb 5oz)
	acrylic	(D)	1500g	(3lb 5oz)
		(S)	1000g	(2lb 3oz)
Cot Sheet			200g	(7oz)
Duvet Cover	cotton	(D)	1500g	(3lb 5oz)
	other	(D)	1000g	(2lb 3oz)
Pillow			900g	(2lb)
Pillowslip			125g	(4½oz)
Tablecloth	large		700g	(1lb 8oz)
	small		250g	(9oz)
Tea Towels			100g	(3½ oz)
Towel	bath		700g	(1lb 8oz)
	hand		250g	(9oz)
Sheet	cotton	(D)	1000g	(2lb 3oz)
		(S)	750g	(1lb 10oz)
	other	(D)	500g	(1lb 2oz)
		(S)	350g	(12oz)

D = Double   S = Single

Chapter 37
Understanding the wash process

In order to ensure good wash results, the four FACTORS OF WASHING must be borne in mind – TIME, TEMPERATURE, AGITATION, DETERGENT. If one is to be reduced then another may need to be increased to compensate.

Important points to remember are:

TEMPERATURE AND AGITATION should never be increased beyond that recommended on the garment's wash code label.

TIME can be increased by soaking before or during the wash. **Note:** *some fabrics should not be soaked – check the label of the garment.*

DETERGENCY is constantly being increased as technological developments make it possible to include new and more effective ingredients in the formulation, ensuring cleaning products really do give best results for today's wash.

The composition of the wash load is constantly changing. Today there are more multi-coloured articles than ever before. Man-made fibres are often mixed with natural fibres, e.g. Polyester Cotton. This means that wash temperatures have had to be reduced to prevent any damage to colour or fibres. Currently over 70% of washing is done at 50°C or below.

The WASH PROCESS is also affected by what goes into the machine – WATER, WASH LOAD AND DETERGENT.

WATER – Too high a temperature may cause damage, e.g., colour transfer and creasing. Hard water means that extra detergent is required. Low water pressure can lead to dispensing problems when the detergent is dispensed through the dispenser drawer of the machine. In some areas water contamination in the form of peat, iron or other naturally occurring minerals can cause discoloration to the wash load, or even to parts of the machine, such as the door gasket.

WASH LOAD – The wash load has to be considered carefully to ensure that the correct fabric types are being put together, e.g., cottons and linens; synthetics; machine washable woollens. The colour and size of the load, together with the nature of the soiling, all have to be taken into account. Help is at hand when sorting the wash load if all the wash codes, found on the garment labels, are followed. These advise maximum temperatures and agitation recommended for that particular type of fabric. If the fabrics require different wash conditions then it is advisable to split the load and perhaps use the half load facility on the machine if available. This will ensure better wash results.

DETERGENT – Detergent is available in either a powder, tablets or liquid form. These detergents are then split into high suds, e.g., Persil and Stergene - or low suds, e.g. Persil Automatic and Radion. High suds detergent are for use in twin tub, tub type top loaders and hand washing. Low suds detergents may be used in any type of washing machine as well as for hand washing. The lather level in low suds detergent is controlled so that the vigorous wash action of a front loader does not cause too much foam to be created. Most low lather, or automatic detergents, are now available in concentrated powder or liquid forms.

A detergent, either powder or liquid, is a complex mixture of ingredients, designed to help wet the fabric, remove soiling and suspend the soiling in solution until the machine pumps out. Ingredients are included to cope with every type of soiling found on the average wash load. Also built into the formulation are ingredients designed to soften the water, protect the machine, prolong it's life and efficiency.

Dosage of detergent is therefore crucial. It is important that the dosage information on the individual packets and bottles is followed in order to achieve perfect wash results. The amount of detergent required can only be reduced if the water is soft, smaller loads are being washed or if the items are only lightly soiled.

During the final rinse a fabric conditioner, such as Comfort, should be added to the wash load. Freshness, less creasing, easier ironing and improved spin efficiency are benefits of using a fabric conditioner.

In order to obtain the best possible wash results from a machine, it is important to follow the machine manufacturer's instructions, the care labels on the items being washed, and the information on the detergent packs. These guidelines will help to ensure successful washing, time and time again.

Choosing the correct detergent

Over the last few years there has been a significant increase in the number of different detergents on the market. People have realised that one product cannot necessarily deal with all their laundry needs. The garments making up today's washload have become more varied in terms of fabric type, and colour. Also, types of stain and soiling differ.

People are increasingly choosing to buy two or three different types of detergent to meet their different washing requirements. For example a typical mix may be:

1   A biological powder for whites and heavily stained articles; e.g. Persil Performance or Radion with Sunfresh Automatic.
2   A colour liquid for dark coloured clothing, or matching household linen; e.g. Persil Colour Care Liquid.
3   A light-duty product for delicate garments made of wool or silk; e.g. Persil Finesse.

There are a number of decisions to be made before picking one or more detergents to suit the required criteria:

1   Is an automatic product needed?
2   Is biological or non-biological detergent preferred?
3   Would powder, tablets or liquid be the best choice?
4   What benefits would a concentrated product give?
5   When should a colour product be considered?

Automatic or 'low foaming' detergent

Traditionally, detergents such as Lux Flakes, Persil and Surf for twin tubs produced high foam levels, and the foam level was used as an indicator that sufficient detergent was present in the wash solution.

As front loading, and top loading-type machines now dominate the washing machine market, the majority of detergents now on sale are, 'Automatic' or low foaming. A drum-type machine cannot cope with too much foam, and automatic detergents contain ingredients to prevent excessive foam being produced in the wash. 'Automatic' detergents can be used in any type of clothes washing situation – machine or hand wash. If automatic detergents are used in a twin tub or Hotpoint top loading machine, the dosage given on the pack should be approximately doubled as the water capacity and size of wash load is much greater with this type of machine. All concentrated detergents are low foaming.

Biological or non-biological?

Biological detergents contain enzymes, non-biological detergents do not.

What are enzymes?

Enzymes are natural substances which help to break down different types of soil into smaller particles, making the task of removing stains easier for the detergent.

There can be up to 3 different types of enzyme in a biological detergent, each working on a different type of stain:

• lipase – helps break down fatty stains such as butter or margarine
• protease – helps break down protein based stains such as blood or gravy
• amylase – helps break down starch based stains such as chocolate

Biological detergents are more effective than non-biological at removing the above types of stain. In addition they are especially effective at lower temperature washing i.e. 40-60°C which means both energy and money can be saved by their use on a regular basis. Garments made from delicate fibres, however, such as wool and silk, should not be washed in a biological detergent. Persil Finesse has been especially developed for fabrics of this type. It is fair to say that it is not possible to formulate a detergent which will be suitable for everyone under all conditions, some people with sensitive skin often prefer to use a non-biological detergent.

Liquid or powder?

Liquids are easy to pour out and dissolve quickly. They also have the added benefit of being able to be used neat to pre-treat difficult stains (though colour fastness should be checked first on a piece of the fabric that does not show). Most powders (except 'colour-care' products) include a bleach ingredient for tackling stains like fruit juice, tea, coffee and wine. Liquid detergents do not contain bleaching agents, so are not as efficient as powders at removing this type of stain, particularly on higher temperature washes. Both powders and liquids are now available in refill bags or cartons helping to reduce the waste of packaging materials.

Concentrated or conventional?

A recent development has been to introduce concentrated variants of familiar brands which are now available in powder form, biological, non-biological and colour.

Concentration is all about using fewer resources, fewer chemicals per wash, reducing the impact of manufacturing and transporting the goods, and having to produce, carry, store and dispose of less packaging. They are therefore more acceptable in terms of the environment.

Concentrated powder detergents, will normally give the best results when dispensed using an 'in-the-machine' dosing device, usually a plastic ball. This ensures that all of the detergent is used in the wash and none is wasted, either by remaining in the dispensing drawer, or being washed directly into the sump at the base of the machine.

Special colour detergents

The most recent types of detergent to be launched are those for 'Colour Care'.

Colour detergents are biological, and come as powders or liquids.

The other products previously mentioned are formulated to give maximum cleaning under the toughest wash conditions. Some contain bleach, which can fade certain dark colours, and some contain optical brightening agents which can cause shade changes in some pastel coloured garments. Colour detergents are formulated without bleach or optical brightening agents.

Whilst these products are designed to take care of coloured articles in the washload, they should not be confused with 'light duty' wash products, such as Stergene, Lux Flakes or Persil Finesse, which are suitable for delicate fabrics like wool or silk.

Detergent tablets

The biggest revolution in the use of laundry detergents for more than a decade has been the advent of detergent tablets.

They have been developed in direct response to customer wishes for a more convenient washing product. The new tablets are simpler, less messy and less wasteful than existing products because there is no need to measure out detergent. They also offer great value for money, especially for people who currently use too much powder.

A net is provided for the tablets before being placed on top of the washload inside the machine. Using a net is the best way to make a washing tablet disperse evenly and thoroughly all around the wash. Two tablets normally provide the correct dosage for most wash conditions.

Fabric conditioners

Liquid

Liquid fabric conditioners are added to the final rinse of the washing process to give unbeatable softness to the wash load. The recommended dosage of Comfort is 110mls for regular, and 27mls for concentrated. Full information on the use is given on the packaging.

Tumbledrier sheets

These sheets are placed on top of the washload in the tumbledrier at the start of the drying cycle. Of the 23 million homes in the UK, over 60% have either a tumbledrier or washerdrier. Fabric conditioner sheets can be successfully used in the majority, of these machines. There are, however, a few exceptions. Tumbledrier sheets are made of polyester and are coated with active ingredients to impart fragrance, soften the fabric and reduce static electricity. This can only be done if the tumbledrier sheet is able to tumble freely inside the drum, touching the load as it tumbles and dries. Research has shown that the sheets behave in this manner in all washerdriers, condenser driers and almost all vented tumbledriers. However, due to the position of the filter in some vented tumbledriers, the sheet may position itself near the filter and remain there for the duration of the drying cycle. Although no harm is done to the dryer or the fabrics being dried, the tumbledrier sheet cannot, in this position, impart the softness, perfume, and anti-static properties for which it is being used. Rather than have consumers disappointed with the performance of the tumbledrier sheet it is suggested that they are not used in these machines.

Some of the UK produced machines are 5 kg vented tumbledriers, sold under the Hotpoint, Creda, and (most) Electra brand names since 1991, and whose filter is located immediately below the porthole, at the front of the machine. All other Hotpoint, Creda and Electra driers i.e. 5 kg manufactured before 1991, 3 kg or condenser driers of any age, and all washerdriers, are fully compatible with tumbledrier sheets.

For further information on the use of tumbledrier sheets or fabric conditioners in general can normally be obtained from the manufacturer of the product – see label for details.

Chapter 38

Identifying poor washing problems

Effectively diagnosing the root cause of poor wash problems will help plan the correct course of action needed to alleviate or rectify the problem. Remember, not all problems are a direct result of mechanical failure or malfunction of the appliance. There are a whole range of external criteria that can affect the washing process and lead to poor wash results. Without a thorough understanding of the washing process it is only too easy to embark upon a random stripdown of a correctly functioning machine only to find sometime later that it was an external problem. Worse still you may decide it is time to change your old machine for a new one only to find that the poor wash problem remains!

The following help and advice is a direct result of experience and will be of help in three ways: –

1 To help identify the cause of existing problems.
2 To help prolong the life of the appliance.
3 To give advice on how to achieve the best wash results.

It is essential to understand that any washing machine new or old cannot produce the best possible wash results without the correct use of the detergent. In addition to poor wash results premature failure of components may also result from the incorrect use of detergent or the bad habits of the user!

To help in developing the fault finding process the following information has been split into four sections:

1 How to get the best possible wash results.
2 Help when things go wrong.
3 How to prolong the life of your machine.
4 Major ingredients in detergents and their functions.

How to get the best results

Always ensure that the appliance is correctly installed, set correctly and is being used in accordance with the manufacturers instructions.

Ensure – the correct type of detergent is being used

For front loading washing machines. The detergent, whether powder, liquid or tablet must be specially formulated for use in automatic washing machines. This means it produces a controlled amount of lather. Non-automatic detergents will give too much lather, reducing the agitation of the washload and leading to poor cleaning.

Ensure – the correct amount of detergent is being used

The use of insufficient detergent will lead to poor wash results, and over a period of time will cause damage to the machine itself. Dosage is determined by the size of the washload, the degree of soiling and water hardness. Details of the recommended dosage can be found on the packs; refer to this for guidance. Underdosing will cause garments to dull in colour as soil removed during the washing process is redeposited onto the load. Too little detergent can also mean that stains may not be fully removed. Heavily soiled items should be given a pre-wash to remove most of the soiling prior to the main wash. Good quality detergents contain many ingredients which are not only important for cleaning but also protect components within the machine.

TO MAINTAIN OPTIMUM CLEANING IT IS VITAL THAT DOSAGE IS NOT REDUCED TOO MUCH

Ensure – the detergent is being measured correctly

The instructions on the pack will have details of the correct dosage for the varying levels of soiling. Some concentrated powders and concentrated liquid detergents must be poured into a dosing 'bubble' and placed in the drum of the machine on top of the washload. Tablet detergents are placed inside a mesh bag.

Ensure – the machine is not overloaded

The clothes should be placed one at a time into the drum leaving a section of the back of the drum visible or there is a danger of the machine being overloaded. Man-made fibres are lighter in weight than cottons therefore the weight of a man-made washload must be reduced or the volume of these fibres can lead to reduced agitation and therefore poor wash results.

Ensure – the correct wash programmes are being used

It is important that clothes are washed at the temperature and level of agitation recommended on the garments label especially for synthetic fabrics and machine washable wool. Remember Quick Wash programmes are only for lightly soiled garments. The best wash results are achieved by using the programme recommended on the garment label.

Ensure – correct rinsing takes place

Soiling and detergent residues are removed by rinsing the clothes. Several rinses are necessary to do this effectively. Water taken into the machine mixes thoroughly with the clothes diluting the concentration of the soiling and detergent present. Each rinse further dilutes the soiling and detergent until the garments have been thoroughly rinsed. It is important that you allow the machine to carry out ALL rinses, and that you do not advance the programme during the rinsing stage. Paradoxically, reducing detergent dosage does not generally lead to improved rinsing because, at low dosage, more soil (and detergent residues) are redeposited onto the load (see *Ensure the correct amount of detergent is being used* above). If you are particularly concerned about efficient rinsing (for example because of allergic sensitivity), then the best solution is to give extra rinses and reduce load size.

Fabric conditioner is added during the final rinse to eliminate static, soften the wash and leave a fresh perfume on the clothes.

Over-filling the fabric conditioner compartment can cause premature dispensing of fabric conditioner due to syphoning. This may cause mild blue or peach coloured staining. Conditioner stains should be treated by gentle rubbing with a bar of soap, followed by re-washing in the usual way.

Cloudiness of the rinse water can often be mistaken for poor rinsing. In reality the opposite is often the case as turbidity (cloudiness) during the rinse agitation cycle relates to the efficiency of the machine in removing the soil residues from the washload and is perfectly normal.

Help for when things have gone wrong

Removing redeposition

Regular underdosing or overloading machines can lead to a build-up of soiling on the inner surfaces of the machine. Reintroducing the correct wash procedures can release this build-up which may then be redeposited onto or stain the wash load. In other words the clothes may come out of the wash worse than when they went in.

To avoid this potential problem after identifying an underdosing or overloading problem carry out a maintenance wash to clean the inside of the machine prior to using the machine with a wash load. A 'maintenance wash' consists of selecting the highest temperature programme, using the recommended detergent dose but NO WASHLOAD in the drum.

In situations where redeposition has already occurred the clothes will need to be re-washed using the recommended wash programme and detergent dosage. However, if the soiling is particularly heavy, it may take several washes before any significant improvement is noticed. **Note:** *When efforts to the correct washing procedures are made do not expect instant results. The conditions that caused the problem may have been present for some considerable length of time and in such instances visible improvements may also take a little time. Improvement may be gradual and take several washes – this may lead you to think that nothing is happening and revert back to the old system. Avoid this problem by holding back one of the original items (it helps if it can be one of two similar items), place it in a drawer and do not wash or use it. After five or six normal washes you can compare your 'control' item with those that have been washed correctly. The comparison can often be quite remarkable.*

Washing at lower temperatures

It is now common practice to mix items in the washload, this can be done safely as long as the wash codes are followed. Most fabrics that require maximum agitation can be mixed together but must be washed at the lower temperature i.e. wash a mixture of 90°C, 60°C and 40°C labels at 40°C. Fabrics needing medium agitation can be mixed in the same way 50°C and 40°C, wash at 40°C. However, if fabrics are never washed at their maximum recommended temperature, then stain removal can be a problem. The occasional wash at the full-recommended temperature should ensure perfect results. Care should be taken if white fabric is included in the washload when mixing loads.

Causes of staining during washing

Occasionally, marks may appear on garments during the washing process. In such instances it is all too easy to blame the machine for causing the marks as they were not visible on the garments when they were put into the machine. The following list of common causes of staining is provided to assist you in the correct diagnosis of staining and if used correctly it will help avoid unnecessary repairs to your machine.

	See cause
BLACK/GREY MARKS	DJ
BLUE STAINING	AI
BROWN STAINING	AB
GREEN STAINING	AF
GREY STAINING	ACDFI
LIGHTER PATCHES	CG
WHITE/GREY SPECKS	HI
PINK STAINING	ABCD
RUST STAINING	E

Causes of stains which occur during the wash

A Dye transfer

The most frequent cause of coloured staining is from dye that has leaked in the wash solution. This dye can then be transferred onto other articles in the wash. Nylon and elasticated items tend to pick up loose dye easily. Loose dye may also remain in the sump of a machine and contaminate the next load. Tiny coloured fibres can also attach themselves to other articles being washed, e.g. wool from a blanket onto a sheet, fibres from a sweater onto a shirt.

Treatment. Dye solvent, e.g. Dylon or one of the products from the Stain Devils range may be required.

Prevention. Test new items for colourfastness and never mix white and coloured items. Carry out an occasional maintenance wash, especially before washing valued items. **Note:** *Nylon is particularly good at picking up loose dye.*

B Metallic compounds in wash water

Iron in the water can cause brown, pink or orange marks. Copper causes grey/green stains. The spots often occur in the same pattern as the holes in the drum of the machine.

Treatment. Re-wash when conditions causing contamination have been corrected, e.g. road works, heavy rainfall. **Note:** *Periods of drought can make contamination occur. If possible reduce the spin speed and dosage of fabric conditioner as metallic particles may adhere to the conditioner on the garments.*

Prevention. As above under treatment.

Footnote: *Discoloration of the washload (or even parts of the machine) due to water contamination can be difficult to verify because by the time the problem is identified, the water supply may be back to normal.*

C Chemicals in the wash water

Some chemicals which may already be on the garment can be colourless but react with alkalinity of the wash solution and show up as staining, e.g. pink staining on baby clothes can be caused by phenolphthalein in teething powder. Lighter patches occurring on pillows and sheets can be caused by skin preparations, acne or hair treatments, with the alkalinity of the wash solution. Grey/brown staining can be caused by a high level of grease on garments, e.g. clear petroleum jelly on babies nappies may be contaminated by soiling from the rest of the wash. If this type of redeposition occurs, the grey/brown stains may be in the form of grease balls which collect in the corners of articles such as pillowcases, shirt collars, etc. This type of fault can give a very greasy feel to the stain. **Note:** *Grease balls can also be affected (spread out) by the heat from ironing. In addition to marks on garments burnt residues may build up on the sole plate of the iron.*

Treatment. 'Grease balling' can be removed by re-washing with sufficient detergent. Where a lightening effect has occurred, the damage is usually permanent, Stain Devils may help to remove some of the stains.

Prevention. Pre-treat heavily soiled areas prior to washing or add a pre-wash to the normal washing programme. Try to prevent skin preparations such as acne and hair treatments from coming into contact with fabrics.

D Mildew

Mildew is a mould growth which develops usually on unwashed articles which have been left damp for a length of time. It may also show as pink or red spots, as well as the more usual grey.

Treatment. For white cottons use a very dilute hypochlorite bleach solution – add 1 eggcup full of household bleach (such as Domestos) to 1 gallon of water in a bucket or bowl and mix thoroughly before adding the affected article. For coloureds, rub the affected area with hard soap and allow it to dry naturally before carrying out a pre-wash.

Prevention. Wash damp clothes as soon as possible to prevent mildew growth. Do not store clothes in the damp atmosphere of the washing machine. Ensure washed articles are dried thoroughly before they are stored.

E Rust marks or iron mould

The most common causes of rust stains are direct contact with rusted metals (screws, nails, etc. left in pockets or lodged within the appliance), rusted flakes from water pipe, blood stains (from the iron content), some red wines, medicines, tonics and certain inks.

Treatment. Mild stains can be removed with lemon juice applied to the stain and ironed through a damp cloth. For heavier stains use a proprietary rust remover such as those found in the Stain Devils range is recommended.

Prevention. Pre-treat blood, wine, medicine and ink stains prior to washing.

F Copper staining

Grey/green staining is often the result of a high level of copper in the wash solution from new plumbing or filings on work overalls.

Treatment. Needs specialist treatment. Dry cleaners may be able to help.

Prevention. Loose copper particles that may be within the pipe work after repairs have been carried out should be completely flushed out of the system prior to use. Overalls (especially those of plumbers) should be shaken to remove copper particles prior to washing.
Note: *A high copper content in the wash may also have a damaging effect on the door gasket (see How to prolong the life of the machine).*

G Uneven fluorescers take-up

This problem often makes areas of the fabric appear 'extra white' making the original whiteness look 'yellow' by comparison. This cannot occur during the normal washing process. **Note:** *Most leading washing products contain fluorescers.*

Treatment. Constant re-washing may remove fluorescer, however in some cases the staining may be permanent.

Prevention. This problem can arise if neat liquid detergent is allowed to dry on damp washing. When using liquid detergent for pre-treatment, the item must be washed immediately. DO NOT use undissolved detergent powder directly on wet washing.

H Hard water deposits

In very hard water areas, calcium in the water supply can show up on dark items as small white/grey specks. These are often mistaken for undissolved detergent powder.

Treatment. Re-wash using sufficient detergent. May be necessary to carry out a maintenance wash with detergent but no wash load. This will help remove the build-up of hard water deposits from inside the machine.

Prevention. Use recommended dose of detergent for hard water area.

Note: *Hard water deposits can shorten the life of the heating element.*

I Undiluted fabric conditioner

Blue staining may occur if undiluted fabric conditioner has come into contact with the washing. This may happen if the conditioner is prematurely dispersed. These stains are not expected to be permanent.

Treatment. Rub the affected area gently with a bar of soap and re-wash in the usual way.

Prevention. Always ensure the conditioner is diluted before use. This is done automatically in most front loading automatics. Ensure that the fabric conditioner compartment is not overfilled as this may cause the conditioner to be dispensed prematurely.

J Door seal marks

Marks caused by the door seal normally have a 'rubbery' feel and are the same colour as the seal. The most likely cause is serious overloading or by an article being trapped between the rotating drum and the stationary seal.

Treatment. Very difficult to remove. Dry cleaners may be able to help.

Prevention. Don't overload the machine. Reduce load for man-made fibres. Ensure the washload is placed well into the drum before door is closed and ensure nothing is trapped e.g. buttons, shirt cuffs, collars, etc. See notes on door gaskets in *How to prolong the life of the machine*. Also ensure that the machine is level to prevent clothes in the drum from riding forward.

Fair wear and tear

Occasionally physical damage to washed garments is blamed on the machine when in fact it is due to fair wear and tear. Marks that occur during the wash may follow a pattern and may be limited to parts of the garment such as the collar and cuffs of a man's shirt. However, if water contamination or dye transfer had caused the problem, then the marks would be across the whole garment. Therefore in this instance the indications are that the cause of the problem was most likely on the garment prior to washing.

Pulled threads on knitted or loosely woven garments are often caused by jewellery or buckles and zips on other garments in the same washload. Fabric damage to the backs of shirts/sweaters is mostly the result of rough surfaces on chairs. Inspect as many items as possible to see if a pattern of damage is present.

Many synthetic fabrics will 'pill' (go bobbly) due to friction caused when the garment is being worn. A good example of this is the 'baby grow' all-in-one suit. As the child crawls the fabric is rubbed against the carpet or the underside of the sleeve of a jumper. The same type of damage can be caused in the washing machine if the wrong wash agitation programme is selected, for instance if synthetic items are washed as cotton items. **Note:** *Synthetic fibres are weak when wet and are therefore more susceptible to damage. Care must be taken when washing and then handling wet synthetic fabrics.*

When physical damage has occurred to garments, careful assessment of the problem must be made.

How to prolong the life of the machine

How long a particular machine will last depends on a number of factors, the most important being that the machine is being used for the purpose for which it was designed. Many small businesses (hairdressers, care homes, etc.) purchase domestic clothes washing machines and tumbledriers when in reality they should use their commercial and more robust counterparts. Factors which most often lead to a reduction in the life of the machine generally relate directly to the way in which it is used and the level of attention given to correct use and maintenance.

Excessive lather. Excessive lather in the wash can lead to poor wash results, due to the reduction in agitation given to the washing, as the foam provides a cushioning effect. It can also result in over-foaming and malfunction of the drain pump, should it become 'locked' with lather. Modern machines with narrow drum-to-outer tub gaps can also be affected by foam locking due to excessive lather caused by overdosing of detergent. Excessive foam between the drum and outer tub can create a braking effect which in severe cases can cause the wash motor to over heat and trip its internal TOC. Blocking of the pressure vessel resulting in nuisance tripping of the pressure switch may also occur. A wide range of problems may ensue, depending on the make and model of machine and computer controlled machines may terminate the wash programme altogether. To avoid the problem ensure the correct amount of high quality automatic detergent is used as they contain ingredients to suppress lather.

Pre-treating heavy stains with dish washing up liquid, or chemicals within the soiling can also lead to excessive lather. The use of water softening additives can also lead to excessive lather as they can lead the user in to believing that it is possible to reduce the amount of detergent required. Where a domestic water softener is installed in the house it should be recommended that the washing machine is connected to the mains supply, and not to the artificially softened water, or excessive foaming, even when using an automatic detergent may occur. In extreme circumstances, in very soft water areas, excessive foaming may occur when a vigorous wash action has been selected and serious underdosing of detergent has taken place.

Door seal deterioration. Rubber is naturally an unstable substance. For this reason, rubber items that are intended to give long service have special stabilisers added to them prior to moulding. Washing machine door seals fall into this category. In normal use, the stabilisers remain in the rubber for between 4-6 years, protecting it from decomposition. However the rate of decomposition of the door seal fitted to a machine is influenced by the original quality of the gasket, by the frequency of machine use, and to some extent by the number of higher temperature wash cycles used (higher temperatures tend to increase the rate of decomposition). Most high temperature or 'boil'

washes are for babies nappies, where hygiene is as important as good wash results. Modern biological detergents can now achieve 'Boil wash' hygiene at temperatures as low as 50°C. In addition to time and temperature there are certain substances that can have adverse affects on the composition of the door seal and greatly reduce its working life. These substances fall into 3 main categories.

a) Oils, fats, grease and solvents such as polish, baby ointments, petroleum jelly, solvents on working clothes, etc. Many of these substances are absorbed into the rubber causing it to swell and deform whilst others cause the stabilisers to migrate from the rubber, leaving it sticky to the touch.

b) Metal in the wash water (copper and iron). Copper is a known catalyst of many chemical reactions. In other words, high concentrations of metals like copper and iron can speed up the decomposition processes. In addition to increasing decomposition, copper and iron in the wash can also cause discoloration of the door seal.

c) Pre-treatment products. The use of certain pre-treatment products containing high levels of non-ionic detergent or hypochlorite-based bleaching agents can also accelerate door gasket decomposition. This most often occurs when articles treated with these types of products are placed directly into the machine without first rinsing to remove the pre-treatment product, e.g. nappy sterilising solutions. Another common cause is the use of clothes previously used with bleach solutions being used to mop and wipe the door seal after use. This simple action can greatly reduce the life of a door seal.

To prolong the life of the door gasket:

1 Always use recommended dosage of detergent, taking the size of load, degree of soiling and water hardness into account.

2 For heavily soiled articles use the pre-wash facility.

3 Always dry the door gasket after use with a clean bleach-free cloth and if possible leave the door of the machine slightly open to allow circulation of air. **Note:** *Take care to avoid creating a hazard and to prevent children from gaining access to the drum of the machine.*

Constant overloading. Overloading of the machine can result in poor washing, rinsing and spin efficiency and can also lead to machine damage. Remember when washing man-made fibres the load must be reduced. In extreme cases of overloading, the pressure of the fabric against the door of the machine can lead to marks being left on the washload from the door gasket.

Enamel and aluminium alloys. Heavy duty washing products create an alkaline wash solution which can slowly disssolve enamel and aluminium components. High quality detergents contain an ingredient which chemically prevents this happening, thereby ensuring that components such as vitreous enamel outer tubs, aluminium alloy back plates or drum spiders, etc. do not fail prematurely. **Note:** *Protection will only occur when sufficient detergent is used. As mentioned previously it is inadvisable to reduce the dosage of detergent products especially where alkaline water softeners (some wash additives), which contain no corrosion inhibitor, are included in the wash.*

Heating elements. The formation of scale on a heating element can reduce its efficiency and lead to premature failure. Hard water requires the full dosage of detergent to prevent heater scale. Reducing the amount of detergent will reduce the life of the heating element.

Summary

Automatic washing machines and automatic detergents are designed to work together to provide the best wash results. In dealing with faults with your machine you may find that the problem is not due directly to a fault of the machine, or that a component has failed prematurely due to an external factor. It is necessary to think beyond the mechanics of the machine and try and establish what factors may have contributed to the problem in hand.

Many problems arise from not fully appreciating or understanding how your machine or the wash process works and this in turn can lead to either poor wash results or premature component failure. I advise you to read and ensure you fully understand your machine's instruction book and the information given on the pack of detergent that you use.

Chapter 39
Common causes of poor washing results

Poor washing is mainly due to the incorrect operation of the machine by the user, rather than a mechanical or electrical fault of the machine. The most common user faults are listed below.

1 Have you read the manufacturer's manual?

Improvements on poor colours and whites will not happen magically, the process is very gradual. Good results can only be achieved if the correct programme and dosing is followed.

2 Incorrect programme control

a) To achieve good consistent results, you must have a good understanding of your machine and its controls. Always remember – you tell the machine what to do. If in doubt, read the manufacturer's manual.
b) Does the selected programme have the right water temperature, agitation and length of wash for the fabrics being washed?

3 Incorrect dosage

a) The amount of detergent that should be used is usually displayed on the pack. Please remember that this is only a guide, and the amounts have to be adjusted to load size, type and degree of soiling, and the hardness of the water supply.
b) Is the container used for measuring the detergent accurate? With the recent advent of 'compact' powders, use the scoop provided.
c) Have you made allowances for special types of soiling? Ointments, thick creams, heavy perspiration and the like, use up the suds activity very quickly. **Note:** *Poor soil and stain removal, the greying of whites or the appearance of 'greasy balls' on washed clothes is a clear indication of underdosing. It is never due to overdosing.*

4 Detergency

Detergents are formulated to do several tasks.
a) Overcome water hardness.
b) Wet-out the fabrics.
c) Remove the soiling from the clothes.
d) Hold the soiling in suspension, away from the clothes so that it can be pumped out with the water.

The harder the water, the harder the detergent has to work. More detergent should be added in the case of hard water, less in the case of soft water – simply follow the dosage information given on the detergent pack. The local area water authority should be able to inform you of the hardness of water in your area.

5 Incorrect loading

a) Overloading the machine will result in the clothes not being able to move freely inside the drum, resulting in poor soil removal.
b) Some programmes require reduced loads. If one of these programmes is used, reduce the load. If you are not sure, check the manufacturer's manual.

6 Other factors

a) How old is the machine? Like any mechanical/electrical item, a washing machine has a limited life span. In the case of an automatic washer, the average life span is approximately eight years.
b) When was the machine last serviced?
c) Poor whiteness is a result of constant underdosing (See 4). With the soiling not being removed, there is a gradual build-up of deposits in the clothes. This can only be corrected by always washing with the correct loads.
d) Domestic changes can reflect the quality of the wash, i.e., have you moved area? Is there a new addition to the family?
e) Are the poor results evident on all programmes or only on specific programmes? (See 4.)
f) Most of the manufacturers recommend a maintenance wash with detergent, but no load, 2 to 3 times a year to keep the machine clean and free from deposits.

Six golden rules for best results

1 Wash clothes frequently.
2 Use the right amount of detergent. Refer to the detergent pack for the correct dosage. Remember underdosing leads to poor soil and stain removal, and the greying of whites.
3 Choose the recommended programme for the fabric. To safeguard colour and finish, preserve shape and minimise creasing, never wash hotter, wash longer or spin longer than indicated by the correct wash code for the fabric.
4 Rinse thoroughly. Thorough rinsing is essential – always allow the machine to complete its full programme.
5 Treat stains quickly. Never allow stains to dry in. Blot out as much as possible and keep wet until the item can be washed thoroughly. Never rub a stain as this may push it further into the fabric.
6 Dry fabrics correctly. Check the instructions on the garment label for line dry, dry flat, tumbledry, etc.
7 Do not forget to check pockets for coins and tissues, etc., and fasten all zippers.

Marks which appear on the wash

If, during use, certain chemicals come into contact with fabrics, irreparable damage may occur. This is often not apparent until after the item is washed.

These chemicals may be present in relatively innocent personal products – skin preparations, hair mousse, perfumes, etc. as well as household products such as cleaning agents, polishes, etc.

The position of the marks and the type of item on which they appear can help to identify the cause. In most situations the marks appear ONLY on certain items in the wash – very often towels, or perhaps only women's tops or men's trousers. The fabric is almost always cotton, linen, viscose or poly-cotton, all of which are absorbent, and will hold the chemical within the fibre.

The marks can be split into two different types –
Light marks – where colour loss has occurred.
Greyish darker marks – where dye transfer is the most likely cause.

Light marks

The most common cause of this type of marking is skin creams and ointments containing benzoyl peroxide. This colourless ingredient reacts to the temperature of the wash water to release peroxide bleach, removing the dye from the item with which it has come into contact. Skin creams usually have an oil base, which helps them adhere to the skin, but this does mean that they can rub off onto towels from the hands after washing, onto bed linen, and onto the necks of T-shirts, etc. The marks are usually only present on the garments or items used by the person using the preparation. No problem will be apparent until the item is washed and the wash temperature activates the bleach. Most, although not all, of these products will state on the label 'contact with fabrics should be avoided', and the presence of benzoyl peroxide may also be listed under the ingredients. Unfortunately, as these marks are colour loss due to the bleaching action, they are permanent and the colour cannot be restored.

Darker marks

The most common cause of this type of marking is from a chemical which has come into contact with the fabric during use, and which acts as a scavenger during the wash, attracting soiling or dye from the wash solution on to it.

Hair mousse, hair treatments and skin preparations may contain chemicals which can act as scavengers during the wash.

The majority of problems in this area involve hand towels, which have been used in the bathroom and have inadvertently come into contact with a preparation, which has then attracted loose dye from the wash solution.

It is also possible for dye from a previous wash to remain in the sump of the washing machine or around the inside of the machine's outer tub and subsequently transfer on to articles in the following wash.

Soiling removed from other items in the same washload and suspended in the wash water can also be attracted to the affected area of the article.

As previously mentioned the marks only normally appear on items which have been used by the person using the preparation, and once again, in most instances, these marks are permanent and cannot be removed.

Chapter 40

Successful stain removal

Stains on washable fabrics fall into two groups:

Group one –
stains that will wash out in soap or detergent suds

Type of stain
Beetroot, Blood, Blackcurrant and other fruit juices, Chocolate, Cream, Cocoa, Coffee, Egg, Gravy, Ice lollies, Jam, Meat juice, Mud, Milk, Nappy stains, Pickles, Soft drinks, Sauces, Soup, Stews, Syrup, Tea, Tomato Ketchup, Wines and Spirits and Washable Ink.

Method
Fresh stains – Soak in cold suds to keep the stain from becoming set in the fabric. Then wash in the normal way according to the fabric.
Old dried-in stains – Lubricate with glycerine. Apply a mixture of one part glycerine to two parts water to the stain and leave for 10 minutes. Then treat as fresh stains.
Residual marks – White fabrics only. Bleach out with Hydrogen Peroxide solution (One part 20 volume hydrogen peroxide to nine parts water). Leave soaking in this solution for 1 hour, then wash in the normal way. Blood stains may leave residual iron mould marks, which should be treated as for iron mould.

   Special Note: *For 'built' stains such as egg (cooked), chocolate and mud, scrape off surplus staining matter first before putting to soak. Blood and meat juice stains, whether fresh or old should be soaked in cold water first.*

Group two–
'treat-n-wash' stains

What you will need
Glycerine (for lubrication).
Methylated Spirit (handle carefully: inflammable and poisonous).
Turpentine (inflammable).
Armyl Acetate (handle carefully: highly inflammable).
Hydrogen peroxide.
Proprietary grease solvent – 'Thawpit', 'Beaucare', 'Dab-it-off', etc., (do not breathe the vapour; use in a well ventilated room).
Photographic Hypo.
White vinegar (acetic acid).
Household ammonia (keep away from eyes).
Cotton wool, paper tissues, etc.

Handy hints
1   Act quickly to remove a stain and prevent it 'setting'. The faster you act, the milder the remedy needed.
2   Never rub a stain, as this pushes it further into the fabric. 'Pinch out' as much as you can, using a clean cloth or a paper tissue.
3   Never neglect a stain. The more drastic remedies for 'set' stains may harm delicate fabrics. If some stains are left on man-made and drip-dry fabrics in particular, they can be absorbed permanently into the fabric itself. Stains such as iron mould (rust) can weaken cellulosic fabrics and may eventually cause holes.
4   When applying solvents, always work from outside the stain towards the centre to avoid making a ring.
5   Always try a solvent on a hidden part first (e.g. under hem or seam allowance) to make sure it does not harm colours or fabric.
6   Stains on garments to be 'dry-cleaned' should be indicated on the garment (e.g. with a coloured tacking thread). Tell the cleaners what has caused the stain. This facilitates the task of removal and lessens the risk of the stain becoming permanently set by incorrect treatment.

Absorbent pad method
Use two absorbent pads of cotton wool, one soaked with the solvent and the other held against the stain. Dab the underside of the stain with solvent and the staining matter will be transferred from the material to the top pad. Change this pad around to a clean part and continue working in this way until no more staining matter comes through. To remove last traces of the stain, wash in usual way.

Type of stain	Solvent	Method
Ballpoint ink	Methylated spirit. (INF) (Benzine for acetate and 'Tricel')	Absorbent pad method
Bicycle oil	Proprietary grease solvent	Absorbent pad method or follow manufacturer's instructions
Black lead	Proprietary grease solvent	Absorbent pad method or follow manufacturer's instructions
Chalks and Crayons (Washable)		Brush off as much as possible while dry. Then brush stained area with suds (one dessertspoonful to a pint of water). Wash in the usual way
Chalks and Crayons (Indelible)	Methylated spirit. (INF) (Benzine for acetate and 'Tricel'.)	Absorbent pad method
Chewing gum	Methylated spirit. (INF) (Benzine for acetate and 'Tricel'.)	Absorbent pad method Alternatively rub the gum with an ice cube to harden it. It may then be picked off by hand. Wash as usual to remove final traces

Type of stain	Solvent	Method
Cod Liver Oil, Cooking Fat, Heavy grease stains	Proprietary grease solvent	Absorbent pad method or manufacturer's instructions
Contact adhesives. (e.g. Balsa cement, 'Evostick')	Amyl Acetate. (INF)	Absorbent pad method
Felt pen inks	Methylated spirit. (INF) (Benzine for acetate and 'Tricel'.)	First, lubricate the stain by rubbing with hard soap, and then wash in the usual way. For obstinate stains, use Methylated Spirit and absorbent pad method. Wash again to remove final traces
Grass	Methylated spirit. (INF) (Benzine for acetate and 'Tricel'.)	Absorbent pad method
Greasepaint	Proprietary grease solvent	Absorbent pad method or follow manufacturer's instructions
Hair lacquer	Amyl Acetate (INF)	Absorbent pad method
Iodine	Photographic Hypo	Dissolve one tablespoon hypo crystals in one pint warm water. Soak the stain for about 5 minutes, watching closely. As soon as the stain disappears, rinse thoroughly, then wash in the usual way
Iron mould (rust marks)	a) Lemon juice (for wool, man-made fibres and all fine fabrics)	Apply lemon juice to the stain and leave it for 10-15 minutes. Place a damp cloth over the stain and iron. Repeat several times, as necessary. Rinse and wash as usual
	b) Oxalic acid solution (for white cotton and linen only) use with care	Dissolve ½ teaspoonful oxalic acid crystals in ½ pint hot water. Tie a piece of cotton tightly round the stained area (to prevent the solution spreading) and immerse the stained part only. Leave for 2 or 3 minutes. Rinse thoroughly and wash in rich suds.
Lipstick and Rouge a) light stains b) heavy stains	Proprietary grease solvent	Soak then wash in usual way. Absorbent pad method or follow manufacturer's instructions
Marking ink	Marking ink eradicator (from stationers)	Follow instructions on the bottle label carefully
Metal polish	Proprietary grease solvent	Absorbent pad method or follow manufacturer's instruction
Mildew (mould on articles stored damp) a) coloured articles		The only treatment is regular soaking, followed by washing in rich suds – this will gradually reduce the marks
b) white cottons and linens without special finishes	Household bleach and vinegar	Soak in one part bleach to 100 parts water with one tablespoonful vinegar. Rinse thoroughly, then wash

(continued overleaf)

Type of stain	Solvent	Method
(Mildew continued) c) White, drip-dry fabrics	Hydrogen peroxide solution	Soak in one part hydrogen peroxide (20 volume) and nine parts water until staining has cleared. Rinse thoroughly then wash in the usual way
Nail varnish	Amyl Acetate for all fabrics (INF)	Absorbent pad method
Nicotine (Tobacco juice)	Amyl Acetate for all fabrics (INF). (Benzine for acetate or 'Tricel').	Absorbent pad method
Non-washable ink	Oxalic acid solution (For white cottons and linens only)	See method (b) under iron mould
Paint a) Emulsion	Water	Emulsion paint splashes sponged immediately with cold water will quickly be removed. Dried stains are permanent
b) Oil	Turpentine or amyl Acetate. (INF)	Absorbent pad method
Perspiration a) Fresh stains	**Ammonia. Do not inhale the fumes**	Damp with water, then hold over an open bottle of household ammonia
b) Old stains	White vinegar	Sponge with white vinegar, rinse thoroughly, then wash in usual way
'Plasticine' Modelling clay	Proprietary grease solvent or lighter fuel. (INF)	Scrape or brush off as much as possible. Apply solvent with absorbent pad method – wash to remove final traces
Scorch: a) Light marks		Light stains will sometimes respond to treatment as for Group one – washable stains
	Glycerine	If persistent, moisten with water and rub glycerine into the stained area. Wash through. Residual marks may respond to soaking in hydrogen peroxide solution
b) Heavy marks	Heavy scorch marks that have damaged the fibres cannot be removed	
Shoe polish	Glycerine and proprietary grease solvent	Lubricate stain with glycerine, then use solvent with absorbent pad method or follow manufacturer's instruction. Wash to remove final traces
Sun tan oil	Proprietary grease solvent	Absorbent pad method or follow manufacturer's instruction
Verdigris (green stains from copper pipes, etc).		Treat as iron mould

INF: *Inflammable*
Special Note: *Cotton garments with flame-resistant finishes must not be treated with household (chlorine) bleach or hydrogen peroxide in stain removal treatment, since this may impair the finish*
Keep solvents securely closed, labelled and out of children's reach

Chapter 41
Textile care labelling

For generations, washing advice was passed down from parent to child. Washing was done by hand and the items washed were usually cotton or wool. The arrival of the washing machine, modern detergents and more importantly the introduction of man-made materials meant that more detailed help was needed to ensure fabrics were washed according to their needs.

The Home Laundry Consultative Council (the UK National Textile Care Labelling Authority) introduced a system of wash codes and symbols. The codes and symbols are designed to indicate whether the fabric can be washed, or needs to be dry-cleaned; the maximum temperature the fabric can be washed at, the most suitable means of drying and the temperature the fabric should be ironed at. The original codes were updated in 1987 and this 'new' care labelling scheme is now in line with that used in Europe.

Washing –
what the symbols mean

 The wash tub indicates the most appropriate programme for that particular fabric.

 The maximum temperature is shown in °C. These will be 95, 60, 50, 40 or 30°C.

In addition to the temperature a bar may be present below the wash tub symbol.

 Where there is no bar below the wash tub maximum agitation is recommended. This symbol appears on robust fabrics such as cotton and linen.

 Where a single bar is shown beneath the wash tub, the washing action (agitation) should be reduced. This symbol is found on more delicate fabrics such as poly-cotton, acrylics and viscose.

 A broken or double bar beneath the wash tub symbol shows that only the most gentle wash action is required, as the fabric is likely to contain washable wool or silk.

In addition to indicating the agitation required the 'no bar', 'single bar' and 'broken bar' programmes have different water fill levels on most machines and also different spin speeds which relate to the absorbency of the fabric. For instance 'no bar' will require a long fast spin to remove as much water as possible from the absorbent fabric such as cotton. 'Single bar' fabrics such as poly-cotton and acrylic are less absorbent and may be severely creased if spun too fast or for too long.

 The wash tub symbol with a cross through it means that the fabric is not suitable for washing.

 Where a hand is shown in the wash tub, the garment may be hand washed but should not be machine washed.

Bleaching –
what the symbols mean

In the UK, the use of household hypochlorite bleach, such as Domestos, does not form part of the normal washing process. However, in some European countries, it is used on certain fabrics. Most dyes are sensitive to chlorine bleach and a triangular symbol is used to indicate if the fabric is suitable for bleach treatment. The household hypochlorite bleach should not be confused with the oxygen based bleaching agents which are present in many of the formulations of washing detergents

 Chlorine bleach may be used.

 Do not use chlorine bleach.

Dry-cleaning –
what the symbols mean

The symbol used to indicate that a fabric can be dry-cleaned is a circle.

 The letter within the circle advises the dry cleaner which type of solvent can be used.

 A circle with a cross means that the garment is unsuitable for dry-cleaning.

Ironing –
what the symbols mean

Most irons now carry the same symbols as the garments care label. The 'dot' system takes the guessing out of just how hot the iron should be for different fabrics. The iron shaped symbol carries one, two or three dots, each indicating that the temperature is suitable for fabrics which have care labels with the same number of dots.

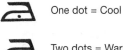

One dot = Cool

Two dots = Warm

Three dots = Hot

Cross = Do not iron

Drying

The vast majority of textile articles can safely be tumbledried. Care labels may be used to indicate either that tumbledrying is the optimum drying method for a particular article, or that tumbledrying should not be used if the article is likely to be harmed by this treatment.

In cases where the tumbledrying prohibition symbol is used, any special positive instructions, such as 'dry flat' for heavier weight knitwear, should be given in words.

Drying – what the symbols mean

The information shown in the square gives the recommended drying method for that particular fabric.

Today many fabrics can be tumble-dried and this is indicated by a circle within the square. The most suitable heat setting for for the garment is indicated by the addition of 'dots' within the circle.

One dot indicates low or half heat is required – normally synthetic fabrics.

Two dots indicates high or full heat is required – normally cotton fabrics.

A cross within the circle, or across the square indicates that the garment should not be tumbledried.

Other less used drying symbols

 Drip drying is recommended

 Hang = line-dry

Dry flat

Mixed fabric group loads

Ideally fabric groups should not be mixed to make up a washload. Unless care is taken it does increase the risk of shrinkage, or dye contamination and discoloration of white things (particularly nylon) from articles which prove non-colourfast under the wash conditions. However, if for convenience or for the sake of economy, there is no alternative, always select the mildest wash conditions.

Fabric conditioning

No matter how thoroughly clothes are rinsed, after repeated washing and rinsing they gradually lose their bulk and softness. Fabric conditioner in the final rinse untangles matted fibres restoring the natural bulk and bounce to the fabric.

Special note on velvet

Velvet is a construction term, not a fibre. It may be silk, cotton or an acetate/nylon blend, e.g., 'Tricelan'. For best results look for the wash-care label and follow the instructions faithfully. If in doubt, dry-clean.

Soft furnishings in velvet weave, e.g., Dralon – it is helpful to remove surface dust with a vacuum cleaner or soft brush. Dralon velvet is not washable. It can be cleaned with a dry-foam shampoo. Avoid saturating cotton backing, vacuum or brush foam off when dry. When dry-cleaning, state fibre content.

Flame-retardant fabrics and finishes

Apart from nylon and wool, which are regarded as being of low flammability, there are two ways of giving fabrics flame-retardant properties:

a) by the application to cotton fabrics of a special finish such as 'Protean', 'Pyrovatex', 'Timonox'. Also in certain cases to wool, though this as yet is not being widely used for apparel purposes.

b) by the modification of the fibre itself, e.g., fibres like acrylic but with modified properties. The generic term for these is modacrylic, e.g., 'Teklan' or Monsanto's modacrylic. They are inherently flame retardant.

Important: *Flame-retardant fabrics, e.g., modacrylics or fabrics with a flame-retardant finish must not be bleached, or soaked in any washing product.*

Fabrics with a flame-retardant finish must not be washed in soap or non-automatic powder as soap can mask the properties of the finish. Other types of washing product, including automatic powder may be used with safety. Rinse very thoroughly.

The appropriate washing codes for the above are:

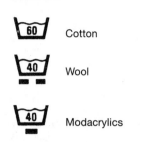

60 Cotton

40 Wool

40 Modacrylics

Hand care

To get the best results in the hand wash make sure the powder is thoroughly dissolved before washing and the clothes thoroughly rinsed afterwards.

After each wash by hand, rinse your hands and dry them thoroughly. People with sensitive or damaged skin should pay particular attention to the instructions for use and avoid prolonged contact with the washing instructions.

'Special finish' labels

E.g. 'machine washable wool'. Sometimes the finish given to a fabric changes its washability.

No label provided

If in doubt wash under the mildest conditions, i.e., use warm 40°C suds only; do not soak; wash through quickly and gently; rinse thoroughly; blot off surplus moisture with a towel and dry carefully. If washing by machine choose the gentlest programme. If ironing seems appropriate, use a cool iron.

Labels with unfamiliar symbols

These will be found detailed.

Wash for the fabric, never mind the shape!

Remember always that it is the fabric and its construction rather than the type of article that decides the washing treatment. A polyester shirt will be grouped with a textured polyester suit, a small boy's polyester trousers and his sister's polyester blouse. They are all different shapes and sizes but all will be washed as polyester requires, in hand-hot suds with cold rinsing and a short spin.

Different fabrics require different washing temperatures and agitation times. So ignore the shape of the article and concern yourself only with what it is made of and then wash it according to the appropriate Care Labelling Code.

Blends and mixtures

A blend fabric is one which has been woven or knitted from yarn made by the blending of two or more fibres, prior to the yarn being spun. A mixture fabric is one where two or more different yarns are used during weaving or knitting (e.g., a nylon warp woven into a viscose or cotton weft). In both cases the fibre which needs the milder treatment influences the wash conditions suitable for the fabric. For example a polyester-wool blend should only be washed in warm suds, because of the wool content; polyester-cotton and acrylic-cotton are both washed at temperatures lower than the maximum for cotton. If in doubt, wash as for the fibre requiring the milder treatment.

Colour fastness

Test for colour fastness by damping a piece of the hem or seam allowance and iron a piece of dry white fabric on to it. If any colour blots off, wash the article separately, in very cool suds, and rinse at once in cold water. Put to dry immediately. If the colour is very loose, dry cleaning may be advisable (check the label).

Soaking

There are occasions when heavily soiled or stained articles benefit from a soak before washing.

Before soaking any coloured article it is important to make sure that:

The dye is fast to soaking – if in doubt do not soak.

The washing powder is completely dissolved before putting in the articles.

The water temperature is not too high for the fabric or the dye.

The article is not bunched up, it should be left as free as possible.

White and coloured articles are not soaked together – this is especially necessary where white nylon is concerned as nylon stockings and tights, for example, are seldom fast to soaking for long periods.

The articles do not have metal buttons or metal fasteners – soaking can encourage iron mould (brown stains).

Articles made from wool or silk or from fabric with a flame-retardant finish, whether white or coloured, should never be soaked in washing products of any type.

Chapter 42
Jargon

Amp – Short for ampere. Used to measure the flow or electricity through a circuit or appliance.

Armature – Wire wound centre of brush motor.

Bi-metal – Two different metals which have been joined together. When heated the strip bends in a known direction.

Boss – Protection around entry point.

Burn-out – Overheated part of item.

Bus bar – An electrical conductor.

Cable – Conductors covered with a protective semi-rigid insulating sheath, used to connect the individual components within a wiring system.

Carbon face (seal) – Watertight flat surface seal.

Centrifugal – Force that increases with rotation causing movement away from its centre.

Circuit – Any complete path for an electric current allowing it to pass along a 'live' conductor to where it is needed and then to return to its source along a 'neutral' conductor.

Clamp band – Large adjustable clip used for holding door boot.

Closed circuit – A normal circuit that allows power to pass through.

Collet – Tapered sleeve of two or more parts designed to grip a shaft passed through its centre.

Commutator – Copper segment on motor armature.

Component – Individual parts of the machine, i.e., pump, valves, motors, are all components.

Conductor – The metallic current carrying 'cores' within cable or flex.

Consumer Unit – Unit governing the supply of electricity to all circuits and containing a main on-off switch and fuses or circuit breakers protecting the circuits emanating from it.

Contact – Point at which switch makes contact.

Continuity – Electrical path with no break.

Corbin – Type of spring hose clip.

Damped – To have reduced movement of suspension, i.e., reduce oscillation of tub unit during distribute and spin cycles.

Dispenser – Compartment that holds detergent ready for use.

Dispenser hose – Hose that supplies the tub with detergent and water from the dispenser compartment.

Distribute – To balance load by centrifugal force, i.e., a set speed calculated to even out wash load prior to faster spin.

Door boot – Flexible seal between door and tub.

Door gasket – Flexible seal between door and tub.

Door seal – Flexible seal between door and tub.

Drift – Soft metal rod used for bearing removal.

ELCB – Earth leakage circuit breaker – see RCCB.

EMF – Electromotive force. Source of energy that can cause a current to flow in a circuit or device.

Early – Machine not currently on the market.

Energize (Energise) – To supply power to.

Energized (Energised) – Having power supplied to.

Flowchart – Method of following complicated steps in a logical fashion.

Functional test – To test machine on a set programme.

Garter ring – Large elastic band or spring used to secure door boot.

Grommet fitting – Method of fitting hoses, etc., requiring no clips.

Harness – electrical wiring within a machine.

Hertz – Periodic cycle of one second, i.e., cycles per second.

Hunting – Oscillating.

IC – Integrated circuit.

OC – Open circuit.

Impeller – The blades of the water pump.

Insulation – Material used to insulate a device or a region.

Isolate – To disconnect from the electrical supply and water supply, etc.

Laminations – Joined metal parts of stator.

Late – Current machine on market.

Lint – Fluff from clothing that may cause a small blockage.

Live – Supply current carrying conductor.

Make – 1 Manufacturer's name.
2 When a switch makes contact it is said to make.

Microprocessor – Miniature integrated circuit containing programme information.

Miniature Circuit Breaker – (MCB) a device used instead of fuses to isolate a circuit if fault/overload occurs.

Neutral – Return current carrying conductor.

OOB – Out of balance detection system.

Open-circuit – Circuit that is broken, i.e., will not let any power through.

Outer casing – Cabinet, 'shell' of the machine.

PCB – Printed circuit board.

PSI – Measurement of water pressure, pounds per square inch, e.g. 38 psi.

PTCR – Positive temperature coefficient resistor.

PME – Protective multiple earthing.

Pawl – Pivoted lever designed to engage ratchet gearing.

Porous – Item that allows water to pass through.

Potentiometer – Variable resistance device.

Processor – Main central processing component of computer control circuitry.

Programmer – See Timer.

RCCB – Residual current circuit breaker *(also known as RCD)*

RCCD – Residual current circuit device.

RCD – Residual current device. *See also – ELCB and RCCB.*

Reciprocating – Mechanical action of backwards and forwards movement.

Reverse polarity – A situation where live and neutral feeds have reversed, e.g., connected incorrectly at supply, socket or plug.

Ribbon cable – Flat cable used for low voltage PCB connections.

Rotor – Central part of an induction motor.

Schematic diagram – Theoretical diagram.

Seal – Piece of pre-shaped rubber that usually fits into a purpose built groove or between two surfaces, therefore creating a watertight seal when subjected to pressure.

Sealant – Rubber substance used for ensuring watertight joints.

Shell – Outer of machine.

Spades – Connections on wires or components – remove gently.

Stat – Abbreviation of thermostat.

Stator – Electrical winding on motor.

Terminal block – A method of connecting wires together safely.

TOC – Thermal overload cut-out. At a pre-set temperature, the TOC will break electrical circuit to whatever it is in circuit with, i.e., prevents motors, etc., overheating.

Thermistor – A semi-conductor device, the resistance of which is affected by temperatures.

Thermostat – Device used to monitor temperature.

Thyristor – Electronic switching device.

Timer – Programme switch.

Triac – Electronic switching device.

Volt – Unit of electrical pressure (potential) difference. In most British homes the mains voltage is 230 V.

Volatile *(when relating to computer control applications)* – Unable to store information when power is turned off.

Non-Volatile *(when relating to computer control applications)* – Retains information for a set period even with power turned off.

Watt – Unit of power consumed by an appliance or circuit, the product of the mains voltage and the current drawn (in amps). 1000 W = 1 kilowatt (kW).

Index